Environmental Science: Teacher's Edition

Contents in Brief

Teacher's Edition

See Program Component List on page ii

Student Edition

Prentice Hall Science Explorer

Series Tables of Contents

Life Science

The Nature of Science and Technology

1. What Is Science?
2. The Work of Scientists
3. Technology and Engineering

From Bacteria to Plants

1. Living Things
2. Viruses and Bacteria
3. Protists and Fungi
4. Introduction to Plants
5. Seed Plants

Animals

1. Sponges, Cnidarians, and Worms
2. Mollusks, Arthropods, and Echinoderms
3. Fishes, Amphibians, and Reptiles
4. Birds and Mammals
5. Animal Behavior

Cells and Heredity

1. Cell Structure and Function
2. Cell Processes and Energy
3. Genetics: The Science of Heredity
4. Modern Genetics
5. Changes Over Time

Human Biology and Health

1. Bones, Muscles, and Skin
2. Food and Digestion
3. Circulation
4. Respiration and Excretion
5. Fighting Disease
6. The Nervous System
7. The Endocrine System and Reproduction

Environmental Science

1. Populations and Communities
2. Ecosystems and Biomes
3. Living Resources
4. Land, Water, and Air Resources
5. Energy Resources

Earth Science

Inside Earth

1. Plate Tectonics
2. Earthquakes
3. Volcanoes
4. Minerals
5. Rocks

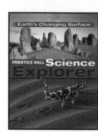

Earth's Changing Surface

1. Mapping Earth's Surface
2. Weathering and Soil Formation
3. Erosion and Deposition
4. A Trip Through Geologic Time

Earth's Waters

1. Earth: The Water Planet
2. Freshwater Resources
3. Ocean Motions
4. Ocean Resources

Weather and Climate

1. The Atmosphere
2. Weather Factors
3. Weather Patterns
4. Climate and Climate Change

Astronomy

1. Earth, Moon, and Sun
2. Exploring Space
3. The Solar System
4. Stars, Galaxies, and the Universe

Physical Science

Chemical Building Blocks

1. Introduction to Matter
2. Solids, Liquids, and Gases
3. Elements and the Periodic Table
4. Exploring Materials

Chemical Interactions

1. Atoms and Bonding
2. Chemical Reactions
3. Acids, Bases, and Solutions
4. Carbon Chemistry

Motion, Forces, and Energy

1. Motion
2. Forces
3. Forces in Fluids
4. Work and Machines
5. Energy
6. Thermal Energy and Heat

Electricity and Magnetism

1. Magnetism
2. Electricity
3. Electromagnetism
4. Electronics

Sound and Light

1. Characteristics of Waves
2. Sound
3. The Electromagnetic Spectrum
4. Light

Teacher's Edition

The Nature of Science and Technology

PRENTICE HALL Science Explorer

PEARSON

Prentice Hall

Needham, Massachusetts
Upper Saddle River, New Jersey

Pearson Prentice Hall™ is a trademark of Pearson Education, Inc.
Pearson® is a registered trademark of Pearson plc.
Prentice Hall® is a registered trademark of Pearson Education, Inc.
Lab zone™ is a trademark of Pearson Education, Inc.

Planet Diary® is a registered trademark of Addison Wesley Longman, Inc.

Discovery Channel School® is a registered trademark of Discovery Communications, Inc., used under license.
The Discovery Channel logo is a trademark of Discovery Communications, Inc.

SciLinks® is a trademark of the National Science Teachers Association. The SciLinks® service includes copyrighted materials and is owned and provided by the National Science Teachers Association. All rights reserved.

Science News® is a registered trademark of Science Services, Inc.

ISBN 0-13-181143-6   1 2 3 4 5 6 7 8 9 10   08 07 06 05 04

Pacing Options

SCIENCE EXPLORER offers many aids to help you plan your instruction time, whether regular class periods or block scheduling. Section-by-section lesson plans for each chapter include suggested times for Student Edition activities. TeacherExpress™ and the Lab zone™ Easy Planner CD-ROM will help you manage your time electronically.

PRENTICE HALL
TeacherEXPRESS™
Plan · Teach · Assess

Lab zone™

Pacing Chart

	PERIODS	BLOCKS
Careers: Super Inventor	1	$1/2$
Chapter 1 What Is Science?		
Chapter 1 Project: Is It Really True?	Ongoing	Ongoing
1 Thinking Like a Scientist	2–3	1–$1^1/_2$
2 Scientific Inquiry	4–5	2–$2^1/_2$
3 Why Study Science?	2–3	1–$1^1/_2$
4 Careers in Science	2–3	1–$1^1/_2$
Chapter 1 Review and Assessment	1	$1/2$
Chapter 2 The Work of Scientists		
Chapter 2 Project: Design and Build a Scale Model	Ongoing	Ongoing
1 Measurement—A Common Language	3–4	$1^1/_2$–2
2 Integrating Mathematics: Mathematics and Science	3–4	$1^1/_2$–2
3 Graphs in Science	3–4	$1^1/_2$–2
4 Safety in the Science Laboratory	1–2	$1/2$–1
Chapter 2 Review and Assessment	1	$1/2$

	PERIODS	BLOCKS
Chapter 3 Technology and Engineering		
Chapter Project: Design and Build a Chair	Ongoing	Ongoing
1 Understanding Technology	3–4	$1^1/_2$–2
2 Technology Design Skills	3–4	$1^1/_2$–2
3 Technology and Society	2–3	1–$1^1/_2$
Chapter 3 Review and Assessment	1	$1/2$
Interdisciplinary Exploration: Edison—Genius of Invention	2–3	1–$1^1/_2$

Research-Based and Proven to Work

As the originator of the small book concept in middle school science, and as the nation's number one science publisher, Prentice Hall takes pride in the fact that we've always listened closely to teachers. In doing so, we've developed programs that effectively meet the needs of your classroom.

As we continue to listen, we realize that raising the achievement level of all students is the number one challenge facing teachers today. To assist you in meeting this latest challenge, Prentice Hall has combined the very best author team with solid research to create a program that meets your high standards and will assure that no child is left behind.

With Prentice Hall, you can be confident not only that your students will be motivated, inspired, and excited to learn science, but that they will also achieve the success needed in today's environment of the No Child Left Behind (NCLB) legislation and testing reform.

On the following pages, you will read about the key elements found throughout *Science Explorer* that truly set this program apart and assure success for you and your students.

> As we continue to listen, we realize that raising the achievement level of all students is the number one challenge facing teachers today.

A Science Program Backed by Research

In developing Prentice Hall *Science Explorer*, we used research studies as a central, guiding element. Research on *Science Explorer* indicated key elements of a textbook program that ensure students' success: support for reading and mathematics in science, consistent opportunities for inquiry, and an ongoing assessment strand. This research was conducted in phases and continues today.

1. Exploratory: Needs Assessment

Along with periodic surveys concerning state and national standards as well as curriculum issues and challenges, we conducted specific product development research, which included discussions with teachers and advisory panels, focus groups, and quantitative surveys. We explored the specific needs of teachers, students, and other educators regarding each book we developed in Prentice Hall *Science Explorer*.

2. Formative: Prototype Development and Field-Testing

During this phase of research, we worked to develop prototype materials. Then we tested the materials by field-testing with students and teachers and by performing qualitative and quantitative surveys. In our early prototype testing, we received feedback about our lesson structure. Results were channeled back into the program development for improvement.

3. Summative: Validation Research

Finally, we conducted and continue to conduct long-term research based on scientific, experimental designs under actual classroom conditions. This research identifies what works and what can be improved in the next revision of Prentice Hall *Science Explorer*. We also continue to monitor the program in the market. We talk to our users about what works, and then we begin the cycle over again. The next section contains highlights of this research.

A Science Program With Proven Results

In a year-long study in 2000–2001, students in six states using Prentice Hall *Science Explorer* outscored students using other science programs on a nationally normed standardized test.

The study investigated the effects of science textbook programs at the eighth-grade level. Twelve eighth-grade science classes with a total of 223 students participated in the study. The selected classes were of similar student ability levels.

Each class was tested at the beginning of the school year using the TerraNova CTBS Basic Battery Plus, and then retested at the end of the school year. The final results, shown in the graph, show a significant improvement in test scores from the pre-test to the post-test evaluation.

• All tests were scored by CTB/McGraw-Hill, the publisher of the TerraNova exam. Statistical analyses and conclusions were performed by an independent firm, Pulse Analytics, Inc.

In Japan, Lesson Study Research has been employed for a number of years as a tool for teachers to improve their curriculum. In April 2003, Prentice Hall adapted this methodology to focus on a lesson from this edition. Our goal was to test the effectiveness of lesson pedagogy and improve it while in the program development stage. In all three classrooms tested, student learning increased an average of 10 points from the pre- to the post-assessment.

• Detailed results of these studies can be obtained at **www.PHSchool.com/research.**

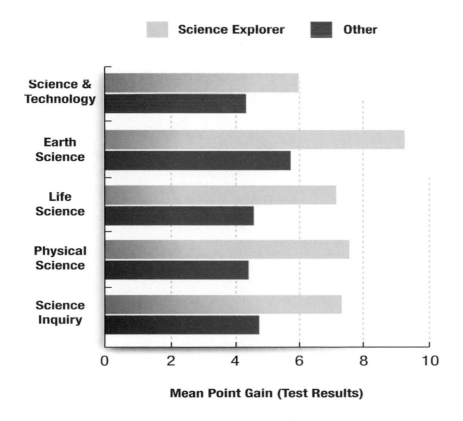

Mean Point Gain (Test Results)

Foundational Research: Inquiry in the Science Classroom

"How do I know if my students are inquiring?" "If students are busy doing lots of hands-on activities, are they using inquiry?" "What is inquiry, anyway?" If you're confused, you are not alone. Inquiry is the heart and soul of science education, with most of us in continuous pursuit of achieving it with our students!

Defining Science Inquiry

What is it? Simply put, inquiry is the intellectual side of science. It is thinking like a scientist—being inquisitive, asking why, and searching for answers. The National Science Education Content Standards define inquiry as the process in which students begin with a question, design an investigation, gather evidence, formulate an answer to the original question, and communicate the investigative process and results. Since it is often difficult to accomplish all this in one class period, the standards also acknowledge that at times students need to practice only one or two inquiry components.

Understanding Inquiry

The National Research Council in Inquiry and the National Science Education Standards (2000) identified several "essential features" of classroom inquiry. We have modified these essential features into questions to guide you in your quest for enhanced and more thoughtful student inquiry.

1. **Who asks the question?** In most curricula, these focusing questions are an element given in the materials. As a teacher you can look for labs that, at least on a periodic basis, allow students to pursue their own questions.

2. **Who designs the procedures?** To gain experience with the logic underlying experimentation, students need continuous practice with designing procedures. Some labs in which the primary target is content acquisition designate procedures. But others should ask students to do so.

3. **Who decides what data to collect?** Students need practice in determining the data to collect.

4. **Who formulates explanations based upon the data?** Students should be challenged to think—to analyze and draw conclusions based on their data, not just copy answers from the text materials.

5. **Who communicates and justifies the results?** Activities should push students to not only communicate but justify their answers. Activities also should be thoughtfully designed and interesting so that students want to share their results and argue about conclusions.

Making Time for Inquiry

One last question—Must each and every activity have students do all of this? The answer is an obvious and emphatic No. You will find a great variety of activities in *Science Explorer*. Some activities focus on content acquisition, and thus they specify the question and most of the procedures. But many others stress in-depth inquiry from start to finish. Because inquiry is an intellectual pursuit, it cannot merely be characterized by keeping students busy and active. Too many students have a knack for being physically but not intellectually engaged in science. It is our job to help them engage intellectually.

Michael J. Padilla, Ph.D.
Program Author of *Science Explorer*
Professor of Science Education
University of Georgia
Athens, Georgia

"Because inquiry is an intellectual pursuit, it cannot merely be characterized by keeping students busy and active."

Evaluator's Checklist

Does your science program promote inquiry by—

✔ Enabling students to pursue their own questions

✔ Allowing students to design their own procedures

✔ Letting students determine what data are best to collect

✔ Challenging students to think critically

✔ Pushing students to justify their answers

Inquiry in *Science Explorer*

Science Explorer offers the most opportunities to get students to think like a scientist. By providing inquiry opportunities throughout the program, *Science Explorer* enables students to enhance their understanding by participating in the discovery.

Student Edition Inquiry

Six lab and activity options are included in every chapter, structured from directed to open-ended—providing you the flexibility to address all types of learners and accommodate your class time and equipment requirements. As Michael Padilla notes, some focus on content acquisition, and thus the question and most of the procedures are specified. But many others stress in-depth inquiry from start to finish. The graph below shows how, in general, inquiry levels are addressed in the Student Edition.

Science Explorer encourages students to develop inquiry skills across the spectrum from teacher-guided to open-ended. Even more opportunities for real-life applications of inquiry are included in Science & Society, Science & Technology, Careers in Science, and Interdisciplinary Exploration features.

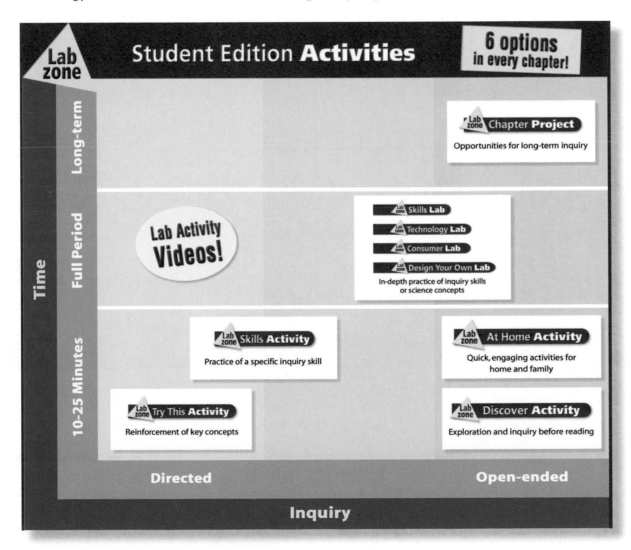

Inquiry Skills Chart

SCIENCE EXPLORER provides comprehensive teaching, practice, and assessment of science skills, with an emphasis on the process skills necessary for inquiry. This chart lists the skills covered in the program and cites the page numbers where each skill is covered.

Basic Process SKILLS				
	Student Text: Projects and Labs	Student Text: Activities	Student Text: Caption and Review Questions	Teacher's Edition: Extensions
Observing	35, 56–57, 96	6	49, 50, 54	7, 17
Inferring	35, 96	24, 30, 44, 68, 108, 111	8, 40, 52, 69, 105, 110, 120	8
Predicting	35, 96	60, 73, 77, 93, 101	9, 34, 40, 55, 84,120	9, 74
Classifying		12, 14, 37, 90	12, 22, 31, 37, 120	10, 11, 37, 89, 90, 92, 93, 94, 98
Making Models	43, 87, 106–107			
Communicating	5, 23, 35, 42, 56–57, 76, 87, 96	22, 29, 39, 58–59, 75, 81, 83, 95, 105, 112–113, 115, 116–117, 119	12, 46–47	7, 12, 25, 27, 31, 33, 37, 45, 61, 67, 69, 78, 81, 89, 99, 101, 104, 109, 111, 115
Measuring	43, 56–57	49, 64	63	46, 48, 54
Calculating	43, 56–57, 76	52, 55, 61, 65, 67, 73, 111	45, 55, 67, 84, 120	51, 66
Creating Data Tables	56–57, 76			54
Graphing	23, 76	75		19, 70, 75
Advanced Process SKILLS				
Posing Questions	23	13, 26	19, 25, 32	14, 15
Developing Hypotheses	5, 23	95	15, 22, 40	19
Designing Experiments	5, 23		40	16, 19

Advanced Process SKILLS (continued)

	Student Text: Projects and Labs	Student Text: Activities	Student Text: Caption and Review Questions	Teacher's Edition: Extensions
Controlling Variables	23	16	17, 40	17
Forming Operational Definitions	96	88		
Interpreting Data	5	73	18, 67, 75, 120	
Drawing Conclusions	5, 23, 56–57, 76	19, 58–59, 73, 111	120	28

Critical Thinking SKILLS

Comparing and Contrasting			12, 22, 75, 84, 95, 98	31, 45, 109
Applying Concepts	23, 35, 42, 56–57, 76, 87, 96, 106–107	37, 95, 116–117	15, 22, 29, 37, 39, 53, 55, 67, 80, 81, 84, 95, 115	7, 20, 21, 25, 26, 27, 28, 29, 33, 36, 46, 48, 50, 51, 54, 61, 63, 64, 80, 89, 90, 92, 94, 100, 101, 103, 104, 109, 110, 113, 114
Interpreting Diagrams, Graphs, Photographs, and Maps	76	9, 73, 111	11, 41, 74, 75, 81, 84, 85, 121	18, 61, 72, 74
Relating Cause and Effect	106–107		72, 84, 91, 100, 115, 120	
Making Generalizations			40, 81	
Making Judgments	106–107	58–59	12, 26, 37, 40, 81, 84, 92, 95, 104, 105, 115, 120	103
Problem Solving	87, 106–107	97	22, 29, 37, 40, 55, 67, 114, 115, 120	

Informational Organizational SKILLS

Concept Maps			39, 83	
Compare/Contrast Tables				34, 67 91
Venn Diagrams			119	
Flowcharts				22, 51, 71, 101, 105
Cycle Diagrams				

The *Science Explorer* program provides additional teaching, reinforcement, and assessment of skills in the *Inquiry Skills Activities Book* and the *Integrated Science Laboratory Manual*.

A National Look at Science Education

Project 2061 was established by the American Association for the Advancement of Science (AAAS) as a long-term project to improve science education nationwide. A primary goal of Project 2061 is to define a "common core of learning"—the knowledge and skills we want all students to achieve. Project 2061 published *Science for All Americans* in 1989 and followed this with Benchmarks for Science Literacy in 1993. Benchmarks recommends what students should know and be able to do by the end of grades 2, 5, 8, and 12. Project 2061 clearly states that *Benchmarks* is not a curriculum but a tool for designing successful curricula.

The National Research Council (NRC) used *Science for All Americans* and *Benchmarks* to develop the National Science Education Standards (NSES), which were published in 1996. The NSES are organized into six categories (Content, Teaching, Assessment, Professional Development, Program, and System) to help schools establish the conditions necessary to achieve scientific literacy for all students.

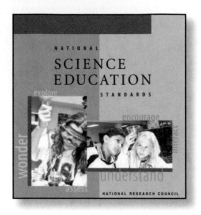

Michael Padilla, the program author of *Science Explorer,* guided one of six teams of teachers whose work led to the publication of *Benchmarks.* He also was a contributing writer of the National Science Education Standards. Under his guidance, *Science Explorer* has implemented these standards through its inquiry approach, a focus on student learning of important concepts and skills, and teacher support aligned with the NSES teaching standards.

Neither *Benchmarks* nor the NSES requires a single, uniform national curriculum, and in fact there is a great diversity nationwide in science curricula. The correlations that follow are designed to help you use the *Science Explorer* program to meet your particular curriculum needs.

Meeting the National Science Education Standards

WHAT IS SCIENCE?

Science as Inquiry (Content Standard A)

● **Design and conduct a scientific investigation** Students design and conduct a scientific experiment to test whether or not a common belief is true. Students design an experiment to investigate how cut flowers can stay fresher longer. *(Chapter Project; Design Your Own Lab)*

● **Develop descriptions, explanations, predictions, and models using evidence** Students use the skills of observing and inferring to model how scientists piece together information. *(Skills Lab)*

● **Understandings about scientific inquiry** Scientists use skills of observing, inferring, predicting, classifying, and making models to learn more about the world. Scientific inquiry refers to the diverse ways in which scientists study the natural world and propose explanations based on the evidence they gather. *(Thinking Like a Scientist; Scientific Inquiry)*

Science in Personal and Social Perspectives (Content Standard F)

● **Science and technology in society** Being able to understand scientific principles and think scientifically can help you solve problems and answer questions in your everyday life. *(Why Study Science?)*

History and Nature of Science (Content Standard G)

● **Science as a human endeavor** Scientists organize their work into three major branches: Earth and space science, life science, and physical science. *(Careers in Science)*

THE WORK OF SCIENTISTS

Science as Inquiry (Content Standard A)

● **Use appropriate tools and techniques to gather, analyze, and interpret data** Using SI as the standard system of measurement allows scientists to compare data and communicate results with each other. Students investigate backpacks to determine which is the best choice for safely carrying books. *(Measurement—A Common Language; Consumer Lab)*

A National Look at Science Education (continued)

● **Develop descriptions, explanations, predictions, and models using evidence** Students create a three-dimensional model that shows the size relationships among the different parts of the model. *(Chapter Project)*

● **Communicate scientific procedures and explanations** Good preparation helps you stay safe when doing science activities in the laboratory and in the field. *(Safety in the Science Laboratory)*

● **Use mathematics in all aspects of scientific inquiry** Scientists use various math skills to collect and analyze data. Graphs are powerful tools in science. *(Mathematics and Science; Graphs in Science)*

Science in Personal and Social Perspectives (Content Standard F)

● **Science and technology in society** Students evaluate whether or not the United States should convert to the metric system. *(Science and Society)*

History and Nature of Science (Content Standard G)

● **History of science** Systems of measurement developed gradually over time in different parts of the world. *(Science and History)*

TECHNOLOGY AND ENGINEERING

Science and Technology (Content Standard E)

● **Identifying appropriate problems for technological design** When engineers identify a need, they clearly define the problem they are trying to solve. *(Understanding Technology)*

● **Design a solution or product** Students design a chair made of cardboard. Students design packaging for a breakable object. *(Chapter Project; Technology Lab)*

● **Implement a proposed design** Students build their proposed designs for a cardboard chair. Students build their proposed designs for packaging for a breakable object. *(Chapter Project; Technology Lab)*

● **Evaluate completed technological designs or products** Students investigate how the parts of a pen work together as a system. Troubleshooting and redesigning are two important steps in the technology design process.*(Skills Lab; Technology Design Skills)*

● **Communicate the process of technological design** Students explain their design process for their cardboard chairs. Students create ads to promote their packaging designs. *(Chapter Project; Technology Lab)*

● **Understandings about science and technology** Science is the study of the natural world to understand how it functions while technology modifies the natural world to meet human needs or solve problems. In addition to positive effects, technology can have negative consequences. *(Understanding Technology; Technology and Society)*

Science in Personal and Social Perspectives (Content Standard F)

● **Science and technology in society** People must analyze the possible risks and benefits of new technologies. Students research the reliability of Internet sources. *(Technology and Society; Tech & Design)*

History and Nature of Science (Content Standard G)

● **History of science** In every age of history, technology has had a large impact on society. *(Technology and Society; Tech & Design in History)*

Note: To see how the benchmarks are supported by *SCIENCE EXPLORER,* go to **PHSchool.com.**

Reading Comprehension in the Science Classroom

Q&A

Q: Why are science texts often difficult for students to read and comprehend?

A: In general, science texts make complex literacy and knowledge demands on learners. They have a more technical vocabulary, a more demanding syntax, and place a greater emphasis on inferential reasoning.

Q: What does research say about facilitating comprehension?

A: Studies comparing novices and experts show that the conceptual organization of experts' knowledge is very different from that of novices. For example, experts emphasize core concepts when organizing knowledge, while novices focus on superficial details. To facilitate comprehension, effective teaching strategies should support and scaffold students as they build an understanding of the key concepts and concept relationships within a text unit.

Q: What strategies can teachers use to facilitate comprehension?

A: Three complementary strategies are very important in facilitating student comprehension of science texts. First, guide student interaction with the text using the built-in strategies. Second, organize the curriculum in terms of core concepts (e.g., the **Key Concepts** in each section). Third, develop visual representations of the relationships among the key concepts and vocabulary that can be referred to during instruction.

Nancy Romance, Ph.D.
Professor of Science Education
Florida Atlantic University
Fort Lauderdale, Florida

"Effective teaching strategies should support and scaffold students as they build an understanding of the key concepts and concept relationships within a text unit."

Reading Support in *Science Explorer*

The latest research emphasizes the importance of activating learners' prior knowledge and teaching them to distinguish core concepts from less important information. These skills are now more important than ever, because success in science requires students to read, understand, and connect complex terms and concepts.

Before students read—
Reading Preview introduces students to the key concepts and key terms they'll find in each section. The **Target Reading Skill** is identified and applied with a graphic organizer.

During the section—
Boldface Sentences identify each key concept and encourage students to focus on the big ideas of science.

Reading Checkpoints reinforce students' understanding by slowing them down to review after every concept is discussed.

Caption Questions draw students into the art and photos, helping them connect the content to the images.

After students read—
Section Assessment revisits the **Target Reading Skill** and encourages students to use the graphic organizer.

Each review question is scaffolded and models the way students think, by first easing them into a review and then challenging them with increasingly more difficult questions.

Evaluator's Checklist

Does your science program promote reading comprehension with—

✔ Text structured in an outline format and key concepts highlighted in boldface type

✔ Real-world applications to activate prior knowledge

✔ Key concepts, critical vocabulary, and a reading skill for every section

✔ Sample graphic organizers for each section

✔ Relevant photos and carefully constructed graphics with questions

✔ Reading checkpoints that appear in each section

✔ Scaffolded questions in section assessments

Math in the Science Classroom

Why should students concern themselves with mathematics in your science class?

Good science requires good data from which to draw conclusions. Technology enhances the ability to measure in a variety of ways. Often the scientist must measure large amounts of data, and thus an aim of analysis is to reduce the data to a summary that makes sense and is consistent with established norms of communication— i.e., mathematics.

Calculating measures of central tendency (e.g., mean, median, or mode), variability (e.g., range), and shape (graphic representations) can effectively reduce 500 data points to 3 without losing the essential characteristics of the data. Scientists understand that a trade-off exists between precision and richness as data are folded into categories, and so margins of error can be quantified in mathematical terms and factored into all scientific findings.

Mathematics is the language used by scientists to model change in the world. Understanding change is a vital part of the inquiry process. Mathematics serves as a common language to communicate across the sciences. Fields of scientific research that originated as separate disciplines are now integrated, such as happened with bioengineering. What do the sciences have in common? Each uses the language of mathematics to communicate about data and the process of data analysis. Recognizing this need, *Science Explorer* integrates mathematics practice throughout the program and gives students ample opportunity to hone their math skills.

Clearly, mathematics plays an important role in your science classroom!

William Tate, Ph.D.
Professor of Education and
American Culture Studies
Washington University
St. Louis, Missouri

> "Mathematics is the language used by scientists to model change in the world."

Integrated Math Support

In the Student Edition

The math instruction is based on principles derived from Prentice Hall's research-based mathematics program.

Sample Problems, Math Practice, Analyzing Data, and a Math Skills Handbook all help to provide practice at point of use, encouraging students to Read and Understand, Plan and Solve, and then Look Back and Check.

Color-coded variables aid student navigation and help reinforce their comprehension.

In the Teacher's Edition

Math teaching notes enable the science teacher to support math instruction and math objectives on high-stakes tests.

In the Guided Reading and Study Workbook

These unique worksheets help students master reading and enhance their study and math skills. Students can create a record of their work for study and review.

Evaluator's Checklist

Does your science program promote math skills by—

✔ Giving students opportunities to collect data

✔ Providing students opportunities to analyze data

✔ Enabling students to practice math skills

✔ Helping students solve equations by using color-coded variables

✔ Using sample problems to apply science concepts

Technology and Design

Technology and Design in the Science Classroom

Much of the world we live in is designed and made by humans. The buildings in which we live, the cars we drive, the medicines we take, and often the food we eat are products of technology. The knowledge and skills needed to understand the processes used to create these products should be a component of every student's basic literacy.

Some schools offer hands-on instruction on how technology development works through industrial arts curricula. Even then, there is a disconnect among science (understanding how nature works), mathematics (understanding data-driven models), and technology (understanding the human-made world). The link among these fields of study is the engineering design process—that process by which one identifies a human need and uses science knowledge and human ingenuity to create a technology to satisfy the need. Engineering gives students the problem-solving and design skills they will need to succeed in our sophisticated, three-dimensional, technological world.

As a complement to "science as inquiry," the National Science Education Standards (NRC, 1996) call for students at all age levels to develop the abilities related to "technology as design," including the ability to identify and frame a problem and then to design, implement, and evaluate a solution. At the 5–8 grade level, the standards call for students to be engaged in complex problem-solving and to learn more about how science and technology complement each other. It's also important for students to understand that there are often constraints involved in design as well as trade-offs and unintended consequences of technological solutions to problems.

As the *Standards for Technological Literacy* (ITEA, 2000) state, "Science and technology are like conjoined twins. While they have separate identities they must remain inextricably connected." Both sets of standards emphasize how progress in science leads to new developments in technology, while technological innovation in turn drives advances in science.

Ioannis Miaoulis, Ph.D.
President
Museum of Science
Boston, Massachusetts

"Engineering gives students the problem-solving and design skills they will need to succeed in our sophisticated, three-dimensional, technological world."

Evaluator's Checklist

Does your science program promote technology and design by—

✔ Incorporating technology and design concepts and skills into the science curriculum

✔ Giving students opportunities to identify and solve technological design problems

✔ Providing students opportunities to analyze the impact of technology on society

✔ Enabling students to practice technology and design skills

Technology and Design

Technology and Design in *Science Explorer*

How often do you hear your students ask: "Why do I need to learn this?" Connecting them to the world of technology and design in their everyday life is one way to help answer this question. It is also why so many state science curricula are now emphasizing technology and design concepts and skills.

Science Explorer makes a special effort to include a technology and design strand that encourages students to not only identify a need but to take what they learned in science and apply it to design a possible solution, build a prototype, test and evaluate the design, and/or troubleshoot the design. This strand also provides definitions of technology and engineering and discusses the similarities and differences between these endeavors and science. Students will learn to analyze the risks and benefits of a new technology and to consider the tradeoffs, such as safety, costs, efficiency, and appearance.

In the Student Edition

Integrated Technology & Design Sections

Sections throughout *Science Explorer* specifically integrate technology and design with the content of the text. For example, students not only learn how seismographs work but also learn what role seismographs play in society and how people use the data that are gathered.

Technology Labs

These labs help students gain experience in designing and building a device or product that meets a particular need or solves a problem. Students follow a design process of Research and Investigate, Design and Build, and Evaluate and Redesign.

Chapter Projects

Chapter Projects work hand-in-hand with the chapter content. Students design, build, and test based on real-world situations. They have the opportunity to apply the knowledge and skills learned to building a product.

Special Features

This technology and design strand is also reflected in Technology & Society and Science & Society features as well as Technology & History timelines. These highly visual features introduce a technology and its impact on society. For example, students learn how a hybrid car differs from a traditional car.

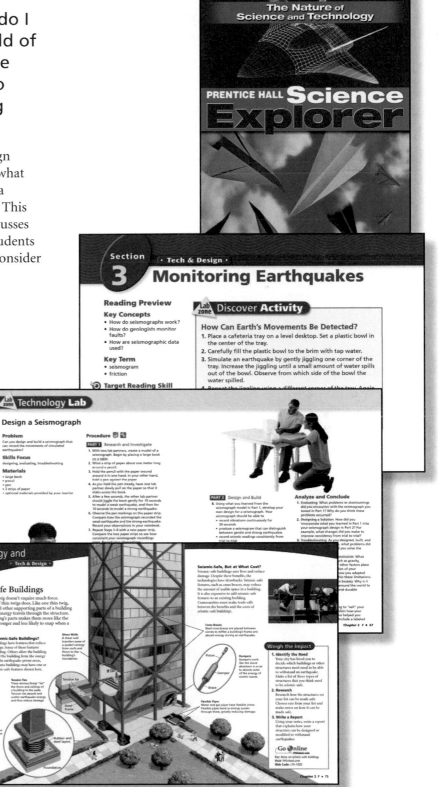

Assessment in the Science Curriculum

No Child Left Behind clearly challenges school districts across the nation to raise expectations for all students with testing of student achievement in science beginning in 2007–2008.

A primary goal of NCLB is to provide classroom teachers with better data from scientifically valid assessments in order to inform instructional planning and to identify students who are at risk and require intervention. It has been a common practice to teach a science lesson, administer a test, grade it, and move on. This practice is a thing of the past. With the spotlight now on improving student performance, it is essential to use assessment results as a way to identify student strengths and challenges. Providing student feedback and obtaining student input is a valuable, essential part of the assessment process.

Assessment is a never-ending cycle, as is shown in the following diagram. Although you may begin at any point in the assessment cycle, the basic process is the same.

An important assessment strategy is to ensure that students have ample opportunities to check their understanding of skills and concepts before moving on to the next topic. Checking for understanding also includes asking appropriate, probing questions with each example presented. This enables students and teachers to know whether the skills or concepts being introduced are actually understood.

Eileen Depka
Supervisor of Standards
and Assessment
Waukesha, Wisconsin

"Meeting the NCLB challenge will necessitate an integrated approach to assessment with a variety of assessment tools."

Implement the plan with a focus on gathering and using assessment information throughout.

Use a variety of assessment tools to gain information and strengthen student understanding.

Analyze assessment results to create a picture of student strengths and challenges.

Identify strategies to achieve the target, create a plan for implementation, and choose assessments tools.

Choose a target to create a focused path on which to proceed.

IMPLEMENT   ASSESS   ANALYZE   STRATEGIZE   TARGET

Evaluator's Checklist

Does your science program include assessments that—

✔ Are embedded before, during, and after lesson instruction

✔ Align to standards and to the instructional program

✔ Assess both skill acquisition and understanding

✔ Include meaningful rubrics to guide students

✔ Mirror the various formats of standardized tests

Assessment in *Science Explorer*

Science Explorer's remarkable range of strategies for checking progress will help teachers find the right opportunity for reaching all their students.

The assessment strategies in *Science Explorer* will help both students and teachers alike ensure student success in content mastery as well as high-stakes test performance. A wealth of opportunities built into the Student Edition help students monitor their own progress. Teachers are supported with ongoing assessment opportunities in the Teacher's Edition and an easy-to-use, editable test generator linked to content objectives. These integrated, ongoing assessment tools assure success.

Especially to support state and national testing objectives, Prentice Hall has developed test preparation materials that model the NCLB approach.

- **Diagnostic Assessment** tools provide in-depth analysis of strengths and weaknesses, areas of difficulty, and probable underlying causes that can help teachers make instructional decisions and plan intervention strategies.

- **Progress Monitoring** tools aligned with content objectives and state tests provide ongoing, longitudinal records of student achievement detailing individual student progress toward meeting end-of-year and end-of-schooling grade level, district, or state standards.

- **Outcomes** tools that mimic state and national tests show whether individual students have met the expected standards and can help a school system judge whether it has made adequate progress in improving its performance year by year.

Caption Questions enhance critical thinking skills

Reading Checkpoints reinforce students' understanding

Scaffolded Section Assessment Questions model the way students think

Comprehensive Chapter Reviews and Assessment provide opportunities for students to check their own understanding and practice valuable high-stakes test-taking skills

ExamView®, Computer Test Bank CD-ROM provides teachers access to thousands of modifiable test questions in English and Spanish

Test Preparation Blackline Masters and Student Workbook include diagnostic and prescription tools, progress-monitoring aids, and practice tests that help teachers focus on improving test scores.

Section 3 Assessment

Target Reading Skill Sequencing Refer to your flowchart about seismographs as you answer Question 1.

Reviewing Key Concepts

1. a. **Defining** What is a seismogram?
   b. **Explaining** How can geologists tell apart the different types of seismic waves on a seismogram?
   c. **Comparing and Contrasting** Two identical seismographs are located 1,000 km and 1,200 km from an earthquake's epicenter. How would the two seismograms for the earthquake compare?

2. a. **Reviewing** What changes are measured by the instruments used to monitor faults?
   b. **Describing** How are satellites used to measure movements along a fault?
   c. **Inferring** A satellite that monitors a fault detects an increasing tilt in the land surface along the fault. What could this change in the land surface indicate?

3. a. **Listing** What are three ways in which geologists use seismographic data?
   b. **Explaining** How do geologists use seismographic data to make maps of faults?
   c. **Making Generalizations** Why is it difficult to predict earthquakes?

Writing in Science

Dialogue Geologists in Alaska have just detected an earthquake and located the earthquake's epicenter. Write a dialogue in which the geologists notify a disaster response team that will help people in the earthquake area.

Chapter 2 F ◆ 65

Standardized Test Prep

Test-Taking Tip
When answering questions about diagrams, read all parts of the diagram carefully, including title, captions, and labels. Make sure that you understand the meaning of arrows and other symbols. Determine exactly what the question asks. Then eliminate those answer choices that are not supported by the diagram.

Practice answering this question.
The diagram shows how stress affects a mass of rock in a process called
  A compression.
  B tension.
  C squeezing.
  D shearing.
The correct answer is D because the arrows show rock being pulled in opposite directions.

Choose the letter that best answers the question or completes the statement.

1. In a strike-slip fault, rock masses along the fault move
   A in the same direction.
   B down only.
   C together.
   D sideways past each other.

2. Stress will build until an earthquake occurs if friction along a fault is
   F decreasing.   G high.
   H low.   J changed to heat.

Use the information below and your knowledge of science to answer Questions 3 and 4.

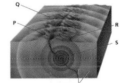

Seismic waves

3. When an earthquake occurs, seismic waves travel
   A from P in all directions.
   B from R to S.
   C from S in all directions.
   D from Q to P.

4. At point R, seismic waves from an earthquake would be
   F weaker than at P.
   G likely to cause little damage.
   H weaker than at Q.
   J likely to cause the most damage.

5. To estimate the total energy released by an earthquake, a geologist should use the
   A Mercalli scale.   B Richter scale.
   C epicenter scale.   D moment magnitude scale.

Constructed Response

6. A geologist discovers a large fault beneath a major city. Why would this information be helpful in determining earthquake risk in the area? What three safety steps should the geologist recommend?

Chapter 2 F ◆ 79

Master Materials List

SCIENCE EXPLORER offers an abundance of activity options in the Student Edition so you can pick and choose those that suit your needs. Prentice Hall has worked with Neo/SCI Corporation to develop Consumable Kits and Nonconsumable Kits that precisely match the needs of the **SCIENCE EXPLORER** labs. Use this Master Materials List or the Materials Ordering CD-ROM to help order your supplies. For more information on materials kits for this program, contact your local Prentice Hall sales representative or Neo/SCI Corporation at 1-800-526-6689 or **www.neosci.com**.

Consumable Materials

Description	Textbook Section(s)	Quantity per class	Description	Textbook Section(s)	Quantity per class
Aluminum foil, roll, 25 sq ft	3-2(DIS)	1			
Bag, plastic, resealable	3-2(Lab)	5			
* Cardboard, 4 square meters	3-1(CP)	5			
Cups, plastic	1-2(SA), 1-2(Lab), 3-1(Lab)	25			
* Eggs	1-2(DIS), 3-2(Lab)	15			
* Flowers, cut	1-2(Lab)	5			
* Graph paper, sheet	2-1(CP), 2-3(Lab)	10			
* Magazine	1-3(SA)	5			
Modeling clay, 1lb	3-2(Lab)	2			
* Packaging material	3-2(Lab)	5			
Paper, sheet	1-2(TT), 1-4(DIS), 2-1(DIS), 3-1(Lab)	35			
* Paperback book	1-4(Lab)	5			
* Pen, retractable	3-1(Lab)	5			
Salt, 100g	1-2(SA)	1			
* Scissors	2-1(DIS), 3-2(Lab)	5			
* Shoe box	2-2(TT)	5			
Spoon, plastic	1-2(Lab)	5			
Sugar, 100g	1-2(Lab), 1-2(SA)	1			
Tape, masking, roll	3-2(Lab)	1			

KEY: CP: Chapter Project; **DIS:** Discover; **SA:** Skills Activity; **TT:** Try This; **Lab:** Skills, Consumer, Design Your Own, & Technology and * items are school supplied.

Quantities based on five groups of six students per class.

Nonconsumable Materials

Description	Textbook Section(s)	Quantity per class	Description	Textbook Section(s)	Quantity per class
* Backpacks	2-1(Lab)	10			
* Balance, triple beam, single pan	2-1(SA), 2-1(Lab), 2-2(TT), 2-3(Lab)	5			
Beaker, low form, 600 mL	1-2(DIS)	10			
Cylinder, graduated, polypropylene, 100 mL	2-3(Lab)	5			
Marbles, jar	2-2(DIS)	5			
Meter stick	2-1(Lab), 3-2(Lab)	5			
Ruler, metric	2-2(TT)	5			
* Scissors	1-4(Lab), 2-1(DIS)	5			
* Stapler	1-4(Lab)	5			

KEY: CP: Chapter Project; **DIS:** Discover; **SA:** Skills Activity; **TT:** Try This; **Lab:** Skills, Consumer, Design Your Own, & Technology and * items are school supplied.

The Nature of Science and Technology

Book-Specific Resources

Student Edition
Interactive Textbook
Teacher's Edition
All-in-One Teaching Resources
Guided Reading and Study Workbook
Student Edition on Audio CD
Discovery Channel Video
Lab Activity Video
Consumable and Nonconsumable Materials Kits

Program Print Resources

Integrated Science Laboratory Manual
Computer Microscope Lab Manual
Inquiry Skills Activity Books
Test Preparation Blackline Masters
Test Preparation Workbook
Test-Taking Tips With Transparencies
Teacher's ELL Handbook
Reading in the Content Area

Program Technology Resources

Teacher Express™ CD-ROM
Interactive Textbook
Presentation Pro CD-ROM
Exam*View*®, Computer Test Bank CD-ROM
Lab zone™ Easy Planner CD-ROM
Student Edition Worksheet Library CD-ROM
Probeware Lab Manual With CD-ROM
Computer Microscope and Lab Manual
Materials Ordering CD-ROM
Discovery Channel DVD Library
Lab Activity DVD Library
Web Site at PHSchool.com

Spanish Print Resources

Spanish Student Edition
Spanish Guided Reading and Study Workbook
Spanish Teaching Guide With Tests

Acknowledgments appear on p. 162, which constitutes an extension of this copyright page.

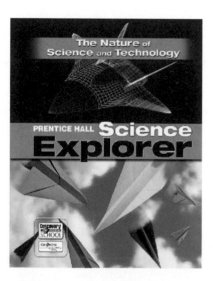

Cover
This model of a proposed spacecraft was generated on a computer (top). Colorful paper airplanes of different designs fly through the air (bottom).

ISBN 0-13-115380-3
1 2 3 4 5 6 7 8 9 10   08 07 06 05 04

Program Authors

Michael J. Padilla, Ph.D.
Professor of Science Education
University of Georgia
Athens, Georgia

Michael Padilla is a leader in middle school science education. He has served as an author and elected officer for the National Science Teachers Association and as a writer of the National Science Education Standards. As lead author of Science Explorer, Mike has inspired the team in developing a program that meets the needs of middle grades students, promotes science inquiry, and is aligned with the National Science Education Standards.

Ioannis Miaoulis, Ph.D.
President
Museum of Science
Boston, Massachusetts

Originally trained as a mechanical engineer, Ioannis Miaoulis is in the forefront of the national movement to increase technological literacy. As dean of the Tufts University School of Engineering, Dr. Miaoulis spearheaded the introduction of engineering into the Massachusetts curriculum. Currently he is working with school systems across the country to engage students in engineering activities and to foster discussions on the impact of science and technology on society.

Martha Cyr, Ph.D.
Director of K–12 Outreach
Worcester Polytechnic Institute
Worcester, Massachusetts

Martha Cyr is a noted expert in engineering outreach. She has over nine years of experience with programs and activities that emphasize the use of engineering principles, through hands-on projects, to excite and motivate students and teachers of mathematics and science in grades K–12. Her goal is to stimulate a continued interest in science and mathematics through engineering.

Book Authors

Andrew C. Kemp, Ph.D.
Assistant Professor of Education
University of Louisville
Louisville, Kentucky

Beth Miaoulis
Technology Writer
Sherborn, Massachusetts

Contributing Writer

Kenneth Welty, Ph.D.
Professor, School of Education
University of Wisconsin-Stout
Menomonie, Wisconsin

Consultants

Reading Consultant

Nancy Romance, Ph.D.
Professor of Science
    Education
Florida Atlantic University
Fort Lauderdale, Florida

Mathematics Consultant

William Tate, Ph.D.
Professor of Education and
    American Culture Studies
Washington University
St. Louis, Missouri

Reviewers

Tufts University Content Reviewers

Faculty from Tufts University in Medford, Massachusetts, participated in the development of *Science Explorer* chapter projects, reviewed the student books for content accuracy, and helped coordinate field testing.

Astier M. Almedom, Ph.D.
Department of Biology

Wayne Chudyk, Ph.D.
Department of Civil and Environmental Engineering

John Durant, Ph.D.
Department of Civil and Environmental Engineering

George S. Ellmore, Ph.D.
Department of Biology

David Kaplan
Department of Chemical Engineering

Samuel Kounaves, Ph.D.
Department of Chemistry

David H. Lee, Ph.D.
Department of Chemistry

Doug Matson, Ph.D.
Department of Mechanical Engineering

Karen Panetta, Ph.D.
Department of Electrical Engineering and Computer Science

John C. Ridge, Ph.D.
Department of Geology

William Waller, Ph.D.
Department of Astronomy

Content Reviewers

Jeff Bodart, Ph.D.
Chipola Junior College
Marianna, Florida

Michael Castellani, Ph.D.
Department of Chemistry
Marshall University
Huntington, West Virginia

Eugene Chiang, Ph.D.
Department of Astronomy
University of California – Berkeley
Berkeley, California

Charles C. Curtis, Ph.D.
Department of Physics
University of Arizona
Tucson, Arizona

Daniel Kirk-Davidoff, Ph.D.
Department of Meteorology
University of Maryland
College Park, Maryland

Diane Doser, Ph.D.
Department of Geological Sciences
University of Texas at El Paso
El Paso, Texas

Richard Duhrkopf, Ph.D.
Department of Biology
Baylor University
Waco, Texas

Michael Hacker
Co-director, Center for Technological Literacy
Hofstra University
Hempstead, New York

Michael W. Hamburger, Ph.D.
Department of Geological Sciences
Indiana University
Bloomington, Indiana

Alice Hankla, Ph.D.
The Galloway School
Atlanta, Georgia

Donald Jackson, Ph.D.
Department of Molecular Pharmacology, Physiology, & Biotechnology
Brown University
Providence, Rhode Island

Jeremiah Jarrett, Ph.D.
Department of Biological Sciences
Central Connecticut State University
New Britain, Connecticut

Becky Mansfield, Ph.D.
Department of Geography
Columbus, Ohio

Joe McCullough, Ph.D.
Department of Natural and Applied Sciences
Cabrillo College
Aptos, California

Robert J. Mellors, Ph.D.
Department of Geological Sciences
San Diego State University
San Diego, California

Joseph M. Moran, Ph.D.
American Meteorological Society
Washington, D.C.

David J. Morrissey, Ph.D.
Department of Chemistry
Michigan State University
East Lansing, Michigan

Philip A. Reed, Ph.D.
Department of Occupational & Technical Studies
Old Dominion University
Norfolk, Virginia

Scott M. Rochette, Ph.D.
Department of Earth Sciences
State University of New York, College at Brockport
Brockport, New York

Laurence D. Rosenheim, Ph.D.
Department of Chemistry
Indiana State University
Terre Haute, Indiana

Ronald Sass, Ph.D.
Department of Ecology & Evolutionary Biology
Rice University
Houston, Texas

George Schatz, Ph.D.
Department of Chemistry
Northwestern University
Evanston, Illinois

Sara Seager, Ph.D.
Carnegie Institution of Washington
Washington, D.C.

Robert M. Thornton, Ph.D.
Department of Biology
University of California
Davis, California

John R. Villarreal, Ph.D.
College of Science and Engineering
The University of Texas – Pan American
Edinburg, Texas

Kenneth Welty, Ph.D.
School of Education
University of Wisconsin–Stout
Menomonie, Wisconsin

Edward J. Zalisko, Ph.D.
Department of Biology
Blackburn College
Carlinville, Illinois

Teacher Reviewers

Steve Barbato
Lower Merion School
Ardmore, Pennsylvania

David R. Blakely
Arlington High School
Arlington, Massachusetts

Jane Callery
Two Rivers Magnet Middle
    School
East Hartford, Connecticut

Melissa Lynn Cook
Oakland Mills High School
Columbia, Maryland

James Fattic
Southside Middle School
Anderson, Indiana

Wayne Goates
Goddard Middle School
Goddard, Kansas

Katherine Bobay Graser
Mint Hill Middle School
Charlotte, North Carolina

Darcy Hampton
Deal Junior High School
Washington, D.C.

Karen Kelly
Pierce Middle School
Waterford, Michigan

David Kelso
Manchester High School Central
Manchester, New Hampshire

John G. Little
St. Mary's High School
Stockton, California

Benigno Lopez, Jr.
Sleepy Hill Middle School
Lakeland, Florida

Angie L. Matamoros, Ph.D.
ALM Consulting
Weston, Florida

Tim McCollum
Charleston Middle School
Charleston, Illinois

Bruce A. Mellin
Brooks School
North Andover, Massachusetts

Ella Jay Parfitt
Southeast Middle School
Baltimore, Maryland

Kathleen Poe
Duncan Fletcher Middle School
Jacksonville, Florida

Shirley Rose
Lewis and Clark Middle School
Tulsa, Oklahoma

Linda Sandersen
Greenfield Middle School
Milwaukee, Wisconsin

Mary E. Solan
Southwest Middle School
Charlotte, North Carolina

Mary Stewart
University of Tulsa
Tulsa, Oklahoma

Paul Swenson
Billings West High School
Billings, Montana

Thomas Vaughn
Arlington High School
Arlington, Massachusetts

Steve Wright
Butler Middle School
Waukesha, Wisconsin

Safety Reviewers

W. H. Breazeale, Ph.D.
Department of Chemistry
College of Charleston
Charleston, South Carolina

Ruth Hathaway, Ph.D.
Hathaway Consulting
Cape Girardeau, Missouri

Douglas Mandt
Science Education Consultant
Edgewood, Washington

Activity Field Testers

Nicki Bibbo
Russell Street School
Littleton, Massachusetts

Connie Boone
Fletcher Middle School
Jacksonville Beach, Florida

Rose-Marie Botting
Broward County School District
Fort Lauderdale, Florida

Colleen Campos
Laredo Middle School
Aurora, Colorado

Elizabeth Chait
W. L. Chenery Middle School
Belmont, Massachusetts

Holly Estes
Hale Middle School
Stow, Massachusetts

Laura Hapgood
Plymouth Community
    Intermediate School
Plymouth, Massachusetts

Sandra M. Harris
Winman Junior High School
Warwick, Rhode Island

Jason Ho
Walter Reed Middle School
Los Angeles, California

Joanne Jackson
Winman Junior High School
Warwick, Rhode Island

Mary F. Lavin
Plymouth Community
    Intermediate School
Plymouth, Massachusetts

James MacNeil, Ph.D.
Concord Public Schools
Concord, Massachusetts

Lauren Magruder
St. Michael's Country
    Day School
Newport, Rhode Island

Jeanne Maurand
Austin Preparatory School
South Hamilton, Massachusetts

Warren Phillips
Plymouth Community
    Intermediate School
Plymouth, Massachusetts

Carol Pirtle
Hale Middle School
Stow, Massachusetts

Kathleen M. Poe
Kirby-Smith Middle School
Jacksonville, Florida

Cynthia B. Pope
Ruffner Middle School
Norfolk, Virginia

Anne Scammell
Geneva Middle School
Geneva, New York

Karen Riley Sievers
Callanan Middle School
Des Moines, Iowa

David M. Smith
Eyer Middle School
Allentown, Pennsylvania

Gene Vitale
Parkland School
McHenry, Illinois

Zenovia Young
Meyer Levi Jr. HS/IS-285
Brooklyn, New York

Contents

The Nature of Science and Technology

Reference Section

Enhance understanding through dynamic video.

Preview Get motivated with this introduction to the chapter content.

Field Trip Explore a real-world story related to the chapter content.

Assessment Review content and take an assessment.

Get connected to exciting Web resources in every lesson.

SciLINKS Find Web links on topics relating to every section.

Active Art Selected visuals from every chapter become interactive online.

Planet Diary® Explore news and natural phenomena through weekly reports.

Science News® Keep up to date with the latest science discoveries.

Experience the complete text-book online and on CD-ROM.

Activities Practice skills and learn content.

Videos Explore content and learn important lab skills.

Audio Support Key terms are spoken and defined.

Self-Assessment Instant feedback helps you track your progress.

Activities

Super Inventor

Inquiry and Inventing

Engineer Lonnie Johnson has made a career as an inventor. By reading about his work, students will gain insights about how products are invented. They will read about how Lonnie Johnson became interested in inventing. They will also learn about the process he uses in developing his inventions, including how he perseveres to overcome problems. The skills that Lonnie Johnson uses in his career as an inventor are the same skills that students need to become successful in their future pursuits.

Build Background Knowledge

Who Invents New Products?

Have students recall products that have come onto the market in the last few years that have made a difference in their lives. Ask: **What new toy or device did not exist a few years ago that you now use all the time?** *(Sample answer: The DVD player came on the market several years ago and has practically replaced the VCR tape player.)* **How do you think this device was invented?** *(Sample answer: It was invented by a large company.)* Explain that new devices are often developed by large companies. But some person always has to come up with ideas for a new product or for a redesign of an existing product. Such a person is an inventor.

Introduce the Career

Before students read the feature, let them read the title, examine the pictures, and read the captions on their own. Then ask: **What questions came to mind as you looked at these pictures?** *(Sample answer: How did the inventor think of these inventions? What process did he use in developing these inventions?)* Explain to students that every invention starts with a basic idea. By reading about Lonnie Johnson, students will find out how an idea becomes reality through the work of an inventor.

Do you recognize this invention by Lonnie Johnson?

Super Inventor

Engineer Lonnie Johnson was working on a new invention. He was experimenting with ways to cool the inside of a refrigerator with plain water instead of with harmful chemicals. As he tested his cooling system with a homemade nozzle in his bathroom sink, he noticed that he could blast a stream of water across the room. He stepped back and thought, "Wouldn't it be great if . . .?"

"That sink nozzle was the idea for a super squirter," says Lonnie. But to make a water gun that could store enough energy to shoot a stream of water forcefully, he had to solve an engineering problem. How could he get a high-pressure water stream from a toy that a child could operate? How could he make the water shoot out in almost the same way that water comes out of a fire hydrant?

Recently, Lonnie set up his own company. He invents new devices to solve tough problems in science and engineering. But he also puts his ideas to work to invent new toys and household products. Lonnie says that whether you're working on a space vehicle or a toy, the process of inventing is much the same.

X ◆ P

Background

Facts and Figures Lonnie Johnson grew up in Marietta, Georgia. After he earned his master's degree at Tuskegee University in 1974, he joined the U.S. Air Force. When he left the service, he went to work for NASA at its Jet Propulsion Laboratory. There, he worked on control systems for space projects. Johnson worked part-time as an inventor on his own while in the Air Force and working for NASA. In 1985, he founded a company in Georgia that would become Johnson Research and Development. Johnson began work on his most famous invention in 1982. In 1991, he and his partner Bruce D'Andrade received a patent for what came to be called the SuperSoaker®, a high-performance pressurized water gun.

Talking With Lonnie Johnson

In high school, Lonnie won first place in a national science-fair competition with a homemade remote-control robot, which he called "Linex."

? **What kind of kid were you?**

I was always interested in how things work—in building and making things. My favorite toy was my erector set. I also liked those plastic building blocks. I used to take my brother's and sister's toys apart to see how they worked. And I used to repair stuff. If there was something broken around the house, like a lamp, I'd try to repair it. I learned from my father, too. He would work on his cars at home and that fascinated me. I was learning about machines by watching and helping him.

? **How did you get interested in engineering?**

The whole interest in building and fixing stuff—I guess that's where the seed came from. Repairing a broken lamp isn't all that different from inventing a super new toy. You need to be able to imagine how something works in your head, to see all the machine parts and how they'd work together—that's the basic skill. I'm usually pretty good at imagining how machines could be put together and work, whether they're big or small, simple or complex.

Career Path

Lonnie Johnson grew up in Alabama. He attended Tuskegee University and received a B.S. in mechanical engineering, an M.S. in nuclear engineering, and an honorary Ph.D. in science. He worked for the Jet Propulsion Laboratory in Pasadena, California. Now Lonnie owns his own company in Georgia.

P ◆ 1

Explore the Career

Choose from among the teaching strategies on these pages as you help your students explore the practical application of inquiry skills.

Use Visuals Have students look at the photo of the robot Lonnie Johnson made while in high school. Explain that he built this robot out of junkyard scraps. Ask: **How did Lonnie Johnson learn how to make such a complicated device?** *(He learned by taking toys apart, repairing broken lamps and other items around the house, and by watching his father work on cars and other machines around the house.)* **What have you ever had to repair on your own?** *(Sample answer: Repairing a broken bike was a necessity when there was no one else to turn to.)*

Demonstrate Lonnie Johnson talks of learning about devices by repairing lamps. Most students don't understand how a lamp works. Have a student read aloud Johnson's answer to the question, "How did you get interested in engineering?" Then demonstrate to students how to take apart a lamp. Make sure the lamp is unplugged. Then unscrew the light bulb and take apart the light-bulb socket. Point out how the wire is attached to the socket, and explain that such sockets can be purchased for little money in many stores. Show students how the wire runs down through and out the lamp.

Build Inquiry Skills Point out that Lonnie Johnson emphasizes that his ability to build things and his interest in engineering came from "building and fixing stuff." Divide the class into small groups, and give each group a common device that no longer works, such as a clock, a lamp, or a coffee maker. Ask students to examine the devices and take them apart as much as possible. Have each group prepare a report, including a labeled drawing, about how the device works and how it might be fixed. Ask groups to present their reports to the class.

Discuss Ask: **What is the need that motivated Lonnie Johnson to make a thermionic engine?** (*He wanted to make an engine that does not pollute the environment.*) **What was his first idea about this engine?** (*To make a mechanical engine, with moving parts*) **Why didn't that work out?** (*He faced problems when he tried to make the engine.*) **Did he give up on inventing a thermionic engine?** (*No. He devised a plan to make an engine with no moving parts.*) Emphasize that one quality an inventor has is not easily giving up. One failure did not deter Lonnie Johnson from trying to find a solution to the problem.

Build Science Skills Divide the class into small groups. Challenge each group to use Lonnie Johnson's answers to all the questions to infer a step-by-step process that he might use when working on a new invention. Using his answers as a guide, students might devise this process:

1. Think of a problem that needs to be solved.
2. Look for a solution to that problem.
3. Design technology to solve the problem.
4. Try out the technology, and redesign if necessary.
5. Keep looking for new solutions until the solution is right.
6. Build a model and obtain a patent.

When all groups have devised a process, call on a member of each group to read the process to the class. Write each process on the board, and lead a discussion about which group's process comes closest to how Lonnie Johnson explained how he proceeds. Finally, compare Johnson's process with the technology design process introduced in *Technology and Engineering*:

1. Identify a need
2. Research the problem
3. Design a solution
4. Build a prototype
5. Troubleshoot and redesign
6. Communicate the solution

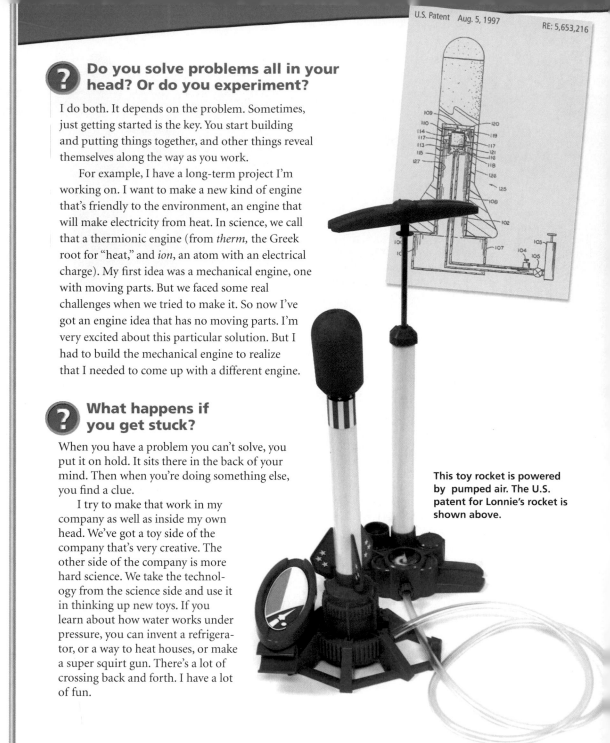

U.S. Patent   Aug. 5, 1997   RE: 5,653,216

? Do you solve problems all in your head? Or do you experiment?

I do both. It depends on the problem. Sometimes, just getting started is the key. You start building and putting things together, and other things reveal themselves along the way as you work.

For example, I have a long-term project I'm working on. I want to make a new kind of engine that's friendly to the environment, an engine that will make electricity from heat. In science, we call that a thermionic engine (from *therm*, the Greek root for "heat," and *ion*, an atom with an electrical charge). My first idea was a mechanical engine, one with moving parts. But we faced some real challenges when we tried to make it. So now I've got an engine idea that has no moving parts. I'm very excited about this particular solution. But I had to build the mechanical engine to realize that I needed to come up with a different engine.

? What happens if you get stuck?

When you have a problem you can't solve, you put it on hold. It sits there in the back of your mind. Then when you're doing something else, you find a clue.

I try to make that work in my company as well as inside my own head. We've got a toy side of the company that's very creative. The other side of the company is more hard science. We take the technology from the science side and use it in thinking up new toys. If you learn about how water works under pressure, you can invent a refrigerator, or a way to heat houses, or make a super squirt gun. There's a lot of crossing back and forth. I have a lot of fun.

This toy rocket is powered by pumped air. The U.S. patent for Lonnie's rocket is shown above.

Background

Facts and Figures Maintaining a career as an inventor is not easy. The myth of the inventor is that of a person working alone, in a primitive lab at home. That may have been true for inventors in the past, but most modern inventors work in the laboratories of large corporations. Most inventors first earn degrees in science or engineering, and then they work many years for companies in product design and development. After extensive experience, some inventors leave companies to work on their own—about 20 percent of patents are issued each year to private inventors. Many inventors work part-time at universities or as corporate engineers.

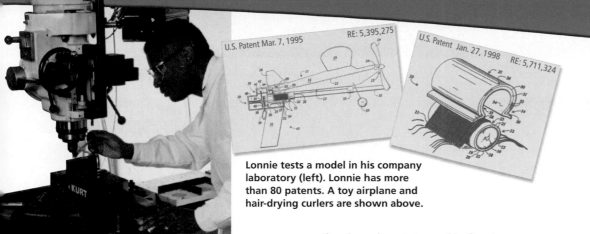

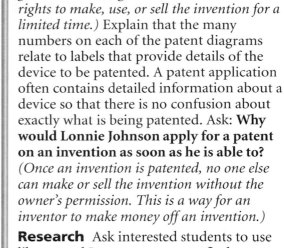

U.S. Patent Mar. 7, 1995   RE: 5,395,275

U.S. Patent Jan. 27, 1998   RE: 5,711,324

Lonnie tests a model in his company laboratory (left). Lonnie has more than 80 patents. A toy airplane and hair-drying curlers are shown above.

? How do you get started on an invention?

You ask the question: What would be a great thing to have? You develop an overall idea. Then you define it by thinking of the specific problems that need to be solved.

Think about model rockets. I used to build model rockets when I was a kid. I'd order them through the mail, assemble them, and launch them. After a while, I made my own. I went to the library and found a book on how to build them. But those rockets used explosive chemicals for fuel. I wanted to make toy rockets that were cleaner and safer. So now I've invented rockets that use pumped air and water for power.

? Is inventing hard?

If you can focus and work for a long time, you get very good at what you do. Problem solving is a process. There can be so many pieces to the puzzle. It's like a jigsaw puzzle. Sometimes all the pieces are there. Yet you can't even see them at first. But if you get your hands in and touch them and start working on it, you can start feeling the shapes. You start to understand how the pieces fit together.

I've always been interested in figuring out how to make things go and in working with new and different sources of power. When I was an engineer at NASA, I worked on the nuclear power source for the Galileo spacecraft. But I've also worked on powering toys with water and air, and making toy planes fly with rubber bands. The basic ideas are the same.

The trick is to keep working at it. Know what you're aiming for and keep looking for new solutions. Following through is also key to my philosophy: Believe in yourself and persevere. That's what I tell kids whenever I get the chance.

Writing in Science

Career Link Lonnie says the first step in an invention is the idea. Think of something that would be "a great thing to have," such as a toy or gadget. As an inventor, write a paragraph that describes your idea. Then, in a second paragraph, identify clearly some of the "little problems" you'll need to solve to make your idea work. (Remember, you don't need to know what the solutions will be.)

Go Online
PHSchool.com
For: More on this career
Visit: PHSchool.com
Web Code: cgb-6000

Go Online
PHSchool.com
For: More on this career
Visit: PHSchool.com
Web Code: cgb-6000

Students can do further research on this career and others that are related to science and technology.

Chapter at a Glance

 Chapter Project *Is It Really True?*

 **Teaching Resources**

- Chapter Project Teacher Notes, pp. 39–40
- Chapter Project Student Introduction, pp. 41–42
- Chapter Project Student Worksheets 1–2, pp. 43–44
- Chapter Project Scoring Rubric, p. 45

Technology

Video Preview

Local Standards

Section 1

2–3 periods
1–1 1/2 blocks

Thinking Like a Scientist

P.1.1.1 Identify skills scientists use to learn about the world.

P.1.1.2 Describe the attitudes, or habits of mind, that are important in science.

PHSchool.com

Section 2

4–5 periods
2–2 1/2 blocks

Scientific Inquiry

P.1.2.1 Explain what scientific inquiry involves.

P.1.2.2 Describe how to develop a hypothesis and design an experiment.

P.1.2.3 Differentiate between a scientific theory and a scientific law.

Video Field Trip

active art

Section 3

2–3 periods
1–1 1/2 blocks

Why Study Science?

P.1.3.1 Explain why people need to understand scientific principles and think scientifically.

P.1.3.2 Explain what scientific literacy is and why it is important.

SciLINKS NSTA

Section 4

2–3 periods
1–1 1/2 blocks

Careers in Science

P.1.4.1 List the three main branches of science.

P.1.4.2 Explain why it is important for scientists in different fields to work together.

P.1.4.3 Explain how science is important in nonscience careers.

SciLINKS NSTA

Review and Assessment

 Teaching Resources

- Key Terms Review, p. 82
- Transparency P5
- Performance Assessment Teacher Notes, p. 88
- Performance Assessment Scoring Rubric, p. 89
- Performance Assessment Student Worksheet, p. 90
- Chapter Test, pp. 91–94

Video Assessment

PHSchool.com

Test Preparation

Test Preparation Blackline Masters

- Diagnostic Test
- Benchmark Test

PRENTICE HALL
TeacherEXPRESS
Plan • Teach • Assess

Chapter Activities Planner

For more activities
LAB ZONE Easy Planner CD-ROM

Student Edition	Inquiry	Time	Materials	Skills	Resources
Chapter Project	Open-ended	Ongoing (2–3 weeks)	**All in One Teaching Resources** See p. 39	Developing hypotheses, designing experiments, interpreting data, drawing conclusions, communicating	**Lab zone Easy Planner** **All in One Teaching Resources** Support pp. 39–40
Section 1					
Discover Activity, p. 6	Open-ended	10 minutes		Observing	**Lab zone Easy Planner**
At-Home Activity, p. 12	Open-ended	Home		Classifying	**Lab zone Easy Planner**
Section 2					
Discover Activity, p. 13	Open-ended	15 minutes	2 eggs, 2 beakers	Posing questions	**Lab zone Easy Planner**
Skills Activity, p. 14	Directed	10 minutes		Classifying	**Lab zone Easy Planner**
Skills Activity, p. 16	Directed	10 minutes	Plastic cup, sugar or salt	Controlling variables	**Lab zone Easy Planner**
Try This Activity, p. 19	Directed	15 minutes	3 sheets of paper	Drawing conclusions	**Lab zone Easy Planner**
Skills Lab, p. 23	Guided	40 minutes	Plastic cups, cut flowers, spoon, sugar	Developing hypotheses, designing experiments, drawing conclusions	**Lab zone Easy Planner** **Lab Activity Video** **All in One Teaching Resources** Skills Lab: *Keeping Flowers Fresh*
Section 3					
Discover Activity, p. 24	Open-ended	5–10 minutes		Inferring	**Lab zone Easy Planner**
Skills Activity, p. 26	Directed	10–15 minutes	Magazine	Posing questions	**Lab zone Easy Planner**
Section 4					
Discover Activity, p. 30	Open-ended	10–15 minutes	Sheet of paper	Inferring	**Lab zone Easy Planner**
Skills Lab, p. 35	Guided	40 minutes	Paperback book, cut into sections and stapled together	Observing, inferring, predicting	**Lab zone Easy Planner** **Lab Activity Video** **All in One Teaching Resources** Skills Lab: *Piecing Information Together*
At-Home Activity, p. 37	Open-ended	Home		Classifying	**Lab zone Easy Planner**

Section 1 **Thinking Like a Scientist**

 *3–4 periods, 1 1/2–2 blocks*

Objectives

P.1.1.1 Identify skills scientists use to learn about the world.

P.1.1.2 Describe the attitudes, or habits of mind, that are important in science.

Local Standards

Key Terms

• observing • quantitative • qualitative • inferring • predicting • classifying
• making models • science • skepticism

Preteach

Build Background Knowledge

Students describe their experiences in science from previous years that involved observing.

Lab zone **Discover Activity** *How Keen Are Your Senses?*

Targeted Print and Technology Resources

 **Teaching Resources**

L2 Reading Strategy Transparency
P1: *Asking Questions*

○ **Presentation-Pro CD-ROM**

Transparency P1

Instruct

Observing Have students make quantitative and qualitative observations of the classroom.

Inferring Ask leading questions for a discussion on making inferences from observations.

Predicting Use the definition of *predicting* to help students understand how predictions are made.

Classifying Teach students about classifying by focusing on Jane Goodall's work with chimps.

Making Models Have groups make a list of models that would be useful in studying chimps.

Scientific Attitudes Ask leading questions for a discussion on scientists' habits of mind.

Targeted Print and Technology Resources

Teaching Resources

L2 Guided Reading, pp. 48–51

www.PHSchool.com Web Code: cgd-6011

○ **Student Edition on Audio CD**

Assess

Section Assessment Questions

Have students use their completed questions and answers to answer the questions.

Reteach

Students give examples of each of the skills scientists use to learn about the world.

Targeted Print and Technology Resources

Teaching Resources

• Section Summary, p. 47
L1 Review and Reinforce, p. 52
L3 Enrich, p. 53

Section 2 **Scientific Inquiry**

 4–5 periods, 2–2 1/2 blocks

ABILITY LEVELS
L1 Basic to Average
L2 For All Students
L3 Average to Advanced

Objectives

P.1.2.1 Explain what scientific inquiry involves.

P.1.2.2 Describe how to develop a hypothesis and design an experiment.

P.1.2.3 Differentiate between a scientific theory and a scientific law.

Key Terms

• scientific inquiry • hypothesis • variable • manipulated variable
• responding variable • controlled experiment • operational definition
• data • communicating • scientific theory • scientific law

Local Standards

Preteach

Build Background Knowledge

Students relate the steps they used in solving an everyday problem.

 **Discover Activity** *What's Happening?*

Targeted Print and Technology Resources

 **Teaching Resources**

L2 Reading Strategy: *Building Vocabulary*

⊙ **Presentation-Pro CD-ROM**

Instruct

Posing Questions Have students assess questions about how they might lead to scientific inquiry.

Developing a Hypothesis Use as an example the hypotheses proposed in the text.

Designing an Experiment Call on volunteers to define key terms related to a controlled experiment.

Collecting and Interpreting Data Use the cricket experiment as an example of how to collect and interpret data.

Drawing Conclusions Ask leading questions for a discussion on drawing conclusions.

Communicating Allow students to examine a variety of scientific publications.

Scientific Theories and Laws Make distinctions between common definitions and scientific usage.

 Skills Lab *Keeping Flowers Fresh*

Targeted Print and Technology Resources

 **Teaching Resources**

L2 Guided Reading, pp. 56–59
L2 Transparency P2
L2 Skills Lab: *Keeping Flowers Fresh*, pp. 62–64

📼 **Lab Activity Video/DVD**
Skills Lab: *Keeping Flowers Fresh*

www.PHSchool.com Web Code: cgp-6012

⊙ **Student Edition on Audio CD**

Transparency P2

P2 Nature of Inquiry

Video Field Trip

Assess

Section Assessment Questions

Have students use their completed definitions of each key term to answer the questions.

Reteach

Students describe scientific inquiry in terms of the cricket experiment.

Targeted Print and Technology Resources

Teaching Resources

• Section Summary, p. 55
L1 Review and Reinforce, p. 60
L3 Enrich, p. 61

Section 3 Why Study Science?

2–3 periods, 1–1 1/2 blocks

Objectives

P.1.3.1 Explain why people need to understand scientific principles and think scientifically.

P.1.3.2 Explain what scientific literacy is and why it is important.

Key Term
• scientific literacy

Local Standards

Preteach

Build Background Knowledge

Students consider why they need to know science to evaluate an environmental group's claim about pollution in a river.

Lab zone Discover Activity *How Much Do You See or Hear About Science?*

Targeted Print and Technology Resources

All in One Teaching Resources

L2 Reading Strategy Transparency P3: *Identifying Main Ideas*

⊙ **Presentation-Pro CD-ROM**

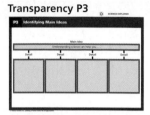
Transparency P3

Instruct

How Does It Work? Have students brainstorm a list of devices they use every day and should know about.

How Can I Stay Healthy? Ask leading questions for a discussion on how knowing science can help to stay healthy.

How Do I Become an Informed Citizen? Have students brainstorm a list of public issues involving science.

What Is the Best Use of Earth's Resources? Use the example of water use during a shower to discuss use of Earth's resources.

Scientific Literacy Define *scientific literacy* and discuss whether most people are scientifically literate.

Targeted Print and Technology Resources

All in One Teaching Resources

L2 Guided Reading, pp. 67–69

www.SciLinks.org Web Code: scn-1613

⊙ **Student Edition on Audio CD**

Assess

Section Assessment Questions

⟳ Have students use their completed graphic organizers about Identifying Main Ideas to answer the questions.

Reteach

Students explain how having scientific literacy could help in evaluating whether a river is polluted.

Targeted Print and Technology Resources

All in One Teaching Resources

• Section Summary, p. 66
L1 Review and Reinforce, p. 70
L3 Enrich, p. 71

Section 4 **Careers in Science**

🕐 *2–3 periods, 1–1 1/2 blocks*

ABILITY LEVELS
L1 Basic to Average
L2 For All Students
L3 Average to Advanced

Objectives

P.1.4.1 List the three main branches of science.

P.1.4.2 Explain why it is important for scientists in different fields to work together.

P.1.4.3 Explain how science is important in nonscience careers.

Local Standards

Preteach

Build Background Knowledge

Students discuss adults they know who use science in performing a job or pursuing a hobby.

Lab zone Discover Activity *What Do Scientists Look Like?*

Targeted Print and Technology Resources

All in One Teaching Resources

L2 Reading Strategy Transparency P4: *Using Prior Knowledge*

◉ **Presentation-Pro CD-ROM**

Transparency P4

Instruct

Branches of Science Write the three main branches of science on the board and ask students to list areas of study each includes.

Scientists Working Together Use the analogy of a sports team to explain how scientists work together.

Science in Nonscience Careers Use the nonscientists shown in the figure to discuss why everyone needs to know science.

Lab zone Skills Lab *Piecing Information Together*

Targeted Print and Technology Resources

All in One Teaching Resources

L2 Guided Reading, pp. 74–76

L2 Skills Lab: *Piecing Information Together,* pp. 79–81

📼 **Lab Activity Video/DVD**
Skills Lab: *Piecing Information Together*

www.SciLinks.org Web Code: scn-1614

◉ **Student Edition on Audio CD**

Assess

Section Assessment Questions

Have students use their completed graphic organizers about What You Know and What You Learned to answer the questions.

Reteach

Students classify different fields of study into one of the three main branches of science.

Targeted Print and Technology Resources

All in One Teaching Resources

• Section Summary, p. 73

L1 Review and Reinforce, p. 77

L3 Enrich, p. 78

Chapter 1 **Content Refresher**

Go Online
NSTA-PDi LINKS

For: Professional Development Support
Visit: www.SciLinks.org/PDLinks
Web Code: TK

Professional Development

Section 1 **Thinking Like a Scientist**

Skills and Attitudes A good example of a scientist with the proper skills and attitudes is Jane Goodall (1934–). She grew up in England and was working as a secretary in Kenya when she was recruited to do research on chimpanzees by famed physical anthropologist Louis Leakey. Goodall began her observations on the shore of Lake Tanganyika in Tanzania in 1960. Among her many important discoveries about these primates was that chimpanzees strip leaves off twigs to make a tool for finding termites in nests. Until this discovery, scientists thought only humans made tools. She also observed that chimps eat meat, disproving the widely accepted notion that they were herbivores. In 1977, she established the Jane Goodall Institute for Wildlife Research, Education, and Conservation. Goodall's field of biology is called ethology, which is the comparative study of animal behavior in the natural environment.

Address Misconceptions

An inference made from an observation may be incorrect, even when the inference seems obvious. For a strategy for overcoming this misconception, see **Address Misconceptions** in Section 1, *Thinking Like a Scientist.*

Section 2 **Scientific Inquiry**

A Process of Inquiry Many textbooks present the process of scientific inquiry in terms of a straight-line "scientific method" instead of the multipath process of scientific inquiry outlined in the section. Versions of the scientific method vary, but in its simplest form it includes the steps shown below. This general method originated during what has been called the Scientific Revolution in Europe, which occurred during the Renaissance period. Yet, doing science doesn't necessarily involve rigidly following a set method. The process of science is less structured than a strict "method" implies. Therefore, this textbook instead presents a process of scientific inquiry that incorporates the traditional scientific method but has no set path along which every scientific investigation proceeds. Central to this inquiry process—and a common theme in any explanation of how science proceeds—is the idea of using deductive reasoning to test hypotheses. Deduction is reasoning from the general to the specific. A hypothesis is

often a general statement. From that hypothesis, a scientist predicts that specific events or data will result under certain conditions. The scientist then sets up an experiment to test whether the predicted results will occur. In practice, a hypothesis is rarely confirmed with just one experiment. The experiment must be duplicated over and over. And the results of those experiments suggest other paths to follow in testing that hypothesis or related hypotheses. When a wide range of hypotheses are confirmed, an overarching scientific theory may be developed that explains a phenomenon. Scientists can also consolidate observations into scientific laws, or predictions of what is expected to happen every time under a certain set of conditions.

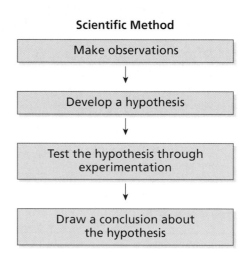

Scientific Method

Make observations

↓

Develop a hypothesis

↓

Test the hypothesis through experimentation

↓

Draw a conclusion about the hypothesis

Section 3 Why Study Science?

Science in Everyday Life Scientists and nonscientists use scientific terms and principles every day to understand the nature and technology around them. For example, most students have ridden on rollercoasters but know little about them. Rollercoasters vary in building materials. Old rollercoasters were large wooden constructions, and the cars moved up and down wooden hills. More modern rollercoasters are constructed mainly of long steel tubes—tubular tracks are supported by a large structure of steel tubes and beams. The steel tubes allow for complex loops, twists, and turns in the track. The whole structure is tied to concrete footers below, or holes dug into the ground and filled with concrete. Rollercoasters don't fall off the track when they go upside down because the cars have wheels that run on top of the steel-tube track and wheels that run both on the bottom of the track and on the sides. As the car reaches the top of a loop, a rider often feels weightless for a moment because of opposing forces—the force of gravity pulls the rider down while the acceleration of the car upward counterbalances that force of gravity.

Section 4 Careers in Science

Using Science in the Workplace Fields of Earth science include geology, oceanography, paleontology (fossils and ancient life), and meteorology (climate and weather). Fields of space science include astronomy and space exploration. The primary division in physical science is between physics and chemistry. Fields of physics include nuclear physics, particle physics, acoustics, electricity, magnetism, and thermodynamics. Branches of chemistry include organic chemistry (carbon-based chemistry), inorganic chemistry, and structural chemistry (quantitative explanations of chemical events). Branches of life science (biology) include zoology (animals), botany (plants), microbiology (microscopic organisms), and ecology (organisms and their environments). Knowledge of science is essential in performing many nonscientific jobs. For example, water is effective in putting out many fires, but not all. A firefighter learns that many materials react unfavorably to water. Sodium, for instance, reacts violently to the addition of water. Fires in sodium and other similar chemicals are put out with special foam, not water, and a firefighter must know

about these and other hazardous materials. To work in auditoriums and other halls, a sound technician must learn the basics of acoustics, a branch of physics. A chef must understand how to use the fungal organisms called yeasts. Through the process of alcoholic fermentation, the yeast *Saccharomyces* causes bread to rise.

Address Misconceptions

Many students may think that all scientists work through the complete science inquiry process on every project. Most scientists, though, have a more narrow focus. For a strategy for overcoming this misconception, see **Address Misconceptions** in Section 4, *Careers in Science*.

Help Student Read

Relating Text and Figures
Using Graphic Elements to Clarify and Extend

Strategy Help students relate figures to text in order to clarify difficult concepts in the text or to understand information beyond that stated in the text. This strategy enables students to focus on their own thought processes as they actively make use of photos and illustrations as tools to support comprehension. Before students begin, choose a subsection in Chapter 1, such as *Designing an Experiment* in Section 2.

Example
1. Have students keep their books closed as you read a few paragraphs aloud, including text that refers to a figure. You may want to think aloud as you read, saying, for example, "I wonder what that would be like?"
2. Then have the students open their books to the passage that you have read. Tell them to reread it and then study the figure and its caption carefully. Ask what parts of the passage make more sense when students look at the figure.
3. Point out that visuals also sometimes communicate information that is not in the text. Have students identify any new information that can be learned from the figure.
4. Have students work in pairs, with one reading aloud through the next reference to a figure, and then both working together to discuss how the figure helps them understand the passage or provides additional information.

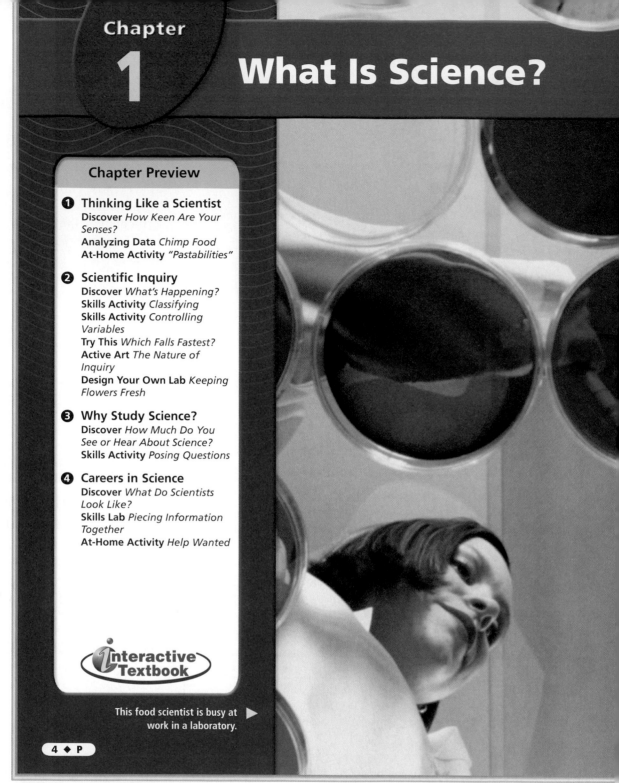

Chapter

1

What Is Science?

Chapter Preview

❶ Thinking Like a Scientist
Discover *How Keen Are Your Senses?*
Analyzing Data *Chimp Food*
At-Home Activity *"Pastabilities"*

❷ Scientific Inquiry
Discover *What's Happening?*
Skills Activity *Classifying*
Skills Activity *Controlling Variables*
Try This *Which Falls Fastest?*
Active Art *The Nature of Inquiry*
Design Your Own Lab *Keeping Flowers Fresh*

❸ Why Study Science?
Discover *How Much Do You See or Hear About Science?*
Skills Activity *Posing Questions*

❹ Careers in Science
Discover *What Do Scientists Look Like?*
Skills Lab *Piecing Information Together*
At-Home Activity *Help Wanted*

i̇nteractive Textbook

This food scientist is busy at ▶ work in a laboratory.

4 ◆ P

 Chapter **Project**

Objectives
Students will design and conduct a scientific experiment to test whether a common belief is true or false. After completing this Chapter Project, students will be able to
- develop a hypothesis about whether a common belief is true or false
- design a controlled experiment that will test the hypothesis
- interpret the data from the experiment and draw a conclusion about the hypothesis
- communicate results to the class

Skills Focus
Developing hypotheses, designing experiments, interpreting data, drawing conclusions, communicating

Project Time Line 2 weeks

All in One Teaching Resources
- Chapter Project Teacher Notes
- Chapter Project Worksheet 1
- Chapter Project Worksheet 2
- Chapter Project Scoring Rubric

4 ● P

Developing a Plan
Students should first brainstorm a list of common beliefs, starting with the three described in their text. Others include: the measure of a person's left fingertip to the right fingertip equals that person's height and warm water freezes faster than cold water. Then, each student should decide which common belief to investigate. All students should follow the process of scientific inquiry described under the heading *Scientific Inquiry*. Have students preview Figure 13 to get an idea about how they should proceed in this project.

Possible Materials
Materials may vary greatly from student to student, depending on the common belief each investigates. For example, to investigate the belief that yawning is contagious, students may not require any materials. An experiment to investigate that belief may focus on observing several groups of students. In contrast, to investigate the belief that a watched pot takes longer to boil, a group may need water, two pots, a heat source, and a clock. As students present their procedures to you, discuss what materials are

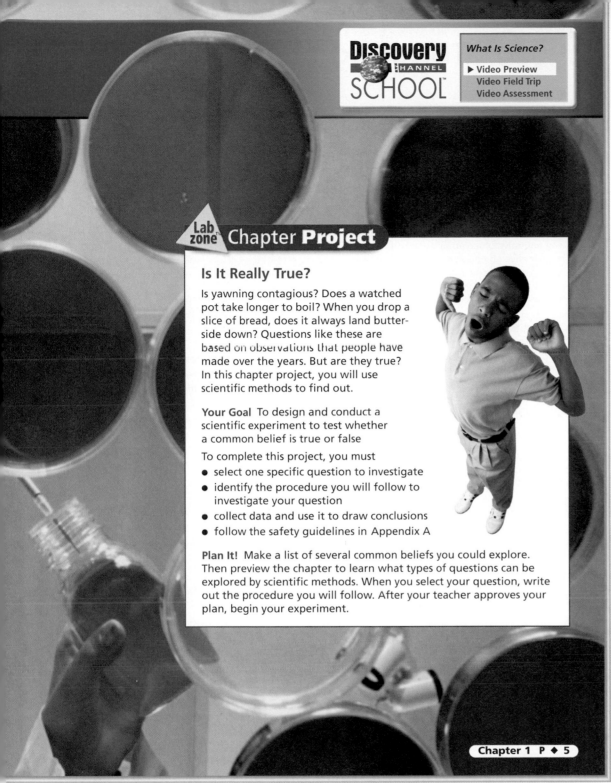

Lab zone ▸ Chapter **Project**

Is It Really True?

Is yawning contagious? Does a watched pot take longer to boil? When you drop a slice of bread, does it always land butter-side down? Questions like these are based on observations that people have made over the years. But are they true? In this chapter project, you will use scientific methods to find out.

Your Goal To design and conduct a scientific experiment to test whether a common belief is true or false

To complete this project, you must
● select one specific question to investigate
● identify the procedure you will follow to investigate your question
● collect data and use it to draw conclusions
● follow the safety guidelines in Appendix A

Plan It! Make a list of several common beliefs you could explore. Then preview the chapter to learn what types of questions can be explored by scientific methods. When you select your question, write out the procedure you will follow. After your teacher approves your plan, begin your experiment.

Chapter 1 P ◆ 5

What Is Science?

Show the Video Preview to introduce the Chapter Project and overview the chapter content. Discussion question: **How did the scientists follow the steps of observing, inferring, predicting, and modeling in their study of the Iceman?** *(They observed an arrowhead lodged in his back and inferred that he was murdered. They observed his remains and predicted that he was a shepherd and was perhaps killed for his sheep. To test their hypothesis, they created a model of his clothes and tough life as an alpine shepherd. Their observations of this model disproved their hypothesis.)*

Performance Assessment

The Chapter Project Scoring Rubric will help you evaluate how well students complete the Chapter Project. You may want to share the scoring rubric with your students so they are clear about what will be expected of them. Students will be assessed on
● how well they develop a hypothesis that can be tested
● how well they plan a procedure for a controlled experiment to test the hypothesis
● how well they carry out the procedure and collect the data that result
● how well they communicate their conclusion to the class
   Students can keep their hypotheses, test data, and conclusions in their portfolios.

Portfolio

needed to carry out the planned experiment and decide with students how those materials can be obtained.

Possible Shortcuts
● You can make this project shorter by dividing the class into groups rather than having individual students do investigations. All groups could focus on the same common belief.
● You could have groups choose a common belief, develop a hypothesis, and plan a

procedure. Then, you could choose one procedure to carry out as a demonstration.

Launching the Project
To introduce the project, lead a discussion about common beliefs concerning people and everyday objects that students have heard expressed among family or peers. Then, explain that they will be investigating whether one of those common beliefs is true or false using a process of scientific inquiry that they will learn about in this chapter.

Objectives

After this lesson, students will be able to
P.1.1.1 Identify skills scientists use to learn about the world.
P.1.1.2 Describe the attitudes, or habits of mind, that are important in science.

Target Reading Skill

Asking Questions Explain that changing a head into a question helps students anticipate the ideas, facts, and events they are about to read.

Answers

Sample questions and answers: **What does observing involve?** *(Observing involves using one or more of your senses to gather information.)* **What is inferring?** *(Inferring means to explain or interpret the things you observe.)* **What does predicting mean?** *(Predicting means making a forecast of what will happen in the future based on past experience or evidence.)* **What does making models involve?** *(Making models involves creating representations of complex objects or processes.)* **What is classifying?** *(Classifying is the process of grouping together items that are alike in some way.)* **What do scientific attitudes include?** *(Scientific attitudes include curiosity, honesty, open-mindedness, skepticism, and creativity.)*

All in One **Teaching Resources**
• Transparency P1

Preteach

Build Background Knowledge **L2**

Experience With Scientific Thinking
Encourage students to describe experiences in science from previous years that involved observing and then making an inference or a prediction from the observations. Then, ask students to draw from those experiences to describe the attitudes that a person should possess when observing or making inferences or predictions.

Reading Preview

Key Concepts
• What skills do scientist use to learn about the world?
• What attitudes are important in science?

Key Terms
• observing
• quantitative observation
• qualitative observation
• inferring • predicting
• classifying • making models
• science • skepticism

Target Reading Skill

Asking Questions Before you read, preview the red headings. In a graphic organizer like the one below, ask a *what, how,* or *why* question for each heading. As you read, write answers to your questions.

Scientific Skills

Question	Answer
What does observing involve?	Observing involves . . .

Go Online
PHSchool.com

For: More on scientific thinking
Visit: PHSchool.com
Web Code: cgd-6011

Discover Activity

How Keen Are Your Senses?

1. Your teacher has arranged for an unexpected event to occur. At the count of three, the event will begin.
2. List as many details as you can remember about the event.
3. Compare your list with those of your classmates.

Think It Over
Observing How many details could you list? Which of your senses did you use to gather information?

> Once, as I walked through thick forest in a downpour, I suddenly saw a chimp hunched in front of me. Quickly I stopped. Then I heard a sound from above. I looked up and there was a big chimp there, too. When he saw me he gave a loud, clear wailing *wraaaaah*—a spine-chilling call that is used to threaten a dangerous animal. To my right I saw a large black hand shaking a branch and bright eyes glaring threateningly through the foliage. Then came another savage *wraaaah* from behind. Up above, the big male began to sway the vegetation. I was surrounded.

These words are from the writings of Jane Goodall, a scientist who studies wild chimpanzees in Gombe National Park in Tanzania, Africa. What would you have done if you were in Jane's shoes? Would you have screamed or tried to run away? Jane did neither of these things. Instead, she crouched down and stayed still so she wouldn't startle the chimps. Not feeling threatened by her, the chimps eventually moved on.

It is not always easy to study animals in their natural homes. But Jane was determined to learn all she could about these great apes. One of the most remarkable things about Jane Goodall is that she essentially trained herself to be a scientist. **Scientists use skills such as observing, inferring, predicting, classifying, and making models to learn more about the world.** However, these skills are not unique to scientists. You, too, think like a scientist every day.

Discover Activity

Skills Focus Observing

Time 10 minutes

Tips Have a school staff member run into and out of the classroom wearing some distinct outfit, ringing a bell, and carrying something that smells strongly, such as a piece of pizza. Advise this person not to do anything that would frighten or disturb students.

Expected Outcome Most students will recall in general what occurred, but the details listed among students will vary widely.

Think It Over Some students may list two or three details, while others may list several or more. Students may report that they used sight, hearing, and smell in gathering information.

Observing

Jane Goodall has spent countless hours among the chimpanzees—quietly following them, taking notes, and carefully observing. **Observing** means using one or more of your senses to gather information. Your senses include sight, hearing, touch, taste, and smell. By using her senses, Jane learned what chimpanzees eat, what sounds they make, and even what games they play! During her time in Gombe, Jane made many surprising observations. For example, she observed how chimpanzees use stems or long blades of grass as tools to "fish" out a tasty meal from termite mounds.

Like Jane, you use your senses to gather information. Look around you. What do you see? What do you hear and smell? You depend on your observations to help you make decisions throughout the day. For example, if it feels chilly when you wake up, you'll probably dress warmly.

Observations can be either quantitative or qualitative. **Quantitative observations** deal with a number, or amount. Seeing that you have eight new e-mails in your inbox is a quantitative observation. **Qualitative observations,** on the other hand, deal with descriptions that cannot be expressed in numbers. Noticing that a bike is blue or that a grape tastes sour are qualitative observations.

 Reading Checkpoint What senses can the skill of observation involve?

Figure 1
Observing
By patiently observing chimpanzees, Jane Goodall learned many things about chimpanzee behavior. The inset shows one of Jane's earliest discoveries—that chimps use sticks as tools to fish for termites.

Observing

Teach Key Concepts　L2
Gathering Information

Focus Tell students that to explain how something occurs or to predict what may occur in the future, a scientist first gathers information about a topic, a skill called observing.

Teach To understand scientific observation, students need to understand the difference between quantitative and qualitative observations. Ask: **What is a quantitative observation?** *(A quantitative observation deals with a number, or amount.)* **What is a qualitative observation?** *(A qualitative observation deals with descriptions that cannot be expressed in numbers.)*

Apply Have students observe the classroom and everything in it and then make a list of five quantitative observations and five qualitative observations. **learning modality: visual**

	For: More on scientific thinking
Go Online PHSchool.com	Visit: PHSchool.com Web Code: cgd-6011

Students can review scientific thinking in an online interactivity.

Independent Practice　L2
All in One Teaching Resources

- Guided Reading and Study Worksheet: *Thinking Like a Scientist*

◉ **Student Edition on Audio CD**

Monitor Progress ——— L2

Oral Presentation Call on students to list skills scientists use to learn about the world and to differentiate between quantitative and qualitative observations.

Answer

 Reading Checkpoint Sight, hearing, touch, taste, and smell

Differentiated Instruction

Special Needs　L1
Classifying and Communicating Ask students in small groups to create a poster that differentiates between the two different kinds of observations. Students could use labeled drawings or pictures from magazines in constructing their posters. **learning modality: visual**

Gifted and Talented　L3
Methods of Observation The scientist discussed in this section, Jane Goodall, became world famous for her years of observing chimpanzees in Africa. Have students research this scientist's life and prepare a report to the class about the methods she used in making her observations. **learning modality: verbal**

Inferring

Teach Key Concepts [L2]

Interpreting Observations

Focus Tell students that making observations begins the process of learning about the world. A next step may be to explain or interpret one observation or several observations taken together.

Teach Ask: **What observations did Jane Goodall make concerning chimpanzees and tree hollows?** (*She observed a chimp chew leaves, push them in a tree hollow, and then put them back into its mouth. She also observed the gleam of water on the leaves when pulled out of the tree hollow.*) **What inference did she make from her observations?** (*She inferred that the chimp was using the leaves like a sponge to soak up water in the tree hollow.*) Emphasize that Goodall's inference was based on reasoning and was not simply a wild guess.

Apply Give students this fictional scenario: A student is missing from his usual bus to school, and when he arrives he looks tired. Then ask students what they might infer from these observations. (*Given these observations as well as past experience, students may infer that the student overslept.*)
learning modality: logical/mathematical

🚩 Address Misconceptions [L1]

Making Incorrect Inferences

Focus Explain that an inference made from an observation may be incorrect, even when the inference seems obvious.

Teach Ask: **If you skipped breakfast on a day that you aced a math test, would a reasonable inference be that skipping a meal caused your success?** (*Some students may say yes. Others will argue that skipping the meal had nothing to do with acing the test.*)

Apply Point out that many people take vitamin C whenever they get a cold. Because they've quickly recovered from a cold when taking vitamin C in the past, they infer that the vitamin "cures" colds. Ask: **What is the observation?** (*The person quickly recovered from a cold after taking vitamin C.*) **What is the inference?** (*Vitamin C cured the cold.*) **How could you prove that taking vitamin C cures colds?** (*Carry out experiments testing whether people who took vitamin C recovered from colds faster than those who didn't.*)
learning modality: logical/mathematical

Inferring

One day, Jane Goodall saw something peculiar. She watched as a chimpanzee peered into a hollow in a tree. The chimp picked off a handful of leaves from the tree and chewed on them. Then it took the leaves out of its mouth and pushed them into the tree hollow. When the chimp pulled the leaves back out, Jane saw the gleam of water. The chimp then put the wet leaves back in its mouth.

What was the chimpanzee doing? Jane reasoned that the chimpanzee might be using the chewed leaves like a sponge to soak up water. Seeing the chimp chew on leaves, put them in the hollow, and then squeeze the liquid out are all examples of observations. But Jane went beyond simply observing when she reasoned why the chimpanzee was doing these things. When you explain or interpret the things you observe, you are **inferring,** or making an inference.

Making an inference doesn't mean guessing wildly. Inferences are based on reasoning from what you already know. Jane knew that chimpanzees, like all other animals, need water, and that rainwater collects in tree hollows. She reasoned that the chimp was using chewed leaves to get the water out of the tree.

You, too, make inferences all the time. Because your brain processes observations and other information so quickly, you may not even realize when you have made an inference. For example, if you see your friend smile after getting back an exam, you might automatically infer that she got a good grade. Inferences are not always correct, however. Your friend's smile might not have anything to do with the test.

✓ **Reading Checkpoint** What is inferring?

FIGURE 2
Inferring
When you explain or interpret your observations, you are making an inference. **Inferring** *List three inferences you can make about this chimp.*

Predicting

Jane's understanding of chimpanzee behavior grew as time went by. Sometimes, she could even predict what a chimp was going to do next. **Predicting** means making a forecast of what will happen in the future based on past experience or evidence.

Through her observations, Jane learned that when a chimpanzee is frightened or angry, its hairs stand on end. This response is sometimes followed by threatening gestures such as charging, throwing rocks, and shaking trees, or even an attack. Therefore, if Jane sees a chimp with its hairs on end, she can predict that there might be danger and move away.

Likewise, you would probably move away if you saw a dog growling or baring its teeth. Why? Because predicting is part of your everyday thinking. You might predict, for example, that your basketball team will win tonight's game if you have always beaten the other team in the past. Predictions, of course, are not always correct. New players this year may increase the other team's chances of winning.

Predictions and inferences are closely related. While inferences are attempts to explain what is happening or *has* happened, predictions are forecasts of what *will* happen. If you see a broken egg on the floor by a table, you might infer that the egg had rolled off the table. If, however, you see an egg rolling toward the edge of a table, you can predict that it's about to create a mess.

FIGURE 3
Predicting
Predictions are forecasts of what will happen next.
Predicting *What do you think this chimp will do next?*

 Reading Checkpoint What are predictions based on?

Math ▶ Analyzing Data

Chimp Food

This graph shows the diet of chimps at Gombe National Park during May of one year.

1. **Reading Graphs** According to the graph, what foods do chimps eat?

2. **Interpreting Data** Did chimps feed more on seeds or leaves during this month?

3. **Calculating** What percentage of the diet did blossoms, seeds, leaves, and fruit make up?

4. **Predicting** Suppose you learn that November is the main termite-fishing season, when chimps spend a large part of their time eating termites. Predict how the chimp diet might change in November.

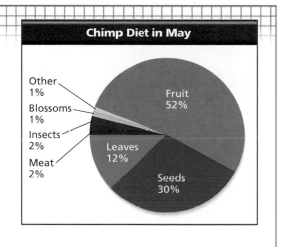

Chimp Diet in May

- Other 1%
- Blossoms 1%
- Insects 2%
- Meat 2%
- Leaves 12%
- Seeds 30%
- Fruit 52%

Predicting

Teach Key Concepts   L2

Making a Forecast

Focus Tell students that scientists make predictions of what will happen in the future based both on observations and experience.

Teach Ask: **What is predicting?** (*Making a forecast of what will happen in the future based on past experience or evidence*) Emphasize that a scientific prediction should be based on evidence and is always placed in the context of a scientist's past experience.

Apply Ask: **If, on a sunny afternoon, you observe a massive line of large, dark clouds quickly advancing on your area, what prediction might you make?** (*Most students will predict that rain and even thunderstorms may soon arrive.*) **What would you base your prediction on?** (*On the observation of advancing clouds and on past experience with weather in your area*) **learning modality: logical/mathematical**

Math ▶ Analyzing Data

Math Skill Making and interpreting graphs

Focus Point out the circle graph, and remind students that this type of graph is used to show portions of a whole.

Teach Ask: **How can a circle graph be used in making a prediction?** (*It shows evidence about the different portions of a whole.*)

Answers

1. Fruit, seeds, leaves, meat, insects, blossoms, and other foods
2. Seeds
3. 95%
4. Insects will constitute a much greater portion of the chimps' diet, with other foods diminishing proportionately.

Monitor Progress   L2

Answers

Figure 2 Sample answer: The chimp is hungry. The chimp is using the rock as a tool. The chimp eats nuts.

Figure 3 Sample answer: The chimp appears to be angry, and it may charge or attack.

 Reading Checkpoint Explaining or interpreting an observation

 Reading Checkpoint Past experience or evidence

Classifying

Teach Key Concepts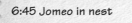
Grouping Items

Focus Tell students that one way scientists organize their observations is by classifying.

Teach Ask: **Jane grouped together information about Jomeo's feeding habits. What kind of information would she have classified in that grouping?** *(What foods Jomeo ate and the proportions of each type of food, when Jomeo fed, whether Jomeo ate with other chimps or ate alone, and so on)* **How would this sort of classifying aid her in understanding chimpanzees?** *(By classifying behaviors, Jane could better compare her observations of various chimps. She could also compare her observations of chimps with those of other scientists. She might also better see patterns and trends.)*

Apply Explain the basic difference between evergreen and deciduous plants. Then students can make a survey of all the plants on the school grounds, classifying each plant into one or the other category. **learning modality: visual**

Classifying Objects

Materials various small objects of different sizes, shapes, and colors

Time 15 minutes

Focus Tell students that scientists often collect a great variety of observations in doing an investigation and classifying what they have observed may be difficult.

Teach Place the objects on a table in the classroom. Challenge students to observe the objects and devise a classification system that might be useful.

Apply After all students have completed their classifications, have students present their systems to the class. Ask: **What is the value of classifying things, as you have with objects in the classroom?** *(Sample answer: Classifying objects helps in understanding the various kinds of objects in a place and the proportions of each kind.)* **learning modality: verbal**

FIGURE 4
Classifying
Field notes like these contain many details about a chimp's daily activities. By grouping together all the information related to resting, climbing, or feeding, Jane can better understand the chimp's behavior.

6:45 Jomeo in nest

6:50 Jomeo leaves nest, climbs, feeds on viazi pori fruit

7:16 Wanders along, feeding on budyankende fruits

8:08 Stops feeding, climbs, and feeds on viazi pori fruit again

8:35 Travels

Resting

Classifying

What do chimps do all day? To find out, Jane and her assistants followed the chimpanzees through the forest. They took detailed field notes about the chimps' behaviors. Figure 4 shows a short section of notes about Jomeo, an adult male chimp.

Suppose Jane wanted to know how much time Jomeo spent feeding or resting that morning. She could find out by classifying Jomeo's actions into several categories. **Classifying** is the process of grouping together items that are alike in some way. For example, Jane could group together all the information about Jomeo's feeding habits or his resting behavior. This would also make it easier to compare Jomeo's actions to those of other chimps. For instance, she could determine if other adult males feed or rest as much as Jomeo does.

You, too, classify objects and information all the time. Classifying things helps you to stay organized so you can easily find and use them later. When you put papers in a notebook, you might classify them by subject or date. And, you might have one drawer in your dresser for shirts and another for socks.

 Reading Checkpoint How is classifying objects useful?

Differentiated Instruction

English Learners/Beginning Vocabulary: Science Glossary
Pronounce and define aloud key terms for students. Suggest that they start a personal glossary of key terms for this and subsequent chapters. They might write each term and its definition in English on one side of an index card and in the student's primary language on the other side. **learning modality: verbal**

English Learners/Intermediate Vocabulary: Science Glossary Students can expand on the Beginning activity by adding important terms encountered in the text other than the key terms. In this section, they might add *curiosity, support, disprove,* and *scientific journal.* Have students write sentences that use each of these words. **learning modality: verbal**

Climbing

Feeding

Making Models

How far do chimpanzees travel? Where do they go? Sometimes, Jane's research team would follow a particular chimpanzee for many days at a time. Figure 5 illustrates Jomeo's journey through the forest over the course of one day. The diagram is one example of a model. **Making models** involves creating representations of complex objects or processes. Models help people study and understand things that are complex or that can't be observed directly. Using a model like the one in Figure 5, Jane and her assistants could share information that would otherwise be difficult to explain.

Models are all around you. They include physical objects, such as globes and movie sets used in filming your favorite TV show. Some models are generated by computer, like the ones some architects use to design new buildings. It's important to keep in mind that models are only representations of the real object or process. Because some information may be missing from a model, you may not be able to understand everything about the object or process the model represents.

 **Reading Checkpoint** What is a model?

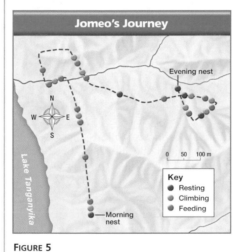

Jomeo's Journey

Evening nest

Lake Tanganyika

Morning nest

0   50   100 m

Key
● Resting
● Climbing
● Feeding

FIGURE 5
Making Models
This map is a model that traces Jomeo's journey through the forest. It represents information that would be hard to explain in words. **Interpreting Maps** *What is the total distance that Jomeo traveled between the morning and evening nests?*

Scientific Attitudes

Teach Key Concepts

Scientists' Habits of Mind

Focus Point out that doing science is also done best with certain attitudes.

Teach List these attitudes on the board: curiosity, honesty, open-mindedness, skepticism, creativity. Call on students to define each attitude and give an example.

Apply Invite students to explain why each attitude would be good for a scientist to have. **learning modality: verbal**

Monitor Progress _____ L2

Answer

✓ **Reading Checkpoint** Having an attitude of doubt

Assess

Reviewing Key Concepts

1. a. Observing, inferring, predicting, classifying, and making models.
b. Observations are information gathered using one or more of your senses. Inferences are explanations or interpretations of the things you have observed. **c.** This is an inference because it does not describe an observation. Rather, it is a reasoned interpretation of the behavior of the cat.
2. a. Curiosity, honesty, open-mindedness, skepticism, and creativity **b.** Open-mindedness helps a scientist consider new and different ideas. Skepticism helps a scientist question whether or not the ideas are correct. **c.** Sample answer: Yes. Without open-mindedness, you would not be capable of accepting new and different ideas. Without skepticism, you might accept new ideas that are incorrect.

Reteach L1

Call on students to explain and give examples of each of the five skills that scientists use to learn more about the world.

Performance Assessment L2

Writing Ask students to write a newspaper article that describes Jane Goodall's work.

All in One Teaching Resources

- Section Summary: *Thinking Like a Scientist*
- Review and Reinforcement: *Thinking Like a Scientist*
- Enrich: *Thinking Like a Scientist*

FIGURE 6
Curiosity
Scientists are driven by a curiosity to learn more about what they are studying.

Scientific Attitudes

Why has Jane Goodall devoted her life to studying chimps? Some people might say that she wants to contribute to "science." **Science** is a way of learning about the natural world. Science also includes all of the knowledge gained by exploring the natural world. **Successful scientists possess certain important attitudes, or habits of mind, including curiosity, honesty, open-mindedness, skepticism, and creativity.**

Curiosity An important attitude that drives scientists is curiosity. Successful scientists are eager to learn more about the topics they study. They stick with problems in spite of setbacks.

Honesty Good scientists always report their observations and results truthfully. Honesty is especially important when a scientist's results go against previous ideas or predictions.

Open-Mindedness and Skepticism Scientists need to be open-minded, or capable of accepting new and different ideas. However, open-mindedness should always be balanced by **skepticism,** which is having an attitude of doubt.

Creativity Whether scientists study chimps or earthquakes, problems may arise in their studies. Sometimes, it takes a bit of creativity to find a solution. Creativity means coming up with inventive ways to solve problems or produce new things.

✓ **Reading Checkpoint** What is skepticism?

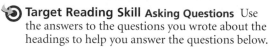

Section 1 Assessment

🎯 **Target Reading Skill Asking Questions** Use the answers to the questions you wrote about the headings to help you answer the questions below.

Reviewing Key Concepts

1. a. Listing Name five skills that are important in scientific thinking.
   b. Comparing and Contrasting How do observations differ from inferences?
   c. Classifying Is this statement an observation or an inference? *The cat must be ill.* Explain your reasoning.
2. a. Identifying What attitudes help scientists succeed in their work?

   b. Explaining Why is it important for scientists to balance open-mindedness and skepticism?
   c. Making Judgments Is it important to be both open-minded and skeptical in your everyday life? Explain.

Lab zone **At-Home Activity**

"Pastabilities" Collect pasta of various shapes and sizes. You and a family member should each devise a system to classify the pasta into three groups. How similar were your groupings?

Lab zone **At Home Activity**

Pastabilities You may want to display some different kinds of pasta in class to give students some idea about the common shapes. Spaghetti, tubes, and bow-tie pasta are examples. Explain that each type of pasta has a common name. Students should avoid these names in making their classification systems.

Lab zone **Chapter Project**

Keep Students on Track By this time, students should have made a list of possible common beliefs and chosen one to investigate. Check to see that each belief students have chosen to study involves a scientific question. Check the procedures students propose for both soundness and safety.

Scientific Inquiry

Reading Preview

Key Concepts
- What is scientific inquiry?
- What makes a hypothesis testable?
- How do scientific theories differ from scientific laws?

Key Terms
- scientific inquiry
- hypothesis • variable
- manipulated variable
- responding variable
- controlled experiment
- operational definition • data
- communicating
- scientific theory • scientific law

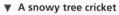
Target Reading Skill
Building Vocabulary A definition states the meaning of a word or phrase by telling about its most important feature or function. After you read this section, reread the paragraphs that contain definitions of Key Terms. Use all the information you have learned to write a definition of each Key Term in your own words.

▼ A snowy tree cricket

Lab zone Discover Activity

What's Happening?

1. Your teacher will give you two eggs and two beakers filled with water.
2. Put one egg in each beaker. Observe what happens.

Think It Over
Posing Questions Write down three questions you have about your observations. How could you find out the answer?

"Chirp, chirp, chirp." It is one of the hottest nights of summer and your bedroom windows are wide open. On most nights, the quiet chirping of crickets gently lulls you to sleep, but not tonight. The noise from the crickets is almost deafening. "Chirp, chirp, chirp, chirp, chirp!"

Why do all the crickets in your neighborhood seem determined to keep you awake tonight? Could the crickets be chirping more because of the heat? How could you find out?

As you lie awake, you are probably not thinking much about science. But, in fact, you are thinking just as a scientist would. You made observations—you heard the loud chirping of the crickets and felt the heat of the summer night. Your observations led you to infer that heat might cause increased chirping. You might even make a prediction: "If it's cooler tomorrow night, the crickets will be quieter, and I can get a good night's sleep!"

Although you might not know it, your thinking and questioning is the start of the **scientific inquiry** process. **Scientific inquiry refers to the diverse ways in which scientists study the natural world and propose explanations based on the evidence they gather.** If you have ever tried to figure out why your CD player has stopped working, then you have used scientific inquiry. Similarly, you could use scientific inquiry to find out whether there is a relationship between the air temperature and crickets' chirping.

Chapter 1 P ◆ 13

Lab zone Discover Activity

Skills Focus Posing questions

Materials 2 raw eggs, 2 beakers, salt

Time 10 minutes

Tips For each student or group, fill two beakers with the same volume of water. Add salt to one beaker to a high enough concentration that when an egg is placed in the water the egg will float— approximately 3 teaspoons of salt.

Expected Outcome Students will observe that the egg placed in one beaker will sink and the egg placed in the other beaker (with saltwater) will float.

Think It Over Sample answer: Why did one egg sink and the other float? The answers could be found out by testing the eggs and the water in each beaker.

Section

2

Scientific Inquiry

Objectives
After this lesson, students will be able to
P.1.2.1 Explain what scientific inquiry involves.
P.1.2.2 Describe how to develop a hypothesis and design an experiment.
P.1.2.3 Differentiate between a scientific theory and a scientific law.

Target Reading Skill
Building Vocabulary Explain that knowing the definitions of key terms helps students understand what they read.

Answers
Sample answers: **scientific inquiry** (*A process that includes the different ways that scientists find out about the natural world*); **hypothesis** (*One possible answer to a scientific question*); **variable** (*Something that can change in an experiment*); **manipulated variable** (*The variable that is changed on purpose during an experiment*); **responding variable** (*The variable that changes in response to changes in the manipulated variable*); **controlled experiment**; (*An experiment in which only one variable is manipulated*); **operational definition**; (*A description of how to measure a variable or define a term*); **data** (*Facts, figures, and other evidence that a scientists collects through observing*) Students should also define *communicating, scientific theory*, and *scientific law*.

Preteach

Build Background Knowledge   L2

Solving Everyday Problems

Ask: **What are some problems you've solved recently, such as having to fix something or having to decide how to proceed in treating an injury or illness?** (*Students might describe fixing a broken bicycle or overcoming a sports injury.*) **What were the steps you used in solving this problem?** (*Sample answer: The first step was trying to figure out exactly what was wrong. The next step was considering alternative solutions and deciding which was best.*)

Instruct

Posing Questions

Teach Key Concepts [L2]

Beginning Inquiry With Questions

Focus Explain to students that a scientist often begins the process of inquiry by posing questions about an observation.

Teach Have students think about the example of a CD player that stopped working. Then, elicit responses from students about what questions they might ask themselves based on the observation that the CD player doesn't work. Have students assess how each question might lead to scientific inquiry that would involve gathering evidence.

Apply Tell students that a local biologist observes one summer that a certain species of bird once common to your area no longer can be found. Ask: **Given this observation, what scientific questions do you think the biologist would ask to begin a scientific inquiry?** *(Sample questions: Why has the bird disappeared from the area? Has a disease wiped out the population? Has the environment changed in some way?)* **learning modality: verbal**

Independent Practice [L2]

All in One Teaching Resources

• Guided Reading and Study Worksheet: *Scientific Inquiry*

⊙ **Student Edition on Audio CD**

---

14 ◆ P

Lab zone Skills Activity

Classifying

Which of the following questions can be answered by scientific inquiry?

• Is running a better sport than swimming?

• Does running make your muscles stronger than swimming does?

• Which brand of running shoes looks best?

How did you make your decision in each case?

FIGURE 7
Posing Questions
Scientific inquiry often begins with a problem or question. Questions often arise from experiences or observations.

The temperature is really warm tonight.

I wonder if the air temperature affects the chirping of crickets.

Posing Questions

Scientific inquiry often begins with a problem or question about an observation. In the case of the crickets, your question might be: Does the air temperature affect the chirping of crickets? Of course, questions don't just come to you from nowhere. Instead, questions come from experiences that you have and from observations and inferences that you make. Curiosity plays a large role as well. Think of a time that you observed something unusual or unexpected. Chances are good that your curiosity sparked a number of questions.

Some questions cannot be investigated by scientific inquiry. Think about the difference between the two questions below.

• Why has my CD player stopped working?

• What kind of music should I listen to on my CD player?

The first question is a scientific question because it can be answered by making observations and gathering evidence. For example, you could change the batteries in your CD player and observe whether it begins to work. In contrast, the second question has to do with personal opinions or values. Scientific inquiry cannot answer questions about personal tastes or judgments.

✓ **Reading Checkpoint** What role does curiosity play in posing questions?

Lab zone Skills Activity

Skills Focus Classifying

Time 10 minutes

Tips This can be either an individual or a group activity.

Expected Outcome Students will typically judge that the first question cannot be answered by scientific inquiry, since the answer may simply be a matter of taste. Some students may say that the word *better* can be interpreted in terms of health or some other measurable quality. The second question is a scientific question because it can be answered by making observations and gathering evidence. The third question is not a scientific question, because any answer would be about personal preferences. **learning modality: verbal**

Developing a Hypothesis

How could you explain your observation of noisy crickets on that summer night? "Perhaps crickets chirp more when the temperature is higher," you think. In trying to answer the question, you are developing a hypothesis. A **hypothesis** (plural: *hypotheses*) is a possible explanation for a set of observations or answer to a scientific question. In this case, your hypothesis would be that cricket chirping increases at higher air temperatures.

It is important to realize that a hypothesis is *not* a fact. Instead, it is only one possible way to explain a group of observations. In the case of the crickets, perhaps they only sounded louder that night because you had left more windows open than you usually do. Or, maybe there were more crickets around that night.

In science, a hypothesis must be testable. This means that researchers must be able to carry out investigations and gather evidence that will either support or disprove the hypothesis. Many trials will be needed before a hypothesis can be accepted as true.

 What is a hypothesis?

Perhaps crickets chirp more when the temperature is higher.

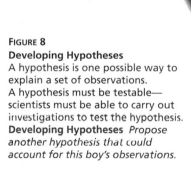

FIGURE 8
Developing Hypotheses
A hypothesis is one possible way to explain a set of observations. A hypothesis must be testable— scientists must be able to carry out investigations to test the hypothesis.
Developing Hypotheses *Propose another hypothesis that could account for this boy's observations.*

Developing a Hypothesis

Teach Key Concepts　L2
A Possible Explanation

Focus Tell students that after posing questions, scientists proceed by focusing on a possible answer to one question in particular.

Teach Ask: **What does it mean that a hypothesis is "testable"?** (*Researchers must be able to carry out investigations and gather evidence that will either support or disprove the hypothesis.*)

Apply Tell students that one explanation for why crickets chirp more on hot summer nights is that the crickets just feel like chirping more on those nights. Ask: **Could this explanation be a scientific hypothesis? Why or why not?** (*It could not be because it is not testable.*) **learning modality: logical/mathematical**

Show the Video Field Trip to let students experience forensic investigators gathering and interpreting evidence to solve a crime. Discussion question: **How much more evidence would modern investigators have about Toms than investigators from 200 years ago?** (*They would have photos of the crime scene, temperature of the victim, cast of the footprint, hair and fibers, DNA analysis of blood, and gun powder residue.*)

Monitor Progress　L2

Writing Ask students to write three scientific questions about today's weather and then develop a hypothesis for each question.

Answers
Figure 8 Sample answer: Maybe there were more crickets around that night.

 Curiosity sparks questions about an observation.

 A possible explanation for a set of observations or answer to a scientific question

---

⌐ Differentiated Instruction ¬

Less Proficient Readers　L1
Answering Questions Select a passage from the text, such as *Developing a Hypothesis*. Read the passage aloud to students as they follow along in their books. After reading, ask some questions about the passage. If they don't know the answers, challenge them to find the answers in the passage. **learning modality: verbal**

Gifted and Talented　L3
Before students read the section on scientific inquiry, ask them to propose in writing a process of scientific inquiry that they think would work best in finding the answer to a scientific question. After they have read the section, ask them to compare the process they proposed with the process described in the text. **learning modality: verbal**

Designing an Experiment

Teach Key Concepts L2
Testing a Hypothesis

Focus Tell students that scientists design an experiment in such a way that an experiment will yield results that will prove or disprove the hypothesis.

Teach After students have read the description of the cricket experiment, call on volunteers to define *variable, manipulated variable,* and *responding variable.* Ask: **What is the manipulated variable and the responding variable in this experiment?** *(Air temperature and number of cricket chirps, respectively)* **Why is this considered a controlled experiment?** *(Only one variable is being tested—air temperature. All other variables are controlled.)*

Apply Have small groups of students design an experiment to test this hypothesis: Crickets are more active at 12:00 midnight than at 12:00 noon. Emphasize that the experiment should have a manipulated variable and a responding variable, and all other variables should be controlled.
learning modality: logical/mathematical

Help Students Read
Relating Text and Figures Refer to the Content Refresher in this chapter, which provides the guidelines for the Relating Text and Figures strategy.

Have students read the text related to designing an experiment. Then, have them use Figure 9 to identify the variables that were designed as part of the cricket experiment. Ask: **What evidence do you see in the photo of what the manipulated variable was in the cricket experiment?** *(Each container is labeled with a different temperature, and thus the manipulated variable is air temperature.)* **What can you see from the photo about variables that were controlled in this experiment?** *(The containers look identical. The environments within the containers look identical or at least very similar. Only one small container is labeled as a cricket holder, and therefore the crickets are the same in each large container. All the containers are aligned in a row, which means they will all receive the same amount of light.)*

Lab zone **Skills Activity**

Controlling Variables
Suppose you are designing an experiment to determine whether sugar or salt dissolves more quickly in water. What is your manipulated variable? What is your responding variable? What other variables would you need to control?

Designing an Experiment

After you state your hypothesis, you are ready to design an experiment to test it. You know that your experiment will involve counting how many times crickets chirp when the air temperature is high. But how will you know how many times the crickets would chirp at a lower temperature? You would need to include other crickets in your experiment for comparison.

Controlling Variables To test your hypothesis, then, you will need to observe crickets at different air temperatures. All other **variables,** or factors that can change in an experiment, must be exactly the same. Other variables include the kind of crickets, the type of container you test them in, and the type of thermometer. By keeping all of these variables the same, you will know that any difference in cricket chirping must be due to temperature alone.

The one variable that is purposely changed to test a hypothesis is called the **manipulated variable** (also called the independent variable). In your cricket experiment, the manipulated variable is the air temperature. The factor that may change in response to the manipulated variable is called the **responding variable** (also called the dependent variable). The responding variable here is the number of cricket chirps.

We've set up the containers to be identical except for the temperature conditions.

Now we have to agree on how to time and count the chirps.

15°C 20°C

16 ◆ P

CRICKETS

Lab zone **Skills Activity**

Skills Focus Controlling variables

Time 10 minutes

Expected Outcome The variables present in such an experiment would include the amount of water in each container, the amount of salt, and the amount of sugar. Some students might also mention the temperature of the water. The manipulated variable is the solute used—either sugar or salt. The responding variable is the time taken for the solute to dissolve.

Extend Challenge students to carry out their experiments. Students should develop a hypothesis and plan how data will be collected before they begin the experiment. **learning modality: logical/ mathematical**

Setting Up a Controlled Experiment An experiment in which only one variable is manipulated at a time is called a **controlled experiment.** Figure 9 shows one way to set up a controlled experiment to test your cricket hypothesis. Notice that identical containers, thermometers, leaves, and crickets are used in each setup. In one container, the temperature will be maintained at 15°C. In the other two containers, the temperatures will be kept at 20°C and 25°C.

The Importance of Controlling Variables Suppose you decide to test the crickets at 15°C in the morning and the crickets at 20°C and 25°C in the afternoon. Is this a controlled experiment? The answer is no. Your experiment would have two variables—temperature and time of day. Would increased chirping be due to the temperature difference? Or are crickets more active at certain times of day? There would be no way to know which variable explained your results.

Forming Operational Definitions One other important aspect of a well-designed experiment is having clear operational definitions. An **operational definition** is a statement that describes how to measure a particular variable or define a particular term. For example, in this experiment you would need to determine what sounds will count as a single "chirp."

 Reading Checkpoint What is a manipulated variable?

FIGURE 9
A Controlled Experiment
In their controlled experiment, these students are using the same kind of containers, thermometers, leaves, and crickets. The manipulated variable in this experiment is temperature. The responding variable is the number of cricket chirps per minute at each temperature.
Controlling Variables *What other variables must the students keep constant in this experiment?*

Chapter 1 P ◆ 17

Lab zone Teacher **Demo**

Time 15 minutes
Materials 2 marbles of different sizes, spring scale, towel, ruler

Focus Explain that one of the best-known experiments in history is an experiment by Galileo. He showed that objects of different weights fall at the same rate and hit the ground at the same time.

Teach Show students that one marble is very much larger than the other, and then weigh both marbles on the spring scale. Have students speculate about which marble will hit the floor first if both are dropped from the same height at the same time. Then, place both marbles on the edge of a desk and position a folded towel on the floor below. Have volunteers in position to see which marble hits the floor first. With the ruler, push both marbles off the desk at the same time. Repeat the procedure several times, allowing all students to observe. Ask: **Which marble hit the floor first?** *(They both hit at the same time.)* Tell students this experiment supports the hypothesis that objects fall at the same rate, no matter what their weight.

Apply Ask: **What is the manipulated variable in this experiment?** *(Marble weight)* **What is the responding variable?** *(Rate of fall)* **What variables are controlled?** *(Height of fall, moment fall begins, landing area, shape and material of falling objects, air temperature)* **learning modality: visual**

Differentiated Instruction

English Learners/Beginning Comprehension: Modified Cloze **L1**
Distribute a simplified paragraph about designing an experiment, but leave some words blank. Model how to fill in the blanks, using a sample sentence on the board. Provide students with the correct answers as choices. **learning modality: verbal**

English Learners/Intermediate Comprehension: Modified Cloze **L2**
Distribute the same paragraph, but include some additional terms as incorrect answer choices. After students complete the paragraph, have them work together to write definitions for the answer choices that were not used. **learning modality: verbal**

Monitor Progress _____ **L2**

Oral Presentation Ask students to explain what a controlled experiment is and why it is always important to control variables in such an experiment.

Answers
Figure 9 Sample answer: Time of day, amount of light, other noises in the environment

 Reading Checkpoint The one variable in an experiment that is purposely changed to test a hypothesis

Collecting and Interpreting Data

Teach Key Concepts   _{L2}
Organizing Data and Graphing Results

Focus Tell students that a good controlled experiment yields quantitative observations that can be recorded in a table or a graph.

Teach Ask a volunteer to read the definition of *data*, and then direct students' attention to Figure 10. Ask: **What data were gathered in the cricket experiment?** *(The number of cricket chirps per minute)* **For what purpose was this data gathered?** *(To test the hypothesis that cricket chirping increases at higher temperatures)* Emphasize that recording data in a data table is a good way of organizing the data in anticipation of drawing a conclusion about the hypothesis.

Apply Show students various data tables and graphs from experiments that have been published in scientific journals. Call on students to describe the kinds of data collected in these tables. **learning modality: visual**

Use Visuals: Figure 10   _{L2}
The Benefits of a Graph

Focus Tell students that a graph is another way of organizing data gathered in a controlled experiment. A graph shows patterns and trends in the data better than a data table does.

Teach Ask volunteers to explain what is measured on the *x*-axis and the *y*-axis of the graph. Have students look at the row of the data table that shows the average number of chirps per minute at the three temperatures tested. Then, correlate those numbers with the points marked on the graph. Ask: **What trend do you observe in the data gathered in the experiment?** *(The number of chirps increase as the temperature rises.)* Point out that the data table provides the specifics of the data, while the graph provides a visual pattern in the data.

Apply Ask: **Suppose the experiment also gathered data about chirps at 30°C. How would the line on the graph be different?** *(Given the trend shown by the graph, the line would likely rise to a point over 200.)* **learning modality: logical/mathematical**

FIGURE 10
Collecting and Interpreting Data
A data table helps you organize the information you collect in an experiment. Graphing the data may reveal any patterns in your data.
Interpreting Data *Did all of the crickets chirp more at 25°C than at 20°C? Did you use the data table or the graph to answer this question?*

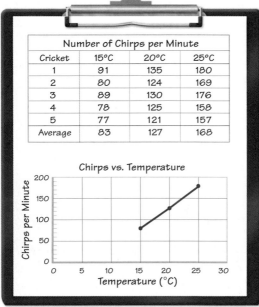

Number of Chirps per Minute			
Cricket	15°C	20°C	25°C
1	91	135	180
2	80	124	169
3	89	130	176
4	78	125	158
5	77	121	157
Average	83	127	168

Chirps vs. Temperature

Collecting and Interpreting Data

You are almost ready to begin your experiment. But first, you must decide how many crickets to test. Because individual differences exist from cricket to cricket, you will need to test more than just one or two. You decide to test five crickets at each temperature.

Organizing Your Data Before you begin your experiment, you should create a table like the one in Figure 10 in which to record your data. **Data** are the facts, figures, and other evidence gathered through observations. A data table provides you with an organized way to collect and record your observations.

Graphing Your Results After all the data have been collected, they need to be interpreted. One useful tool that can help you interpret data is a graph. Graphs will be discussed in more detail in Chapter 2.

Study the graph in Figure 10 to see how graphing can help you make sense of your data. Graphs can reveal patterns or trends in data. For example, notice that your data points seem to fall in a line. You can see that as the temperature increases from 15°C to 25°C, the number of chirps per minute also increases.

Reading Checkpoint   What are data?

Drawing Conclusions

Now that you have gathered and interpreted your data, you can draw conclusions about your hypothesis. A conclusion is a summary of what you have learned from an experiment. In drawing your conclusion, you should ask yourself whether the data supports the hypothesis. You also need to consider whether you collected enough data and whether anything happened during the experiment that might have affected the results. You should address these questions in your summary of the experiment.

After reviewing the data, you decide that the evidence supports your original hypothesis. You conclude that cricket chirping does increase with temperature. It's no wonder that you have trouble sleeping on those warm summer nights!

Inquiry Leads to Inquiry Scientific inquiry usually doesn't end once a set of experiments is done. Often, one scientific inquiry leads into another one. You have found that crickets do indeed chirp more as the temperature rises. But does this apply to all kinds of crickets everywhere? And what happens at lower temperatures? These new questions can lead to new hypotheses and new experiments.

Lab zone Try This **Activity**

Which Falls Fastest?
Design an experiment to determine which falls fastest—an unfolded sheet of paper, a sheet of paper folded in fourths, or a crumpled sheet of paper. Be sure to develop a hypothesis, design a controlled experiment, and collect data.

Drawing Conclusions Does your data support your hypothesis?

Cricket chirping does increase with temperature!

I wonder if temperature affects the rate of bird chirps, too.

FIGURE 11
Drawing Conclusions
Conclusions from an experiment often lead to additional questions to investigate. **Posing Questions** *What new questions does the cricket experiment lead you to ask?*

Chapter 1 P ◆ 19

Lab zone Try This **Activity**

Skills Focus Drawing conclusions

Materials 3 sheets of paper, watch or clock with second hand

Time 15–20 minutes

Expected Outcome Gravity causes objects to fall at the same rate unless another force opposes that downward motion, such as air resistance. The crumpled sheet of paper will fall at about the normal rate, but air resistance will cause the unfolded sheet to fall much slower. The paper folded in fourths will likely fall at a rate between the other two. Possible hypothesis: The crumpled sheet of paper will fall fastest. A typical experiment will involve dropping the different sheets from the same height in the same conditions. **learning modality: visual**

Drawing Conclusions

Teach Key Concepts   L2
A Summary of What's Been Learned

Focus Tell students that the purpose of gathering data from an experiment is to draw a conclusion about whether the data support or disprove the original hypothesis.

Teach Ask: **What was the hypothesis the cricket experiment was designed to test?** (*Cricket chirping increases at higher temperatures.*) **Was this hypothesis supported?** (*Yes*) **What do you base your conclusion on?** (*An interpretation of the data shown in Figure 10*)

Apply Direct students' attention to the new questions that the cricket experiment led to: "Does this apply to all kinds of crickets?" and "What happens at lower temperatures?" Then, divide the class into small groups, and ask each group to write a new hypothesis for one of the questions and describe an experiment that would test that hypothesis.

Extend The *active art* will show students about the process of scientific inquiry.
learning modality: visual

Monitor Progress _____   L2

Skills Check Daily newspapers often have a table that shows the progression of air temperatures on the previous day. Copy the table onto the board. Then ask students to make a line graph from that data and write a description of any pattern or trend they see in the temperatures during the day.

Students can save their graphs in their portfolios.

Portfolio

Answers
Figure 10 They all chirped more at the higher temperature. Only the data table provides information for the answer.
Figure 11 Sample answer: Why does cricket chirping increase with temperature? Does the chirping begin to decrease above a certain temperature? Do crickets increase any other activity as the temperature rises?

✓ **Reading Checkpoint** Facts, figures, and other evidence gathered through observations

Use Visuals: Figure 12

A Process of Many Paths

Focus Have students recall the process involved in investigating crickets chirping. Ask: **What were the steps involved in finally drawing a conclusion about cricket chirping?** *(Make observations, pose questions, develop a hypothesis, design an experiment, gather data, and draw a conclusion)*

Teach Tell students that scientific inquiry is a process of many paths. Direct their attention to Figure 12, and ask: **Why is the phrase *Posing Questions* placed at the center of the process?** *(A surprising observation or accidental discovery at any stage of the process can lead to new questions, which in turn lead to new hypotheses and experiments.)*

Apply Ask: **Would a scientist be wrong to discontinue a long-running experiment before it was completed in order to pursue another direction?** *(No, because a surprising observation or accidental discovery made during the experiment may suggest a better way to proceed)* **learning modality: verbal**

All in One Teaching Resources

• Transparency P2

Go Online
active art

For: The Nature of Inquiry activity
Visit: PHSchool.com
Web Code: cgp-6012

Students can interact with the art of the nature of inquiry online.

The Nature of Inquiry

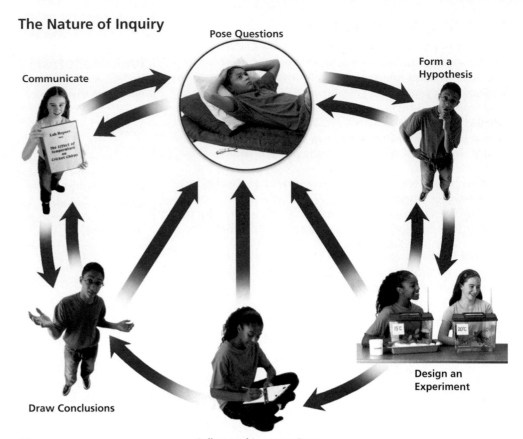

Pose Questions

Communicate

Form a Hypothesis

Draw Conclusions

Design an Experiment

Collect and Interpret Data

FIGURE 12
There is no set path that a scientific inquiry must follow. Observations at each stage of the process may lead you to modify your hypothesis or experiment. Conclusions from one experiment often lead to new questions and experiments.

Go Online
active art

For: The Nature of Inquiry activity
Visit: PHSchool.com
Web Code: cgp-6012

The Nature of Inquiry In this cricket experiment, you decided to test your hypothesis in one particular way. Your friend may do it another way. Furthermore, different questions may require different approaches to finding answers. For example, a scientist studying the moon may rely more on observations rather than controlled experiments to test a hypothesis.

Scientific inquiry is a process with many paths, not a rigid sequence of steps. Often, a surprising observation or accidental discovery leads into inquiry. New information springs up, then a scientist's path takes a different turn. Work may go forward—or even backward—when testing a hunch or fitting a new idea with existing ones.

Reading Checkpoint Why doesn't the scientific inquiry process follow a rigid set of steps?

Communicating

An important part of the scientific inquiry process is communicating your results. **Communicating** is the sharing of ideas and experimental findings with others through writing and speaking. Scientists share their ideas in many ways. For example, they give talks at scientific meetings, exchange information on the Internet, or publish articles in scientific journals.

Sometimes, a scientific inquiry can be part of a huge project with many scientists working together around the world. On such projects, scientists must share their ideas and findings on a regular basis. When scientists communicate their research, they describe their procedures in full detail so that others can repeat their experiments.

 Reading Checkpoint Why is communicating important to scientists?

Scientific Theories and Laws

As a body of knowledge, science is built up cautiously. Scientists do not accept a new hypothesis after just one successful experiment. Rather, a hypothesis is tested repeatedly as many different scientists try to apply it to their own work.

Scientific Theories Sometimes, a large set of related observations can be connected by a single explanation. This can lead to the development of a scientific theory. A **scientific theory** is a well-tested explanation for a wide range of observations or experimental results. For example, according to the atomic theory, all substances are composed of tiny particles called atoms. The atomic theory helps to explain many observations, such as why ice melts at a particular temperature and why iron nails rust.

Scientists accept a theory only when there is a large body of evidence that supports it. However, future testing can still prove an accepted theory to be incorrect. If that happens, scientists may modify the theory, or discard it altogether. This illustrates the ever growing—and exciting—nature of scientific knowledge.

FIGURE 13
A Scientific Theory
Based on observations of sunsets and sunrises, ancient people theorized that the sun revolved around Earth. New evidence led scientists to abandon that ancient theory. Today, scientists know that Earth, along with the other planets in the solar system, revolves around the sun.

Communicating

Teach Key Concepts [L2]

Sharing Ideas and Findings

Focus Tell students that scientists depend on other scientists to communicate their findings fully and accurately.

Teach Ask: **What would happen if a space scientist discovered something new about the solar system but failed to report the discovery to other scientists?** *(Other scientists would continue their work without the new information, and the work might be wasted as a result.)*

Apply Ask students why it is important for scientists to communicate the details of experiments to other scientists and to the public. **learning modality: verbal**

Scientific Theories and Laws

Teach Key Concepts [L2]

Explanations and Patterns

Focus Explain that the words *theory* and *law* have special meanings in science.

Teach Have a volunteer read aloud the definition of *scientific theory*. Discuss how that definition differs from the common meaning of the word. Then, have a volunteer read the definition of *scientific law*, and discuss how its definition differs from the common meaning.

Apply Ask: **Would a scientific law that is true in New York also be true in Alabama?** *(Scientific laws hold true for every state, and throughout the universe. A scientific law is a rule of nature, not a law passed by a human legislature.)* **learning modality: verbal**

Monitor Progress _____ [L2]

Skills Check Ask students to explain the difference between a hypothesis and a theory.

Answers

Reading Checkpoint Different questions may require different approaches to finding answers, and unexpected observations may steer the process in different directions.

Reading Checkpoint Sample answer: A scientific inquiry may be part of a huge project with many scientists working together around the world. When scientists communicate, they describe their procedures in full detail so that others can repeat their experiments.

Answer

✓ **Reading Checkpoint** A scientific law describes what scientists expect to happen every time under a particular set of conditions.

Assess

Reviewing Key Concepts

1. a. Scientific inquiry refers to the diverse ways in which scientists study the natural world and propose explanations based on evidence they gather. **b.** Sample answer: You could because the hypothesis that ceiling fans cool air faster than air conditioners can be tested. **c.** Sample answer: Changes in air temperature over time.

2. a. Researchers must be able to carry out investigations and gather evidence that will either support or disprove the hypothesis. **b.** Sample answer: Studying for an exam together rather than studying individually results in higher test scores for both students.

3. a. A scientific theory is a well-tested explanation for a wide range of observations or experimental results. A scientific law is a statement that describes what scientists expect to happen every time under a particular set of conditions. **b.** Unlike a theory, a scientific law describes an observed pattern in nature without attempting to explain it. **c.** It cannot be called a theory, because a theory is an explanation for a wide range of experimental results.

Reteach L1

Call on volunteers to describe scientific inquiry in terms of the cricket experiment. Ask what the hypothesis was, why it could be tested, what the design of the controlled experiment was, how data was collected, and what conclusion was drawn.

Performance Assessment L2

Skills Check Have students make a flowchart that describes the process of scientific inquiry as outlined in this section.

All in One Teaching Resources
- Section Summary: *Scientific Inquiry*
- Review and Reinforcement: *Scientific Inquiry*
- Enrich: *Scientific Inquiry*

FIGURE 14
A Scientific Law
According to the law of gravity, this parachutist will eventually land back on Earth.

Scientific Laws Have you ever heard someone say, "What goes up must come down"? When scientists repeatedly observe the same result in specific circumstances, they may arrive at a scientific law. A **scientific law** is a statement that describes what scientists expect to happen every time under a particular set of conditions.

Unlike a theory, a scientific law describes an observed pattern in nature without attempting to explain it. You can think of a scientific law as a rule of nature. For example, the law of gravity states that all objects in the universe attract each other. This law has been verified over and over again.

✓ **Reading Checkpoint** What does a scientific law describe?

Section 2 Assessment

⊙ **Target Reading Skill** Building Vocabulary Use your definitions to help you answer the questions below.

Reviewing Key Concepts

1. a. Defining Define the term *scientific inquiry*.
  b. Explaining A friend claims that ceiling fans are better than air conditioning because they cool the air faster than air conditioners do. Could you investigate this through scientific inquiry? Explain.
  c. Problem Solving What kind of data would you need to collect to carry out this experiment?

2. a. Reviewing What is meant by saying that a hypothesis must be testable?
  b. Developing Hypotheses Every time you and your friend study for an exam while listening to classical music, both of you do well on the exam. What testable hypothesis can you develop from your observations?

3. a. Defining What is a scientific theory? What is a scientific law?
  b. Comparing and Contrasting How do scientific theories differ from scientific laws?
  c. Classifying The students who conducted the cricket experiment concluded that their results supported their hypothesis. Can their supported hypothesis be called a theory? Why or why not?

Writing in Science

Summary Suppose you will be traveling to a convention of cricket scientists from around the world. Write a paragraph describing the results of your cricket experiment. Include questions you'd like to ask other cricket scientists while at the conference.

Lab zone Chapter **Project**

Keep Students on Track By this point, students should have developed a hypothesis and described a controlled experiment to test that hypothesis. Check that the procedure of each experiment will result in collecting data that will enable students to draw a conclusion about the belief involved.

Writing in Science

Writing Mode Description
Scoring Rubric
4 Exceeds criteria
3 Meets all criteria
2 Includes only a partial description, does not identify variables, and/or lacks questions
1 Includes only brief and/or inaccurate information

Lab zone — Design Your Own Lab

Keeping Flowers Fresh

Problem
How can cut flowers stay fresher for a longer period of time?

Skills Focus
developing hypotheses, designing experiments, drawing conclusions

Suggested Materials
• plastic cups • cut flowers • spoon • water
• sugar

Design a Plan

1. You have just been given a bouquet of cut flowers. You remember once seeing a gardener put some sugar into the water in a vase before putting flowers in. You wonder if the gardener did that so that the flowers would stay fresh longer. Write a hypothesis for an experiment you could perform to answer your question.

2. Working with a partner, design a controlled experiment to test your hypothesis. Make a list of all of the variables you will need to control. Also decide what data you will need to collect. For example, you could count the number of petals each flower drops. Then write out a detailed experimental plan for your teacher to review.

3. If necessary, revise your plan according to your teacher's instructions. Then set up your experiment and begin collecting your data.

Analyze and Conclude

1. **Developing Hypotheses** What hypothesis did you decide to test? On what information or experience was your hypothesis based?

2. **Designing Experiments** What was the manipulated variable in the experiment you performed? What was the responding variable? What variables were kept constant?

3. **Graphing** Use the data you collected to create one or more graphs of your experimental results. (For more on creating graphs, see the Skills Handbook.) What patterns or trends do your graphs reveal?

4. **Drawing Conclusions** Based on your graphs, what conclusion can you draw about sugar and cut flowers? Do your results support your hypothesis? Why or why not?

5. **Communicating** In a paragraph, describe which aspects of your experimental plan were difficult to carry out. Were any variables hard to control? Was it difficult to collect accurate data? What changes could you make to improve your experimental plan?

More to Explore
Make a list of some additional questions you would like to investigate about how to keep cut flowers fresh. Choose one of the questions and write a hypothesis for an experiment you could perform. Then design a controlled experiment to test your hypothesis. *Obtain your teacher's permission before carrying out your investigation.*

Lab zone — Skills Lab

Keeping Flowers Fresh

Prepare for Inquiry

Key Concept
In a controlled experiment, only one variable is manipulated at a time.

Skills Objectives
After this lab, students will be able to:
• design a controlled experiment in which a manipulated variable is tested
• control all variables in an experiment except the manipulated variable

Prep Time 20 minutes
Class Time 40 minutes class time over 5 days

Advance Planning
Collect the appropriate number of flower bouquets and plastic cups ahead of time. Each pair of students can divide one bouquet in half to carry out an experiment.

Safety
Caution students to be careful when handling sharp objects.

All in One Teaching Resources
• Lab Worksheet: *Keeping Flowers Fresh*

Guide Inquiry

Introduce the Procedure
Before students read the procedure, call on students at random to define the terms *hypothesis*, *manipulated variable*, *responding variable*, and *controlled experiment*. Have students then read through the lab and identify the manipulated variable and the responding variable.

Troubleshooting the Experiment
• Review each student's or group's hypothesis and plan before giving the go-ahead to set up the experiment.
• Review with students how to make a graph.

Expected Outcome
See **Analyze and Conclude**, answers for Questions 1 and 2.

Extend Inquiry

More to Explore A typical controlled experiment might test a hypothesis that focuses on the air temperature the cut flowers are exposed to.

Analyze and Conclude
1. Sample answer: Hypothesis: Placing cut flowers in sugar water keeps the flowers fresh. The hypothesis is based on seeing a gardener put sugar in the water in a vase.

2. Manipulated variable: the presence of sugar in the water. Responding variable: freshness of flowers. Controlled variables include amount of water and sunlight and the air temperature.

3. A typical graph will include two lines, one for each flower, showing petals lost over time.

4. Students should conclude the sugar in the water keeps flowers fresh.

5. Sample answer: Collecting data about the freshness of the cut flowers was most difficult.

Objectives

After this lesson, students will be able to
P.1.3.1 Explain why people need to understand scientific principles and think scientifically.
P.1.3.2 Explain what scientific literacy is and why it is important.

Target Reading Skill

Identifying Main Ideas Explain that identifying main ideas and details helps students sort the facts from the information in groups. Each group can have a main topic, subtopics, and details.

Answers

Sample answer:
Understanding science can help you
- make the right choice when shopping for a bicycle
- evaluate claims in advertisements
- weigh the pros and cons of public issues
- answer questions about the best use of Earth's resources

All in One Teaching Resources
- Transparency P3

Preteach

Build Background Knowledge　　　L2

Using Science Knowledge

Describe for students a scenic river. Then, propose this scenario: An environmental group has issued a press release claiming that this river has been heavily polluted by a local chemical plant. Yet, the river doesn't look polluted. This environmental group is new, and no one has heard of it before. Ask: **Why would a person need to know something about science to judge the validity of this group's claim?** *(A person would need to know about chemicals, how chemicals pollute water, what the evidence would be if the river were polluted, how to detect such pollution, and what the consequences of such pollution would be on humans and wildlife.)* Point out that without such knowledge of science, a citizen would have no basis by which to condemn or defend the local chemical industry.

Reading Preview

Key Concepts
- Why do people need to understand scientific principles and think scientifically?
- What is scientific literacy and why is it important?

Key Term
- scientific literacy

Target Reading Skill
Identifying Main Ideas As you read about the importance of studying science, write the main idea in a graphic organizer like the one below. Then write four supporting details that further explain the idea.

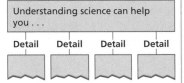

Main Idea

Understanding science can help you . . .

Detail　Detail　Detail　Detail

Lab zone Discover **Activity**

How Much Do You See or Hear About Science?

1. Watch a half-hour evening news broadcast. List all the news stories that have something to do with a science topic.
2. Watch the ads during the broadcast and list the ones that make scientific claims.

Think It Over
Inferring Were you surprised at how often science topics were mentioned on the news or in ads? Based on your observations, why is it important to study science?

Your eyes are glued to the screen. You watch as two explorers from the special investigations unit, Theta 7, activate the matter resequencer and teleport to their next destination. Three thousandths of a second later, they arrive at Sector 1572. The land is inhabited by giant fire ants and other creatures grown out of proportion. Because the explorers' garments make them nearly invisible, they move through the sector without being noticed by the giant creatures.

As the movie ends, you think how great it would be if you could teleport yourself or become invisible. This was only a movie, but could these things be possible some day? What about the giant ants? Could insects that large ever really exist?

From science fiction movies to nightly news reports, science is all around you. That's why you need to have a basic knowledge of science. **Being able to understand scientific principles and think scientifically can help you solve problems and answer many questions in your everyday life.** This section presents some of the questions that people ask every day.

Lab zone Discover **Activity**

Skills Focus Inferring

Time 15 minutes for in-class discussion

Tips Assign this activity for the evening news on the day students begin this section. Advise students that they should make two lists and answer in writing the Think It Over questions.

Expected Outcome The number of news stories having to do with science will vary depending on the news of the day. Science stories might include those about the weather, the environment, and energy. Ads often make scientific claims.

Think It Over Sample answer: How often science topics were mentioned was surprising. It is important to study science to understand these news stories and to assess the validity of claims in the ads.

How Does It Work?

You are standing in line at the grocery store. The cashier scans each item with a laser. The customer in front of you pulls out a credit card and runs the magnetic stripe through a slot. The machine reads information on the card and sends the data to a distant computer. Devices such as these are a common part of our daily lives. They have changed almost every aspect of how people live and work. All of them have some basis in science. But could you explain how any of these devices work?

Of course, as a customer, you don't really need to know how these devices work. But what if you were the cashier and one of the devices stopped working? Or what if you were shopping for a bicycle? Do you know how gears work or which metal is lightweight, yet sturdy? Knowing some science and thinking scientifically could help you make the right choice.

Learning science can also help you understand natural events that affect your daily life. For example, how do tornadoes form? Can listening to loud music damage your hearing? Being able to answer questions like these can help you make wise decisions and stay safe.

Reading Checkpoint How might knowing science help you shop for a bicycle?

What materials are helmets made of? How do they protect your head?

How do different types of brakes work? How quickly can you come to a stop?

How do gears work? How many gears do you need for the biking you plan to do?

FIGURE 15
How Things Work
Learning the science behind how things work can help make everyday activities, such as biking, safer and more enjoyable.
Posing Questions *What other bike-related questions do you have?*

Chapter 1 P ◆ 25

Differentiated Instruction

Less Proficient Readers **L1**
Comprehension: Link to Visual Use Figure 15 to help students understand the importance of knowing how things work. Slowly read aloud the displayed questions in the figure, and note how those questions relate to the photo. Elicit students' previous experiences with fixing bicycles. Then, use the concept of knowing how to fix a bicycle as an analogy for using knowledge of science to help a person understand natural events. Tie that idea to the photo of a shopper in Figure 16, who uses science to evaluate the claims of advertising. **learning modality: visual**

Instruct

How Does It Work?

Teach Key Concepts **L2**
Being Self-Reliant Through Science

Focus Explain that knowing how devices work is essential to being a person who can function intelligently in the modern world.

Teach Have students brainstorm a list of devices they use every day that depend on electrical energy to work. Then ask: **You know that all these devices depend on electrical energy, but do you know what electrical energy is?** *(Some students may know that electrical energy is the energy of moving electrical charges.)* Point out that learning about electrical energy, will help them understand how these devises work.

Apply Take the back off a large pocket watch and encourage students to examine the inner workings of the watch. Ask: **Now that you've examined the watch, how do you think it works?** *(Sample answer: The battery produces electrical energy that turns the various sprockets and wheels that make up the workings of the watch.)* **learning modality: visual**

Independent Practice **L2**

All in One Teaching Resources
• Guided Reading and Study Worksheet: *Why Study Science?*

 **Student Edition on Audio CD**

Monitor Progress _____ **L2**

Writing Ask students to write a short story that demonstrates that knowing how something works could be a benefit in getting out of a dangerous or difficult situation.
Students can save their stories in their portfolios.

Answers
Figure 15 Sample answer: How do the different types of tires aid or hinder smooth riding on the road? How does the chain work? What materials are best for the frame?

Reading Checkpoint Knowing how the gears work and knowing which metal is lightweight could help in choosing the best bicycle to buy.

How Can I Stay Healthy?

Teach Key Concepts L2

Taking Charge of Your Own Health

Focus Tell students that scientific thinking can help them stay healthy.

Teach Ask: **What is the most important thing you should be doing to be the healthiest you can be?** (*Students might mention various diets or exercise regimes.*) As students answer the question, make a list on the board. Then, ask: **What do you need to know to judge which one of these suggestions would be best to follow?** (*Scientific thinking would help in evaluating each suggestion.*)

Apply Read aloud a short newspaper article reporting a new finding about a food, drug, or health product. Ask: **What do you need to know to evaluate whether this is important information to your life?** (*For most articles, a person needs to know about human biology and how food and drugs affect the body.*)
learning modality: verbal

How Do I Become an Informed Citizen?

Teach Key Concepts L2

Knowing About the Issues Facing Society

Focus Tell students that making intelligent decisions about important issues facing society involves understanding science.

Teach Divide the class into small groups, and give each group a copy of a national news magazine. Have each group make a list of public issues they find in the magazine that involve scientific questions. Then, have groups read their lists to the class and discuss which are the most important facing society today. Ask: **How could you become informed about these important public issues?** (*By reading articles and books, attending meetings of groups involved in these issues, and talking to friends and relatives*)

Apply Give small groups a copy of a weekly news magazine. Ask each group to make a list of public issues reported in the magazine that require an understanding of science in order to weigh the pros and cons of the issue. **learning modality: verbal**

FIGURE 16
Staying Healthy
Knowing the science behind health and nutrition issues can help you make wise shopping decisions.
Making Judgments *What scientific information do you rely on when making food choices?*

 Skills Activity

Posing Questions

Look through a magazine and select an ad that makes a scientific claim. Write down five questions that you would want answered before you would believe the claim. Choose one of the questions and plan a way to find the answer.

How Can I Stay Healthy?

"Jump higher, run faster! Improve your athletic abilities with new Superstar Energy Bar. Buy it now!" This is not a real advertisement, but you may have seen ads with similar claims. Would you buy the product based on this ad? If not, suppose the ad went on to say, "Studies have shown that Superstar Energy Bar improves people's athletic abilities more than other brands." Now would you be convinced?

Scientific thinking can help you to evaluate advertised claims. For example, you might question whether the claims are based on a controlled study. You might want to know how the study measured improvement in athletic ability and how many people were studied.

Eating well is one way to maintain your health. Getting enough exercise and avoiding exposure to disease are other ways. Which exercises are best for you? Should you take pills to help your muscles grow stronger? Can going out on a cold, wet day really make you sick? These are the kinds of questions that studying science will help you answer.

 Reading Checkpoint **What information might help you evaluate advertised claims?**

How Do I Become an Informed Citizen?

Have you ever heard people discuss their views on a public issue? For example, should a town restrict water use in the summer? Should scientists continue to explore space? Should old paint in a building be removed? Issues like these often generate much debate.

Take space exploration, for example. What can we learn from space missions? What are the costs and risks? Would the money be better spent on projects closer to home? These are just a few of the questions that might come up during a debate.

As you grow older, you will have more and more opportunities to voice your opinion on public issues—at public hearings, in the voting booth, or by just talking with friends. And more and more public issues involve science. Understanding the science will help you weigh the pros and cons and arrive at a decision.

Reading Checkpoint **Where are some places you can voice your opinions on public issues?**

Skills Activity

Skills Focus Posing questions
Materials popular magazine
Time 15 minutes
Expected Outcome Students may choose any kind of ad from which they will write questions and formulate a plan. A typical ad might be for a food product. Questions might focus on such claims as

great taste or some health benefit. A claim about health benefits could be developed into a testable hypothesis.

Extend Have small groups carry out plans that are particularly well thought out. Check for safety issues, and tell students to review the safety guidelines in Appendix A.
learning modality: verbal

What Is the Best Use of Earth's Resources?

"Paper or plastic?" Have you ever heard this question from a store clerk? Although the question seems simple, it's not. Do you know enough science to arrive at an answer?

You might be surprised to learn that the clerk's question has something to do with science. But think about how these bags were produced and where they might end up after you use them. Is one choice better than the other? That is a complex question that scientists are studying.

Scientists are also studying other topics related to Earth's resources. For example, you may have heard about cars that run on fuels other than gasoline. What are the advantages and disadvantages of these types of cars? What's involved in developing other sources of fuels?

Topics related to Earth's resources may seem far removed from your life, but in fact, they're not. Have you ever wondered where the water in your toilet comes from and where it goes after you flush it? And why do adults always tell you to turn off the lights when you leave a room? Could the world's energy sources ever really run out? Learning science will help you answer questions like these.

 Reading Checkpoint What are two decisions related to Earth's resources that you faced today?

FIGURE 17
Using Earth's Resources Wisely
Should you walk or ride in a car to a nearby destination? Knowing science can help you make wise decisions that impact Earth's resources.

Differentiated Instruction

Gifted and Talented **L3**
Communicating Have students do research to answer the questions about roller coasters that are displayed in Figure 18. Ask that they prepare a presentation to the class, complete with any visuals that might be appropriate to fully explain the concepts involved. Make sure students prepare a list of the sources they used. **learning modality: verbal**

Special Needs **L1**
Organize students into groups of three or four. Have each group brainstorm a list of questions related to science that might arise in daily life. Then have each group use its questions to make a poster that illustrates how people use a knowledge of science to answer the questions. Hang the posters in the classroom. **learning modality: visual**

What Is the Best Use of Earth's Resources?

Teach Key Concepts   **L2**
Natural Resources in Your Life

Focus Tell students that in their lifetimes society will likely be faced with important decisions about the use of Earth's limited natural resources.

Teach Ask: **How long on average does a person in your home spend taking a shower?** (*An average shower might take 5 to 10 minutes.*) Point out that up to 5 gallons of water are used every minute of a shower, and thus a 10-minute shower may use 50 gallons of water. Then, discuss where this water comes from, how it gets to homes, and how it is processed after it leaves the home. Ask students if they think long showers are the best use of this limited natural resource.

Apply Have students find out whether the water supply in their area is abundant or at risk of being rationed in the future. **learning modality: verbal**

Monitor Progress   **L2**

Writing Have students write a newspaper article that describes a debate at a city council about establishing or retaining a city-wide recycling center.

Answers
Figure 16 Information related to biology as well as medicine and other health sciences

Reading Checkpoint Sample answer: Scientific information about the human body, especially information about exercise and health, might help in evaluating advertised claims.

Reading Checkpoint At public hearings and in talking to friends

Reading Checkpoint Sample answer: Two decisions are how water resources should be used in order to protect the limited supply and how energy sources should be used to limit pollution.

Scientific Literacy

Teach Key Concepts

Knowing the Basics of Science

Focus Tell students that understanding basic terms and principles of science is very important in the modern world.

Teach Ask a volunteer to read aloud the definition of *scientific literacy*. Ask students whether they think most people they know are scientifically literate. Ask: **How is having scientific literacy an advantage for a person?** (*Someone who has scientific literacy can keep up with the latest scientific trends and be well qualified for jobs.*)

Apply Ask: **Why would having scientific literacy be an advantage to a person applying for a gardener's job?** (*Gardening involves knowing about different plants, how plants grow, and what kinds of soils are best for growing plants. Scientific literacy includes understanding basic terms and principles of biology and Earth science.*) **learning modality: logical/mathematical**

Build Inquiry

Time 20 minutes

Focus Tell students that a survey is one way of finding out how scientifically literate people are.

Teach Divide the class into groups, and have each group design a 10-question survey questionnaire that asks about basic scientific terms and principles. Once the questionnaires are checked for appropriateness, have groups trade surveys.

Apply When groups receive their completed surveys back, they should gather the data and draw a conclusion about students' scientific literacy. **learning modality: verbal**

What materials make the best support for a roller coaster? What kind of ground should a roller coaster be built on?

FIGURE 18
Scientific Literacy
Even a roller coaster ride can generate many scientific questions! Having scientific literacy can help you identify good sources of scientific information in which to find answers.

Go Online

For: Links on scientific literacy
Visit: www.SciLinks.org
Web Code: scn-1613

Scientific Literacy

Are you still wondering why you should study science? Or, at this point, are you instead wondering how you could possibly learn everything there is to know?

Of course, it is not possible to become an expert in every field of science. Nor is it possible to test everything scientifically by yourself. Instead, you need to have scientific literacy. Having **scientific literacy** means that you understand basic scientific terms and principles well enough that you can evaluate information, make personal decisions, and take part in public affairs. **By having scientific literacy, you will be able to identify good sources of scientific information, evaluate them for accuracy, and apply the knowledge to questions or problems in your life.** You will also be able to keep up with the latest scientific trends and be well qualified for jobs.

So, why should you study science? The real question is, why wouldn't you?

 Reading Checkpoint Why is a good understanding of scientific terms and principles important?

Why don't roller coasters fall off the track when they go upside down?

What causes that feeling of queasiness or exhilaration?

Section 3 Assessment

⟳ **Target Reading Skill**

Identifying Main Ideas Use your graphic organizer about the importance of studying science to answer the questions below.

Reviewing Key Concepts

1. a. **Reviewing** List two questions that a knowledge of science could help you answer.
   b. **Summarizing** How does understanding scientific principles and thinking scientifically apply to your everyday life?
   c. **Applying Concepts** A friend tells you that studying science is only for scientists. How could you convince your friend otherwise?

2. a. **Defining** What is scientific literacy?
   b. **Problem Solving** You are watching the news on TV and hear about "DNA fingerprinting." How could you find out what that is?

Writing in Science

Comic Strip Design a five panel comic strip that illustrates the importance of science education in a humorous way. Your comic strip should show a particular situation in which a knowledge of science would have been important.

Chapter 1 P ◆ 29

Lab zone Chapter Project

Keep Students on Track Students should have finished collecting data. The next task is to interpret the collected data and draw a conclusion about the common belief. Where appropriate, review how to create graphs, how to determine percentages, or how to construct labeled diagrams.

Writing in Science

Writing Mode Persuasion
Scoring Rubric
4 Exceeds criteria
3 Meets all criteria
2 Meets some criteria but is not humorous and/or not well thought out
1 Meets few criteria

Answer

✓ **Reading Checkpoint** By having such scientific literacy, a person will be able to identify good sources of scientific information, evaluate them for accuracy, and apply the knowledge to questions or problems in that person's life.

Assess

Reviewing Key Concepts

1. **a.** Sample answer: How does a bike work? How can I stay healthy? **b.** Being able to understand scientific principles and to think scientifically can help you solve problems and answer many questions in your everyday life. **c.** Sample answer: You could mention a problem or issue the friend is interested in and point out that understanding scientific principles might help the friend solve the problem or take a stand on the issue.
2. **a.** Scientific literacy is understanding basic scientific terms and principles well enough to evaluate information, make personal decisions, and take part in public affairs. **b.** Sample answer: You could check the index of a major encyclopedia or use a search engine to search the Internet.

Reteach L1

Show students a photo of a scenic river. Call on volunteers at random to explain again how having scientific literacy could help in evaluating a claim that this river is polluted.

Performance Assessment L2

Oral Presentation Divide the class into small groups. Have each group write a short scenario involving an everyday problem that could be solved with an understanding of scientific principles and how to think scientifically. Then, have groups exchange scenarios. Each group should collaborate on an explanation using a basic knowledge of science about how the problem might be solved.

All in One Teaching Resources

- Section Summary: *Why Study Science?*
- Review and Reinforce: *Why Study Science?*
- Enrich: *Why Study Science?*

Objectives

After this lesson, students will be able to

P.1.4.1 List the three main branches of science.

P.1.4.2 Explain why it is important for scientists in different fields to work together.

P.1.4.3 Explain how science is important in nonscience careers.

Target Reading Skill

Using Prior Knowledge Explain that using prior knowledge helps students connect what they already know to what they are about to read.

Answers

Sample answers:

What You Know

1. There are different fields of science.

2. Scientists work together.

3. Knowledge of science is used in nonscience careers.

What You Learned

1. The three main branches of science are Earth and space science, life science, and physical science.

2. Most scientific questions being investigated today span the different fields of science, including questions related to exploring beyond Earth and developing new sources of energy.

3. In many nonscience careers, a knowledge of science is essential in order to perform the job.

All in One Teaching Resources

• Transparency P4

Preteach

Build Background Knowledge   L2

Science in the Community

Ask: **What adult do you know who uses science in performing a job or pursuing a hobby?** (*Students may know a variety of people who use basic science in performing a job or pursuing a hobby. Examples include firefighters who must know about materials that are not fire resistant and hobbyists, such as, bird watchers.*)

Section 4

Careers in Science

Reading Preview

Key Concepts

• What are the three main branches of science?

• Why is important for scientists in different fields to work together?

• How is science important in nonscience careers?

Target Reading Skill

Using Prior Knowledge Before you read, look at the section headings and visuals to see what this section is about. Then write what you know about scientists in a graphic organizer like the one below. As you read, continue to write in what you learn.

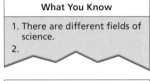

What You Know
1. There are different fields of science.
2.

What You Learned
1.
2.

Lab zone Discover **Activity**

What Do Scientists Look Like?

1. On a sheet of paper, draw a picture of a scientist at work.

2. Compare your picture to that of a classmate.

3. Use both of your pictures to list the characteristics of a "typical" scientist.

Think About It

Inferring Where do you think your ideas about typical scientists come from?

How would you like to live and work on an island? Can you work under challenging conditions, such as extreme heat? Would you like to hike and explore new places? Would you enjoy flying in helicopters? If you answered yes to these questions, maybe you should consider becoming a scientist!

This job description probably doesn't match your idea of what a scientist does. But it accurately describes the work of a volcanologist, a scientist who studies volcanoes. Volcanologists do such things as collect and study samples of molten rock after a volcano has erupted. Other scientists can be found at work in the oceans, in laboratories, on glaciers, and in outer space. Wherever people are asking questions and searching for answers, they are using the skills of scientific inquiry.

◄ Earth science: Volcanologist

Lab zone Discover **Activity**

Skills Focus Inferring

Materials sheet of paper

Time 15 minutes

Expected Outcome Many students will draw a picture of a bespeckled, solitary man in a lab coat working indoors and using a microscope or another piece of scientific equipment. Discussion can counter this stereotype. The characteristics of a "typical" scientist students may mention include high intelligence, curiosity, and a lack of sociability.

Think It Over Sample answer: Ideas about typical scientists come from television news media, newspaper and magazine articles, and experiences with adults who work in science-related fields.

Branches of Science

How many different science careers can you name? Your list would probably include such careers as astronauts, doctors, and engineers. But would it also include crystallographers—scientists who study the three-dimensional structure of chemicals? How about ornithologists—scientists who study birds? As you can see, the term *scientist* spans many diverse fields and interests.

Because the areas of scientific study are so diverse, scientists organize their work into three major branches, or fields of study. **The three main branches of science are earth and space science, life science, and physical science.**

Earth and Space Science Earth and space science is the study of Earth and its place in the universe. Some earth scientists study the forces that have shaped Earth throughout its long history. Others study Earth's oceans or its weather. Space scientists study the planets and stars that exist beyond Earth.

Life Science Life science is the study of living things, including plants, animals, and microscopic life forms. Life scientists also study how living things interact with each other and with their surroundings. The study of the human body is part of life sciences, too.

Physical Science Physical science includes the study of motion, sound, light, electricity, and magnetism. It also includes chemistry—the study of the tiny particles that make up all things, from flowers to stars.

 Reading Checkpoint What topics of study does physical science include?

▲ Life science: Ornithologists

▲ Physical science: Chemist

FIGURE 19
Branches of Science
The diverse topics of scientific study can be classified into three main branches: earth and space science, life science, and physical science. **Classifying** *Which branch of science includes the study of clouds?*

Branches of Science

Teach Key Concepts   L2
Three Main Branches

Focus Tell students that there are three main branches of science into which all the specialized studies of science are classified.

Teach Ask: **What are the three main branches of science?** (*Earth and space science, life science, and physical science*) **In which branch is the human body studied?** (*Life science*) **In which branch is weather studied?** (*Earth science*) **Which branch includes the science of chemistry?** (*Physical science*) **What topics does physical science include other than chemistry?** (*Motion, sound, light, electricity, and magnetism*)

Apply Ask: **Into which main branch would you classify biophysics?** (*Students may infer by the name that biophysics includes aspects of both biology and physics. Students may argue for either life science or physical science.*) Explain that biophysics focuses on the physics of living things, and thus it is classified as a life science. **learning modality: verbal**

Independent Practice   L2

All in One Teaching Resources

• Guided Reading and Study Worksheet: *Careers in Science*

⊙ **Student Edition on Audio CD**

Monitor Progress   L2

Skills Check Ask students to compare and contrast the three main branches of science. Have students explain what fields of study each branch includes and how the three branches could overlap.

Answers
Figure 19 Earth and space science

Reading Checkpoint Physical science includes the study of motion, sound, light, electricity, and magnetism. It also includes chemistry.

For: Links on branches of science
Visit: www.SciLinks.org
Web Code: scn-1614

Download a worksheet that will guide students' review of Internet resources on branches of science.

Scientists Working Together

Teach Key Concepts　L2

Different Scientists Collaborate

Focus Tell students that on many projects, scientists with different specialties and from different fields work together toward a common goal.

Teach Use the analogy of players on a sports team to reinforce this concept. For example, each player on a soccer team has different responsibilities and plays accordingly. Ask: **What responsibilities does a soccer goalkeeper have?** *(The goalkeeper protects against shots on the goal and almost never moves downfield.)* **What are the different responsibilities other players on the team have?** *(Forwards normally stay on the attack at the opposing end, while the sweeper and other defensive backs almost never attack the goal.)* Emphasize that together these players function as a team, blending their skills and talents together with a common purpose of winning. Similarly, scientists of different skills and areas of study often work together toward a common goal.

Apply Challenge students to think of other analogies for scientists working together. Such analogies include the variety of musicians in the school's marching band, and the crew of carpenters, bricklayers, electricians, plumbers, and others who work together in building a house. **learning modality: verbal**

For: Links on branches of science
Visit: www.SciLinks.org
Web Code: scn-1614

Scientists Working Together

Although it is convenient to think of science as divided into three branches, these areas are not really separate at all. Most scientific questions being investigated today span the different fields of science.

If you have ever worked on a difficult jigsaw puzzle with friends, then you can understand how scientists study questions and solve problems. One friend might work on one corner of the puzzle, while you work on another. Similarly, a physical scientist might investigate one piece of a scientific "puzzle" while an earth scientist works on another piece of the same puzzle. As you read about two scientific questions being investigated today, you can see how they involve the cooperation of a wide range of scientists.

Exploring Beyond Earth Will it someday be possible for humans to live in space? The International Space Station was designed in part to study this question. In orbit since 1998, the space station has been home to many crews, who stay for months at a time. On board, scientists explore the challenges of living in space. On the ground, hundreds of other scientists make the work of the crew possible.

FIGURE 20
Exploring Beyond Earth
The International Space Station continually travels around Earth, about 400 km above the ground.
Posing Questions *What questions are the scientists who work on the space station trying to answer?*

FIGURE 21
Scientists Working Together
It takes the work of many scientists for the space station to function smoothly.

Food Scientists
Imagine living in space, far from the the conveniences of home. Now imagine opening a package of your favorite snack food only to have the contents float away. Food scientists develop foods for space flights that are easy to use, nutritious, and perhaps most important, appetizing!

Computer Scientists
Computer scientists manage most aspects of space flight. Some computers keep air and temperature conditions stable. Others control the space station's robotic arm. Computer scientists at Mission Control keep the space station in constant contact with Earth.

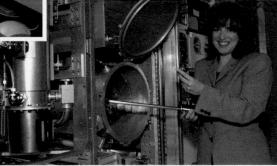

Astronauts
Astronauts perform many tasks on the space station. Some pilot the spacecraft, while others carry out experiments. They may study how living in space affects muscle strength or whether crops can be grown in space.

Materials Scientists
What protects the space station from the harsh environment of space? The answer lies in materials. Materials scientists know that spacecrafts must be strong, lightweight, and heat resistant. They study the properties of materials such as ceramics to understand how they would perform in space.

Chapter 1 P ◆ 33

Address Misconceptions   L1
Scientists May Have Narrow Roles
Focus Tell students that not all scientists work through the whole scientific inquiry process in the jobs that they have.

Teach Explain that, generally, scientists have jobs in which their focus is at one stage of the scientific inquiry process, and those scientists may never continue to another stage. For example, some scientists spend their lives in the field, gathering observations about nature. Other scientists specialize in working in a laboratory conducting experiments. Some scientists concentrate on reviewing other scientists' observations and developing hypotheses for still other scientists to test.

Apply Use the several scientists shown in Figure 21 and Figure 22 to make this point about science work. For example, ask: **What stage of the scientific inquiry process are the food scientists in Figure 21 engaged in?** *(They appear to be conducting an experiment.)* Explain that other scientists may have gathered observations about food in space or developed a hypothesis. These scientists may not draw conclusions or communicate the results about their experiment. **learning modality: visual**

Monitor Progress _____   L2
Writing Ask students to imagine being a scientist on the International Space Station who keeps a journal of daily activities. Have students write a journal entry that describes working on a project with other scientists on board the station.

Answer
Figure 20 Sample answer: Can humans live in space? What foods are best for astronauts living in space? How does living in space affect muscle strength? Can crops be grown in space? What materials are needed to protect spacecraft from the harsh environment of space?

Help Students Read

Relating Text and Figures Refer to the Content Refresher in this chapter, which provides the guidelines for the Relating Text and Figures strategy.

Have students read the text related to scientists working together to develop new sources of energy. Then, have them use Figure 22 to identify the kinds of scientists that are working together on this project and describe the focus of each different scientist. Ask: **What are the three kinds of scientists pictured in this figure?** *(Botanists, chemists, and soil scientists)* **How would you classify each of these scientists in terms of main branches of science?** *(Botanists are life scientists; chemists are physical scientists; and soil scientists are Earth scientists.)* **What can you learn about these scientists by looking at the figure that you cannot by reading the text?** *(Sample answer: Scientist both work in the field and in the laboratory. Here, the botanist and the soil scientist are gathering observations in the field, while the chemists are working in the laboratory.)*

Monitor Progress ———— L2

Skills Check Have students make a table to contain the information about the different scientists shown in Figure 22 and Figure 23. The table could have three columns with these column heads: Type of Scientist, Branch of Science, Area of Study.

Answers

Figure 22 Sample answer: The different scientists might work at cross purposes. For instance, chemists might concentrate on a plant that botanists had already rejected as too difficult to grow and process.

 Fuels made from soybeans or other plant material

FIGURE 22

Developing New Sources of Energy

Many scientists are studying how plants can be used as a source of fuel. **Predicting** *What problems might arise if the scientists on this project didn't communicate with one another?*

Developing New Sources of Energy Imagine boarding a bus that didn't run on gasoline—but on soybeans instead! Buses like these already exist in several cities. Fuels made from soybeans or other plant matter are called biofuels. Unlike gasoline and oil, biofuels are readily available and burn more cleanly than other fuels. Many scientists are studying biofuels as a promising new source of energy.

 What are biofuels?

The soybean bus ▲

Chemists
Chemists study how the energy in plants can be converted into fuels. They analyze the plants' chemical makeup and experiment with different methods of producing fuels. Their goal is to produce high-quality, inexpensive biofuels that don't pollute the environment.

Botanists
What kinds of plants make good fuels? Botanists, or plant biologists, know that fuel crops must be easy to plant, grow, and process. In addition to soybeans, botanists are studying corn, trees, and fast-growing grasses as potential biofuel crops.

Soil Scientists
What kind of soil do fuel crops need? How do fuel crops affect the soil they grow in? Soil scientists help identify crops that may be used both for producing fuel and for improving the soil.

Lab zone Skills Lab

Piecing Information Together

Problem
How do the skills of observing and inferring help scientists piece together information?

Skills Focus
observing, inferring, predicting

Materials
- paperback book, cut into sections and stapled together
- paper
- pencil

Procedure
1. Examine the small section of the book your teacher gives you. Use your observation skills to list any facts you can state confidently about the book, including its characters, setting, or events.
2. Based on your observations, what can you infer the book is about? Write one or two sentences describing the book's storyline.
3. Get together with a partner and share your book sections, observations, inferences, and story descriptions.
4. Together, write a new one- or two-sentence story description based on your shared observations and information.
5. Get together with another pair of students. Repeat Steps 3 and 4.
6. After you have written your description of the story as a group of four, look back over all your story descriptions. Note how they have changed over time.

Analyze and Conclude
1. **Observing** Look over the list of observations you made in Step 1. Were any of the observations really inferences? If so, explain why.
2. **Inferring** How confident did you feel about the inference you made about the storyline in Step 2? How did your confidence level change when your observations included additional sections of the book?
3. **Predicting** How do you think your level of confidence would change if you observed more and more sections of the book? Explain your reasoning.
4. **Communicating** Write a paragraph explaining how this activity resembles the work of scientists. How do the observations and inferences you made relate to those that scientists make? What do your story descriptions represent?

More to Explore
Choose a scientific article from a newspaper or magazine. Read the article and identify three observations and three inferences that the scientists made.

Analyze and Conclude
1. Accept answers that demonstrate an understanding of what an inference is.
2. A good answer is one that demonstrates that as the number of observations increases there is an increase in confidence.
3. The level of confidence would rise because the more observations, the more confidence there is in inferences.
4. Scientists make observations of objects and events in the natural world and then make inferences from those observations. The story descriptions represent the interpretations that scientists make from their observations.

Lab zone Skills Lab

Piecing Information Together

Prepare for Inquiry

Key Concept
The process of science uses observation and inference skills to piece together information and form hypotheses.

Skills Objectives
After this lab, students will be able to:
- observe a small section of a book and list facts about the book
- infer what the storyline of a book is from observations of a small section of the book
- predict how a person's confidence would change if more sections of a book were seen
- communicate how the activity resembles the work of scientists.

 Prep Time 45 minutes
Class Time 40 minutes

Advance Planning
Collect an appropriate number of paperback books. Each book should be age-appropriate and also unfamiliar to students. A guillotine paper cutter is ideal for cutting a book. Do not cut too many pages at a time. Keep pages in order as the book is cut up. Staple pieces together.

All in One Teaching Resources
- Lab Worksheet: *Piecing Information Together*

Guide Inquiry

Introduce the Procedure
Cut out a portion of a paperback book, read the portion to students, and ask for their observations. Write these observations on the board. Then, ask for inferences about the article based on their observations.

Expected Outcome
In the initial pairs, there will likely be little confidence in the inferences that are made. As the groups get larger and the accumulation of observations grows larger, students should become more confident about their inferences.

Science in Nonscience Careers

Teach Key Concepts

Everyone Needs to Know Science

Focus Tell students that most people don't work as scientists, yet most people need to know some science to do their jobs.

Teach Have a volunteer read aloud the paragraph about why firefighters need to know science. Ask: **What could happen to a firefighter if he or she knew nothing about chemistry?** (*The firefighter could be hurt badly or even killed if he or she added water to the wrong material.*) Emphasize that the more knowledge of science a person has, the more qualified that person is for jobs in the modern world.

Apply Ask: **What scientific principles do the adults in your family need to know to do their jobs?** (*Sample answer: An office worker needs to have some knowledge of how a computer and other electronic equipment work, including principles of physical science related to electricity in order to avoid electrical surges and other problems.*) **learning modality: verbal**

FIGURE 23
Science in Nonscience Careers
A knowledge of science is useful in many nonscience careers.

Firefighter ▼

Sound technician ▲

36 ◆ P

Science in Nonscience Careers

Are scientists the only people who need a knowledge of science on the job? The answer, of course, is no. **In many nonscience careers, a knowledge of science is essential in order to perform the job.** Just a few of the careers that involve science are presented here.

Firefighter When a fire alarm goes off, firefighters do not know what type of fire they will encounter. Is it a grease fire, an electrical fire, or something else? Did you know that some materials actually catch on fire if you spray them with water? Understanding chemistry helps firefighters put out fires and clean up hazardous spills quickly and safely.

Sound Technician From concert halls to radio stations, sound technicians are busy behind the scenes. Their job is to make sure that the sound quality is at its best. Sound technicians must understand how sound waves travel and how they interact with different materials. Most sound technicians use electronic equipment to adjust the sound quality in different situations.

Chef ▼

Monitor Progress

Writing Have students explain why a firefighter, sound technician, chef, or artist needs to have some knowledge of science to perform their jobs.

Answer

✓ **Reading Checkpoint** Sample answer: Sculpters must know about the properties of the materials they use.

Chef Whether cooking a simple meal or creating a dessert masterpiece, chefs rely on science in the kitchen. Did you know that scrambling an egg involves chemistry or that living organisms are the key to baking delicious breads and cakes? And would you know how to prevent food from spoiling and causing sickness? A lot of science goes into what you eat!

Artist You might be surprised to learn that the work of artists involves science. But sculptors must know about the properties of the materials they use. For example, would bronze be a good material to use for an outdoor sculpture? Glass artists apply the physics of heating and cooling as they shape glass. And painters must understand the properties of the paints, paper, and other materials they work with.

Artist ▲

✔ **Reading Checkpoint** What is one way that science is involved in an artist's career?

Section 4 Assessment

 Target Reading Skill Using Prior Knowledge Review your graphic organizer and revise it based on what you just learned in the section.

Reviewing Key Concepts

1. a. Listing What are the three major branches of science?
   b. Describing Write a one-sentence description of each of the three branches of science.
   c. Classifying Into which branch of science would you classify the following scientists: a scientist studying the organisms in a river; a scientist studying how a river first formed?

2. a. Identifying Give an example of a scientific investigation that involves scientists from different branches working together.
   b. Problem Solving How might an Earth scientist studying volcanoes work together with scientists in each of the other branches of science?

3. a. Reviewing Why should nonscientists study science?
   b. Applying Concepts How would a knowledge of science benefit a gardener?
   c. Making Judgments A friend tells you he doesn't need to study science because he doesn't even know what career he'll want to pursue. What would you tell your friend?

Lab zone **At-Home Activity**

Help Wanted With a family member, look through the job listings in a local newspaper. Cut out four listings—two for science careers and two for nonscience careers. For the science careers, identify the branch of science and the educational background required. For the nonscience careers, identify what science knowledge is needed to perform the job.

Lab zone **At Home Activity**

Help Wanted Examples students choose will vary, in part depending on local industries. A typical science career will be one in a health-related field, such as nurse or physical therapist. A typical nonscience career might be chef or auto technician.

Study Guide

nteractive Textbook

- Complete student edition
- Section and chapter self-assessments
- Assessment reports for teachers

Help Students Read

Building Vocabulary

Word Origin Have students look up the origin of the word *skeptic*. They will discover that it comes from the Greek word *skeptikos,* meaning "thoughtful." Ask students how being thoughtful is related to being skeptical. (*People who are thoughtful often don't accept explanations without examining them closely with an attitude of doubt.*)

Words in Context Help students learn the meaning of new words or phrases by examining the context. Tell students to look for familiar words or phrases that surround a new term—these are clues to the new term's meaning. Have students reread the second paragraph under the heading Inferring. Ask: **What does the description say that Jane Goodall was doing that could help you remember the meaning of *inferring*?** (*In the first sentence of the paragraph, Jane "reasoned."*)

Connecting Concepts

Concept Maps Help students develop one way to show how the information in this chapter is related. Scientists use characteristic skills and ways of thinking, and they follow a certain process of inquiry. And, science is a body of knowledge that is divided into main branches, each of which includes many fields of study. Have students brainstorm to identify the key concepts, key terms, details, and examples. Then write each one on a self-sticking note and attach it at random on chart paper or on the board.

Tell students that this concept map will be organized in hierarchical order and to begin at the top with key concepts. Ask students these questions to guide them to categorize the information on the self-sticking notes: **What skills do scientists use to learn about the world? What attitudes are important in**

① Thinking Like a Scientist

Key Concepts

- Scientists use skills such as observing, inferring, predicting, classifying, and making models to learn more about the world.
- Successful scientists possess certain important attitudes, or habits of mind, including curiosity, honesty, open-mindedness, skepticism, and creativity.

Key Terms

observing
quantitative observation
qualitative observation
inferring
predicting
classifying
making models
science
skepticism

② Scientific Inquiry

Key Concepts

- Scientific inquiry refers to the diverse ways in which scientists study the natural world and propose explanations based on the evidence they gather.
- In science, a hypothesis must be testable. This means that researchers must be able to carry out investigations and gather evidence that will either support or disprove the hypothesis.
- Unlike a theory, a scientific law describes an observed pattern in nature without attempting to explain it.

Key Terms

scientific inquiry	operational definition
hypothesis	data
variable	communicating
manipulated variable	scientific theory
responding variable	scientific law
controlled experiment	

③ Why Study Science?

Key Concepts

- Being able to understand scientific principles and think scientifically can help you solve problems and answer many questions in your everyday life.
- By having scientific literacy, you will be able to identify good sources of scientific information, evaluate them for accuracy, and apply the knowledge to questions or problems in your life.

Key Term

scientific literacy

④ Careers in Science

Key Concepts

- The three main branches of science are earth and space science, life science, and physical science.
- Although it is convenient to think of science as divided into three branches, these areas are not really separate at all. Most scientific questions being investigated today span the different fields of science.
- In many nonscience careers, a knowledge of science is essential in order to perform the job.

---

science? What stages are important in the scientific inquiry process? What are the main branches of science, and what does each include?

Prompt students by using connecting words or phrases, such as "use," "possess," and "includes," to indicate the basis for the organization of the map. The phrases should form a sentence between or among a set of concepts.

Answer
Accept logical presentations by students.

All in One Teaching Resources

- Key Terms Review: *What Is Science?*
- Transparency P5

Review and Assessment

Organizing Information

Identifying Main Ideas Copy the graphic organizer about scientific skills onto a separate sheet of paper. Then complete it and add a title. (For more on Identifying Main Ideas, see the Skills Handbook.)

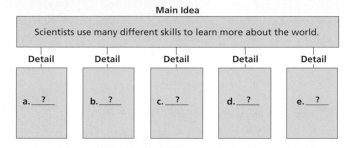

Main Idea

Scientists use many different skills to learn more about the world.

Detail	Detail	Detail	Detail	Detail
a. ?	b. ?	c. ?	d. ?	e. ?

Reviewing Key Terms

Choose the letter of the best answer.

1. When you explain or interpret an observation, you are
   a. making models.   b. classifying.
   c. inferring.   d. predicting.

2. The scientific attitude of having doubt is called
   a. open-mindedness.
   b. curiosity.
   c. honesty.
   d. skepticism.

3. The variable that a scientist intentionally changes in an experiment is called the
   a. manipulated variable.
   b. responding variable.
   c. control.
   d. operational definition.

4. The facts, figures, and other evidence gathered through observations are called
   a. predictions.   b. hypotheses.
   c. conclusions.   d. data.

5. Being able to understand basic scientific terms and principles well enough to apply them to your life is called
   a. classifying.
   b. scientific inquiry.
   c. scientific literacy.
   d. controlling variables.

If the statement is true, write *true*. If it is false, change the underlined word or words to make the statement true.

6. Noticing that the sky is dark and hearing thunder in the distance are examples of <u>inferring</u>.

7. When you are <u>predicting</u>, you are making a forecast of what will happen in the future based on your past experiences.

8. A <u>hypothesis</u> is a factor that can change in an experiment.

9. A <u>scientific theory</u> is a well-tested explanation for a wide range of observations.

10. <u>Life science</u> includes the study of motion, sound, light, electricity, and magnetism.

Writing in Science

Journal Entry Describe one of your daily routines or something interesting that happened to you this week. Illustrate how you thought like a scientist by using at least five of the Key Terms from this chapter.

What Is Science?
Video Preview
Video Field Trip
▶ Video Assessment

Organizing Information
a. Observing
b. Inferring
c. Predicting
d. Classifying
e. Making models

Reviewing Key Terms
1. c 2. d 3. a 4. d 5. c
6. observing
7. true
8. variable
9. true
10. Physical science

Writing in Science

Writing Mode Description
Scoring Rubric
4 Exceeds criteria; includes many more than five key terms and/or it may integrate an interesting event into a description of a daily routine
3 Meets criteria
2 Includes less than five key terms and/or describes an incomplete story
1 Includes only brief and/or inaccurate information

Video Assessment

What Is Science?

Show the Video Assessment to review chapter content and as a prompt for the writing assignment. Discussion questions: **What tools did present-day forensic scientists use to solve this investigation?** (*They used DNA testing and fiber analysis*). **What observations did modern-day forensic scientists make that helped them determine that John Toms was guilty of this historical crime?** (*They could take photos of the crime scene, take the temperature of the victim, make a plaster cast of a footprint, examine hair and fibers, and analyze blood samples and gunpowder residue.*)

Go Online
PHSchool.com
For: Take a practice test.
Visit: PHSchool.com
Web Code: cga-6010

Students can take a practice test online that is automatically scored.

Teaching Resources
- Transparency P6
- Chapter Test
- Performance Assessment Teacher Notes
- Performance Assessment Student Worksheet
- Performance Assessment Scoring Rubric

◉ **ExamView® Computer Test Bank CD-ROM**

Checking Concepts

11. Inferring means explaining or interpreting things you observe, while predicting means forecasting things that will happen in the future.

12. Sample answer: Science is a way of learning about the natural world that includes many skills and processes, as well as existing knowledge.

13. Such results could lead to new ideas and better understanding, even though the original hypothesis was proven incorrect.

14. Scientists share their results by speaking at scientific meetings, exchanging information on the Internet, or publishing articles in scientific journals.

15. Students' answers should describe ways in which they applied scientific information to questions or problems in their lives.

16. Most scientific questions being investigated today span the different fields of science.

Thinking Critically

17. You could infer that the cat climbed in the aquarium in order to eat fish it saw there. But when it became wet, it left the fish alone and began struggling to get out of the aquarium.

18. Sample answer: Type of food, amount of food, time needed for dog to eat food, location, time of day, possible distractions, how much food dog had eaten previously

19. Sample answer: How was the study conducted? What frozen fruits and canned vegetables were involved? How was nutrition measured or determined?

20. Sample answer: No. Astronauts need to know how to conduct many types of experiments, study many properties, and use computers in these and other activities.

Applying Skills

21. The manipulated variable is type of activity (at rest, walking, running); the responding variable is heart rate.

22. Sample answer: A person's heart rate while running is greater than that person's heart rate while walking.

23. Their heart rates would decrease as they rested after a long run.

24. Sample answer: The manipulated variable is a type of activity, such as jumping rope or doing push ups. The responding variable is heart rate. Controlled variables include the same person, time of day, temperature, humidity, and level of physical exertion before the activity.

Review and Assessment

Checking Concepts

11. What is the difference between inferring and predicting?

12. In your own words, explain briefly what science is.

13. Why is it important to report experimental results honestly even when the results go against your hypothesis?

14. What are some ways scientists communicate with one another?

15. Give an example from your life in which having scientific literacy was important.

16. How do the different branches of science depend on one another?

Thinking Critically

17. Inferring Suppose you come home to the scene below. What can you infer happened while you were gone?

18. Problem Solving Suppose you would like to find out which dog food your dog likes best. What variables would you need to control in your experiment?

19. Making Judgments You read an ad claiming that scientific studies prove that frozen fruit is more nutritious than canned vegetables. What questions would you want answered before you accept this claim?

20. Making Generalizations Your friend tells you that she wants to become an astronaut and therefore only needs to study space science. Do you agree with this statement? Why or why not?

Applying Skills

Use the data table below to answer Questions 21–24.

Three students conducted a controlled experiment to find out how walking and running affected their heart rates.

Effect of Activity on Heart Rate (in beats per minute)

Student	Heart Rate (at rest)	Heart Rate (walking)	Heart Rate (running)
1	70	90	115
2	72	80	100
3	80	100	120

21. Controlling Variables What is the manipulated variable in this experiment? What is the responding variable?

22. Developing Hypotheses What hypothesis might this experiment be testing?

23. Predicting Based on this experiment and what you know about exercising, predict how the students' heart rates would change while they are resting after a long run.

24. Designing Experiments Design a controlled experiment to determine which activity has more of an effect on a person's heart rate— jumping rope or doing push-ups.

Lab zone | Chapter **Project**

Performance Assessment Create a poster that summarizes your experiment for the class. Your poster should include the question you tested, how you tested it, the data you collected, and what conclusion you drew from your experiment. What problems did you encounter while carrying out your experiment? Is additional testing necessary?

Lab zone | Chapter **Project**

Performance Assessment Students' posters will vary depending on the common belief tested. Each poster should include a statement of the common belief, the hypothesis, a description of the experiment, the data gathered in the form of a table or graph, and the conclusion drawn from that data. In a summary, students should mention any problems encountered as well as state whether additional testing is necessary.

Standardized Test Prep

The graph below compares how well two different brands of insulated mugs retained heat. Use the graph and your knowledge of science to answer Questions 3–4.

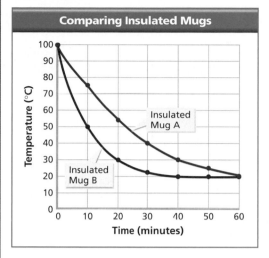

Choose the letter of the best answer.

1. What would be the best way to determine which brand of paper towels is the "strongest when wet"?
   A comparing television commercials that demonstrate the strength of paper towels
   B tearing different brands of towels when they are wet to feel which seems strongest
   C comparing how much weight each brand of towel can hold when wet before it breaks
   D conducting a survey of consumers, professional cooks, and restaurant staff

2. Which of the following habits of mind do good scientists possess?
   F curiosity about the natural world
   G open-mindedness about their findings and those of other scientists
   H honesty in reporting observations and results
   J all of the above

3. What was the manipulated variable in this experiment?
   A the temperature of the water
   B location of the travel mug
   C brand of travel mug
   D the length of time the water was allowed to cool

4. What conclusion can you draw from this experiment?
   F There is no difference between brands A and B.
   G Brand A keeps water warmer longer than brand B.
   H Brand B keeps water warmer longer than brand A.
   J Brand B seems to add heat to the water.

Constructed Response

5. Advertisements for three brands of plant food each claim that their brand makes plants grow fastest. How would you design an experiment to test which brand works best?

Standardized Test Prep

1. C **2.** J **3.** D **4.** G
5. Sample answer: Grow four of the same kind of plants in different pots. Add a different brand of plant food to each of three pots. Add no plant food to the fourth pot. Control all other variables, including soil type, amount of water, amount of sunlight, and temperature. Observe the growth of the four plants over a two-week period, measuring and recording the height of the plant each day. After two weeks, compare the growth data from the four plants and draw a conclusion about which plant food works best.

Chapter at a Glance

 Chapter Project *Design and Build a Scale Model*

Technology

Local Standards

All in One **Teaching Resources**

- Chapter Project Teacher Notes, pp. 105–106
- Chapter Project Student Introduction, pp. 107–108
- Chapter Project Student Worksheets 1–2, pp. 109–110
- Chapter Project Scoring Rubric, p. 111

Video Preview

 Section 1

Measurement—A Common Language

3–4 periods
1 1/2–2 blocks

P.2.1.1 Explain why scientists use a standard measurement system.

P.2.1.2 Identify the SI units of measure for length, mass, volume, density, time, and temperature.

P.2.1.3 Describe how conversion factors are useful.

Video Field Trip

PHSchool.com

 Section 2

Mathematics and Science

3–4 periods
1 1/2-2 blocks

P.2.2.1 Describe what math skills scientists use in collecting data and making measurements.

P.2.2.2 Identify the math skills scientists use to analyze their data.

SCiLINKS

 Section 3

Graphs in Science

3–4 periods
1 1/2-2 blocks

P.2.3.1 Explain what type of data line graphs can display.

P.2.3.2 Describe how you determine a line of best fit or the slope of a graph.

P.2.3.3 Explain why line graphs are powerful tools in science.

active art

PHSchool.com

 Section 4

Safety in the Science Laboratory

1-2 periods
1/2-1 blocks

P.2.4.1 Explain why preparation is important when carrying out scientific investigations in the lab and in the field.

P.2.4.2 Describe what you should do if an accident occurs.

SCiLINKS

Review and Assessment

Test Preparation

All in One **Teaching Resources**

- Key Terms Review, p. 152
- Transparency P30
- Performance Assessment Teacher Notes, p. 159
- Performance Assessment Scoring rubric, p. 160
- Performance Assessment Student Worksheet, p. 161
- Chapter Test, pp. 162–165

Video Assessment

PHSchool.com

Test Preparation Blackline Masters

- Diagnostic test
- Benchmark test

Chapter Activities Planner

For more activities

LAB ZONE Easy Planner CD-ROM

Student Edition	Inquiry	Time	Materials	Skills	Resources
Chapter Project	Open-ended	Ongoing (2–3 weeks)	**All in One Teaching Resources** See p. 105		**Lab zone Easy Planner** **All in One Teaching Resources** Support pp. 105–106
Section 1					
Discover Activity, p. 44	Open-ended	10 minutes	Scissors, sheet of paper	Inferring	**Lab zone Easy Planner**
Skills Activity, p. 49	Directed	15 minutes	Balance, CD, textbook	Measuring	**Lab zone Easy Planner**
Consumer Lab, pp. 56–57	Guided	40 minutes	Balance, 5–6 textbooks, meter stick, 2 backpacks (one large and one small)	Measuring, calculating, drawing conclusions	**Lab zone Easy Planner** **Lab Activity Video** **All in One Teaching Resources** Consumer Lab: *Backpack Basics*
Section 2					
Discover Activity, p. 60	Open-ended	15 minutes	Clear glass jar with top, marbles of different colors	Predicting	**Lab zone Easy Planner**
Try This Activity, p. 64	Directed	15 minutes	Metric ruler, meter stick, balance, penny, shoe box	Measuring	**Lab zone Easy Planner**
Section 3					
Discover Activity, p. 68	Open-ended	5 minutes		Inferring	**Lab zone Easy Planner**
At-Home Activity, p. 75	Open-ended	15 minutes		Graphing	**Lab zone Easy Planner**
Skills Lab, p. 76	Guided	40 minutes	Graduated cylinder, balance, graph paper, 3 samples of a liquid	Graphing, calculating	**Lab zone Easy Planner** **Lab Activity Video** **All in One Teaching Resources** Skills Lab: *Density Graphs*
Section 4					
Discover Activity, p. 77	Open-ended	15 minutes		Predicting	**Lab zone Easy Planner**

Section 1 Measurement—A Common Language

 3–4 periods, 1 1/2–2 blocks

Objectives

P.2.1.1 Explain why scientists use a standard measurement system.

P.2.1.2 Identify the SI units of measure for length, mass, volume, density, time, and temperature.

P.2.1.3 Describe how conversion factors are useful.

Local Standards

Key Terms

• metric system • SI • mass • weight • volume • meniscus • density

Preteach

Build Background Knowledge

Students describe their experiences with metric measurements.

Lab zone Discover Activity *How Many Shoes?*

Targeted Print and Technology Resources

All in One Teaching Resources

L2 Reading Strategy Transparency P7: *Comparing and Contrasting*

Presentation-Pro CD-ROM

Transparency P7

Instruct

A Standard Measurement System Ask leading questions for a discussion of SI units.

Length Ask students what units of length they would use in specific examples.

Mass Call on students to define terms related to measuring mass.

Volume Ask students what unit of measure they would use to measure the volume of objects.

Density Lead a discussion on what density is and how to determine the density of objects.

Time Have students become familiar with the second through a test of a folk measure.

Temperature Ask students to take daily Celsius measurements of air temperature.

Converting Between Units Describe a situation in which a scientist has to convert a measurement.

Lab zone Consumer Lab Backpack Basics

Targeted Print and Technology Resources

All in One Teaching Resources

L2 Guided Reading, pp. 114–118

L2 Transparencies P8, P9, P10, P11, P12, P13, P14, P15

L2 Consumer Lab: *Backpack Basics,* pp. 121–125

Lab Activity Video/DVD
Skills Lab: *Backpack Basics*

www.PHSchool.com
Web Code: cgd-6021

www.PHSchool.com
Web Code: cgh-6020

Discovery CHANNEL SCHOOL
Video Field Trip

Student Edition on Audio CD

Transparencies P8, P9, P10, P11, P12, P13, P14, P15

Assess

Section Assessment Questions

Have students use their completed graphic organizers to answer the questions.

Reteach

Call on volunteers to identify units of measure and the processes used to measure.

Targeted Print and Technology Resources

All in One Teaching Resources

• Section Summary, p. 113

L1 Review and Reinforce, p. 119

L3 Enrich, p. 120

Section 2 **Mathematics and Science**

⏱ *4–5 periods, 2–2 1/2 blocks*

Objectives

P.2.2.1 Describe what math skills scientists use in collecting data and making measurements.

P.2.2.2 Identify the math skills scientists use to analyze their data.

Key Terms

• estimate • accuracy • precision • significant figures • percent error • mean
• median • mode

Local Standards

Preteach

Build Background Knowledge

Students relate their experiences in using math in science activities.

Lab zone ▶ **Discover Activity** *How Many Marbles Are There?*

Targeted Print and Technology Resources

All in One **Teaching Resources**

L2 Reading Strategy Transparency P16: *Asking Questions*

⊙ **Presentation-Pro CD-ROM**

Transparency P16

Instruct

Estimation Ask students how they would estimate the number of students at their school.

Accuracy and Precision Have students classify an example in terms of accuracy and precision.

Significant Figures Have students work problems related to significant figures.

Percent Error Ask students to analyze a scenario in which a scientist has a high percent error.

Mean, Median, and Mode Have students find mean, median, and mode in lists of numbers.

Targeted Print and Technology Resources

All in One **Teaching Resources**

L2 Guided Reading, pp. 136–139

L2 Transparencies P17, P18, P19, P20, P21, P22

www.SciLinks.org
Web Code: scn-1622

⊙ **Student Edition on Audio CD**

Transparencies P17, P18, P19, P20, P21, P22

Assess

Section Assessment Questions

↻ Have students use their questions and answers to answer the questions.

Reteach

Use a figure to reteach the concepts of precision and accuracy.

Targeted Print and Technology Resources

All in One **Teaching Resources**

• Section Summary, p. 127
L1 Review and Reinforce, p. 132
L3 Enrich, p. 133

Section 3 Graphs in Science

 4–5 periods, 2–2 1/2 blocks

ABILITY LEVELS
L1 Basic to Average
L2 For All Students
L3 Average to Advanced

Objectives

P2.3.1 Explain what type of data line graphs can display.

P.2.3.2 Describe how you determine a line of best fit or the slope of a graph.

P.2.3.3 Explain why line graphs are powerful tools in science.

Local Standards

Key Terms

• graph • horizontal axis • vertical axis • origin • coordinate • data point

• line of best fit • linear graph • slope • nonlinear graph

Preteach

Build Background Knowledge

Students relate their experiences with graphs.

 Discover Activity *What's in a Picture?*

Targeted Print and Technology Resources

All in One Teaching Resources

L2 Reading Strategy: *Building Vocabulary*

⊙ **Presentation-Pro CD-ROM**

Instruct

The Importance of Graphs Have students examine examples of graphs in science textbooks and journals.

Why Draw a Line of Best Fit? Ask students to find examples of lines of best fit in science magazines.

Slope Give students data points on a graph line and ask them to determine the slope of the line.

Using Graphs to Identify Trends Have students identify a trend in a graph and make a prediction.

Skills Lab *Density Graphs*

Targeted Print and Technology Resources

All in One Teaching Resources

L2 Guided Reading, pp. 136–139

L2 Transparencies P23, P24, P25, P26

L2 Skills Lab: *Density Graphs*, pp. 142–144

📼 **Lab Activity Video/DVD**
Skills Lab: *Density Graphs*

www.PHSchool.com
Web Code: cgp-6023

www.PHSchool.com
Web Code: cgd-6023

⊙ **Student Edition on Audio CD**

Transparencies P23, P24, P25, P26

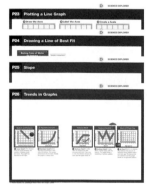

Assess

Section Assessment Questions

↺ Have students use their definitions of key terms to answer the questions.

Reteach

Use the graphs in a figure to reteach concepts related to graphs.

Targeted Print and Technology Resources

All in One Teaching Resources

• Section Summary, p. 135

L1 Review and Reinforce, p. 140

L3 Enrich, p. 141

Section 4 Safety in the Science Laboratory

ABILITY LEVELS
- **L1** Basic to Average
- **L2** For All Students
- **L3** Average to Advanced

🕐 *2–3 periods, 1–1 1/2 blocks*

Objectives

P.2.4.1 Explain why preparation is important when carrying out scientific investigations in the lab and in the field.

P.2.4.2 Describe what you should do if an accident occurs.

Local Standards

Preteach

Build Background Knowledge

Students analyze the safety mistakes of a fictional student in a laboratory.

 **Discover Activity** *Where Is the Safety Equipment in Your School?*

Targeted Print and Technology Resources

 **Teaching Resources**

L2 Reading Strategy Transparency P27: *Outlining*

⊙ **Presentation-Pro CD-ROM**

Transparency P27

Instruct

Safety in the Lab Lead a discussion of how to stay safe in a laboratory.

Safety in the Field Have students assess a situation in which a student violates safety rules.

In Case of an Accident Ask students what they would do if an accident happened in the lab.

Targeted Print and Technology Resources

 **Teaching Resources**

L2 Guided Reading, pp. 147–149
L2 Transparencies P28, P29

www.SciLinks.org Web Code: scn-1624

⊙ **Student Edition on Audio CD**

Transparencies P28, P29

Assess

Section Assessment Questions

🔄 Have students use their outlines to answer the questions.

Reteach

Use a figure to question students about dangers in a laboratory.

Targeted Print and Technology Resources

Teaching Resources

- Section Summary, p. 146
- **L1** Review and Reinforce, p. 150
- **L3** Enrich, p. 151

Chapter 2 **Content Refresher**

Go Online

NSTA-PDi LINKS

For: Professional development support
Visit: www.SciLinks.org/PDLinks
Web Code: scf-1620

Professional Development

Section 1 Measurement— A Common Language

A Common Measurement System Many people think that the metric system is a fairly new system in the United States. Actually, Thomas Jefferson proposed a decimal-based system for the United States in 1790. In 1866, Congress authorized the use of the metric system in the United States. In 1875, the United States was one of seventeen nations to sign the Treaty of the Meter, which established the International Bureau of Weights and Measures and provided measurement standards for the world. It wasn't until 1975, though, that Congress passed the Metric Conversion Act, which had the purpose of preparing the United States to convert to the metric system. No deadline was set, however, and the English system continues to be widely used throughout the United States today. Nevertheless, most federal agencies use the metric system in their various business-related activities. Although private industries do not by law have to convert, the necessities of world trade have caused most industries to replace machinery with metric based systems as older technology wears out. The United States is the only industrial country in the world that does not use the metric system as its main system of measurement.

Section 2 Mathematics and Science

Significant Figures Measuring is not the same as counting. You can count the pennies in your pocket and know exactly how many you have. But you can never measure your height exactly. In fact, in practical terms it is impossible to make an exact measurement. The reason it is impossible is because all measuring instruments have some limitation. For example, suppose you measure the width of a calculator with a metric ruler and determine that the width is to 6.75 cm. In making this measurement, you are sure about the 6 cm, and you can see that the edge of the calculator is slightly more than an additional 7 mm. The metric ruler has no divisions beyond millimeters, and so you estimate an extra 0.05 cm. In this measurement, then, you can know 3 significant figures with some reliability, given the instrument you are using. Notice that a measurement of 6.75 cm could also be expressed as 0.0675 m or even as 0.0000675 km. Each figure is equivalent to 6.75 cm, and each has 3 significant figures. Zeros to the left in a measurement are not considered as significant figures,

because they only position the decimal point. Zeros to the right are significant. A measurement of 7.00 has 3 significant figures, just as 6.75 cm does. Scientists take care to express measurements with the correct significant figures in order to avoid misunderstanding. For example, the average distance from the Earth to the sun is 149 million km, a measurement with 3 significant digits. That distance might also be expressed as 149,000,000 km. Yet, the latter measurement implies 9 significant figures, and that would be misleading.

Address Misconceptions

Students may think that measuring with metric units ensures a more accurate measurement. This misconception is addressed in Section 2, Mathematics and Science.

Section 3 Graphs in Science

Types of Graphs The three main types of graphs are the line graph, the bar graph, and the circle graph. The line graph is perhaps the most widely used in science. It especially provides a good pictorial representation of a continuing process, such as the acceleration of an object. A bar graph, by contrast, provides a good representation of a series of discrete measurements. In ecological studies, a climate graph is used,

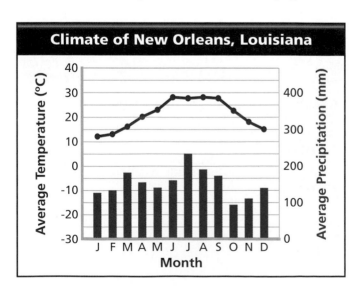

Climate of New Orleans, Louisiana

Composition of Earth's Atmosphere

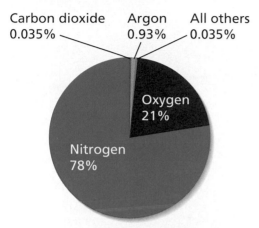

and this graph includes both a line graph and a bar graph, as shown in the figure. Average temperature is represented by a line graph. Since temperature is continuous, a line well represents temperature variations throughout a year. Precipitation, though, is periodic, and the data collected for precipitation are often communicated as a monthly figure. Therefore, a bar graph is a good choice to represent that data.

The third type of graph, the circle graph, is also sometimes called a pie chart because data are shown in a way that is similar to pieces of a pie. This type of representation is a good choice when there are several components of a whole. The figure above shows a common circle graph in Earth science texts for the composition of Earth's atmosphere. A reader of the graph can immediately see the different proportions of the gases that make up the atmosphere.

Section 4 Safety in the Science Laboratory

Safety First Following safety precautions in the science laboratory cannot be overemphasized. In addition to having students follow the safety cautions in their texts, the teacher can take some actions that might further ensure safety. For instance, it is a good idea to lock the laboratory or the lab storeroom when you are not present. This will prevent the enterprising student from continuing an investigation when you are not there to supervise. Also consider having drills on what students should do if a substance catches fire or if there is an accidental chemical exposure or spill. You may want to post the phone numbers of the local poison control center in your laboratory.

Monitoring Your Understanding
Self-Questioning and Self-Adjusting While Reading

Strategy This strategy enables students to focus on their own thought processes as they actively question and apply fix-up strategies to improve comprehension. First, present the three steps in the example below, reviewing the fix-up strategies in Step 2. Then, before students begin, assign a section for them to read, such as *The Importance of Graphs* in Section 3. You might want to model the strategy with a paragraph or two before having students practice it on their own.

Example

1. Self-Question Have students read and think about the paragraphs under each heading, stopping often to ask themselves questions such as "Do I understand this?" and "Is this clear?"

2. Identify Trouble Spots and Apply Fix-Up Strategies

- **Reread/Adjust Reading Pace** When students do not understand a paragraph, have them reread it slowly, making sure they understand each sentence before they continue.

- **Clarify** When students encounter a difficult paragraph, suggest they state what they do understand, talk through confusing points or steps in a process, or relate new information to concepts and examples that are already familiar to them.

- **Read Ahead/Use Visuals and Captions** Show students how to use visuals and captions to help clarify a process or concept. Suggest also that they can read ahead to see whether a process or concept is discussed further.

- **Use Outside Resources** Point out, too, that students should seek assistance from friends, teachers, or other resources.

3. Self-Check After students read, have them check their understanding by summarizing or retelling the main idea of a paragraph or section.

Interactive Textbook
- Complete student edition
- Video and audio
- Simulations and activities
- Section and chapter activities

Chapter 2

The Work of Scientists

Chapter Preview

❶ Measurement—A Common Language
Discover *How Many Shoes?*
Science and History *Measurement Systems*
Skills Activity *Measuring*
Consumer Lab *Backpack Basics*
Science and Society *Should the United States Go Metric?*

❷ Mathematics and Science
Discover *How Many Marbles Are There?*
Math Skills *Calculating Area*
Try This *For Good Measure*

❸ Graphs in Science
Discover *What's in a Picture?*
Active Art *Plotting a Line Graph*
Analyzing Data *Car Travel*
At-Home Activity *Which Line Is Best?*
Skills Lab *Density Graphs*

❹ Safety in the Science Laboratory
Discover *Where Is the Safety Equipment in Your School?*

Interactive Textbook

This scientist studies young bearded seals that live in subzero waters near Norway. ▶

 **Chapter Project**

Objectives

Students will measure or find a structure and construct a three-dimensional model to scale. After completing this Chapter Project, students will be able to

- measure a structure to be modeled, or find the dimensions of a structure
- calculate scaled values for the actual measurements of the model
- construct a scale three-dimensional model of the structure
- communicate a description of the model to the class

Skills Focus

Measuring, calculating, making models, communicating

Project Time Line 2-3 weeks

All in One Teaching Resources

- Chapter Project Teacher Notes
- Chapter Project Worksheet 1
- Chapter Project Worksheet 2
- Chapter Project Scoring Rubric

Developing a Plan

Students can individually make a model of a structure or work in small groups. Students should first make measurements of a chosen room or structure or find out the dimensions of a building or another large structure. They should then write a plan of how to proceed and make a sketch of the model. After you have approved the plans, students can collect building materials and proceed to the building stage. Finally, students will present their models to the class.

Possible Materials

Most models can be made using metric rulers (preferably with millimeter graduations), scissors, glue, and thin sheets of poster board or construction paper. Some students might also choose to use scraps of fabric, plastic sheets, wire, craft sticks, polystyrene shapes, and toothpicks.

Discovery CHANNEL **SCHOOL** Video Preview

Lab zone Chapter **Project**

Design and Build a Scale Model

How do scientists study something as large as the solar system or as tiny as an atom? One tool they use is a model. Models help scientists picture things that are difficult to see or understand. In this chapter project, you will create a three-dimensional model of a building or room.

Your Goal To create a three-dimensional model that shows the size relationships among the different parts of the model

To complete this project, you must
- measure or find the actual dimensions of the structure to be modeled
- sketch your model on graph paper and calculate the size of each part you will include
- construct your three-dimensional model
- follow the safety guidelines in Appendix A

Plan It! Choose a room in your house or school, or a familiar building to model. Think about how you could construct a smaller replica of that room or building. Preview the chapter to find out how scientists make measurements. Then write a brief plan detailing how you will proceed with this project. Make sure your plan includes a sketch and a list of the materials you will use. After your teacher approves your plan, start working on your model.

Chapter 2 P ◆ 43

The Work of Scientists

Show the Video Preview to introduce the chapter. Discussion question: **Why is it important to be able to measure time accurately in a race?** *(Sample answer: Accurate measurement of time is important because a hundredth, even a thousandth, of a second can make the difference in who wins the race.)*

Launching the Project

Bring several toy cars of different sizes to class. Have students contrast these models with the real-life counterparts in terms of composition, color, and realism. Then focus the discussion on size. Ask: **What is a scale model?** *(Sample answer: A scale model is a model in which all of the parts of the model are made in proportion to the parts of the actual structure.)* Point to a table, and ask: **How would you make a scale model of this object?** *(Sample answer: The table would be measured and the values would be reduced or increased proportionally to produce a scale model.)* Ask a volunteer to read aloud the description of this Chapter Project from the student page. Allow a few minutes for students to brainstorm a list of rooms or structures that could be modeled.

Performance Assessment

The Chapter Project Scoring Rubric will help you evaluate how well students complete the Chapter Project. You may want to share the scoring rubric with your students so they are clear about what will be expected of them. Students will be assessed on
- how well they make the measurements of a structure or find the dimensions of the structure
- how accurately they construct their scale models
- how effectively they present their models to the class
- how well they participate in their groups

Students can keep the sketches of their models in their portfolios.

Portfolio

Possible Shortcuts
- You can make this project shorter by assigning several students to make a single scale model of their choice.
- For a class project, have several groups of students work on different parts of the same scale model, such as your school or one of its common rooms. Assign several groups to complete one part of the model. Each group can be given time to add its contribution.

Objectives

After this lesson, students will be able to

P.2.1.1 Explain why scientists use a standard measurement system.

P.2.1.2 Identify the SI units of measure for length, mass, volume, density, time, and temperature.

P.2.1.3 Describe how conversion factors are useful.

Target Reading Skill

Comparing and Contrasting Explain that comparing and contrasting information shows how ideas, facts, and events are similar and different. The results of the comparison can have importance.

Answers

Length—Distance from one point to another, meter (m), metric ruler

Mass—Amount of matter, gram (g), balance

Volume—Amount of space, liter (L), graduated cylinder

Time—Passing of events, second (s), watch or clock

Temperature—Hotness or coldness, degrees Celsius or kelvin, thermometer

All in One Teaching Resources

• Transparency P7

Preteach

Build Background Knowledge   L2

Experience With Metric Measurement

Ask: **What units of measure do you use in everyday life?** *(Sample answer: Pounds, miles, yards, feet, inches, gallons, ounces, degrees Fahrenheit)* **What units of measure have you used in science investigations in the past?** *(Sample answer: Grams, meters, liters, degrees Celsius)* **Why do you think there is a difference in the units of measure people use every day and the units of measure used in science?** *(Sample answer: Scientists all over the world have agreed to use the metric system.)*

Section

1 Measurement—A Common Language

Reading Preview

Key Concepts

• Why do scientists use a standard measurement system?

• What are the SI units of measure for length, mass, volume, density, time, and temperature?

• How are conversion factors useful?

Key Terms

• metric system   • SI   • mass
• weight   • volume   • meniscus
• density

Target Reading Skill

Comparing and Contrasting As you read, compare and contrast different types of measurement by completing a table like the one below.

Measurement

Characteristic	Length	Mass
Definition		
SI unit		
Measuring tool		

Lab zone Discover Activity

How Many Shoes?

1. Trace an outline of your shoe onto a piece of paper. Cut out your pattern.

2. Use your pattern to measure the length of your classroom in "shoes."

3. Compare your measurement to those of three classmates. Did you all measure the same number of "shoes"?

Think About It

Inferring Why do you think it is important that people use standard units of measurement?

Did you ever ask a relative for an old family recipe? If so, the answer might have been, "Use just the right amount of flour and water. Add a spoonful of oil and a pinch of salt. Bake it for awhile until it looks just right."

Instructions like these would be difficult to follow. How much flour is "just the right amount"? How big is a spoonful or a pinch? It would be impossible for you to know what your relative had in mind. You could end up with disastrous results.

In tasks such as cooking, ▶ measurements can be critical!

Lab zone Discover Activity

Skills Focus Inferring

Materials scissors, sheet of paper

Time 15 minutes

Tips Divide the class into groups of four.

Expected Outcome No four students will have measured the same number of "shoes."

Think It Over Sample answer: Using standard units of measure helps to eliminate confusion when people communicate their data, conclusions, and answers.

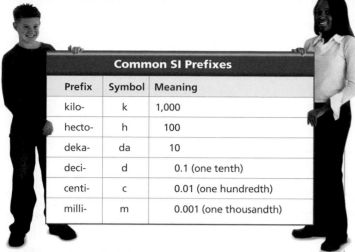

Common SI Prefixes		
Prefix	Symbol	Meaning
kilo-	k	1,000
hecto-	h	100
deka-	da	10
deci-	d	0.1 (one tenth)
centi-	c	0.01 (one hundredth)
milli-	m	0.001 (one thousandth)

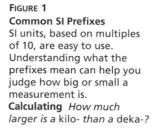

FIGURE 1
Common SI Prefixes
SI units, based on multiples of 10, are easy to use. Understanding what the prefixes mean can help you judge how big or small a measurement is.
Calculating *How much larger is a kilo- than a deka-?*

A Standard Measurement System

The recipe example illustrates the importance of using a standard system of measurement. This is especially true in science. Using the same system of measurement minimizes confusion among scientists all over the world.

The Metric System More than 200 years ago, most countries used their own measurement systems. Sometimes two or more different systems were used in the same country. In the 1790s, scientists in France developed a universal system of measurement called the metric system. The **metric system** is a system of measurement based on the number 10.

The International System of Units (SI) Modern scientists use a version of the metric system called the International System of Units, abbreviated as **SI** (for the French, *Système International d'Unités*). Scientists all over the world use SI units to measure length, volume, mass, density, temperature, and time. **Using SI as the standard system of measurement allows scientists to compare data and communicate with each other about their results.** In this book and others in the *Science Explorer* program, you will use both SI and other metric units.

Figure 1 lists the prefixes used to name the most common SI units. Because they are based on multiples of 10, SI units are easy to use. Each unit is ten times larger than the next smallest unit and one tenth the size of the next largest unit. This is similar to our money system, in which a dime is worth ten times more than a penny, but one tenth as much as a dollar.

 Reading Checkpoint SI units are based on multiples of what number?

The Work of Scientists

Video Preview
▶ Video Field Trip
Video Assessment

Differentiated Instruction

Special Needs **L1**
Communicating Ask students to create a display about each of the measurements described in this section. For each measurement, students should include a definition of the characteristic being measured, the basic SI unit for that measurement, any instructions for making the measurement, and any formulas needed for determining values. **learning modality: visual**

Gifted and Talented **L3**
Comparing and Contrasting Have students investigate how to operate a double-pan balance and prepare a demonstration for the class. In this demonstration, they can compare and contrast the double-pan balance with the triple-beam balance by determining the mass of an object on both instruments. **learning modality: visual**

A Standard Measurement System

Teach Key Concepts **L2**
The Metric System and SI

Focus Tell students that modern scientists use a version of the metric system called the International System of Units, or SI.

Teach Ask: **What do scientists use SI units to measure?** *(Length, volume, mass, density, temperature, and time)*

Apply Ask: **Why is using a standard measurement system important for scientists?** *(Using the same system of measurement minimizes confusion among scientists all over the world.)* **learning modality: logical/mathematical**

All in One Teaching Resources
• Transparency P8

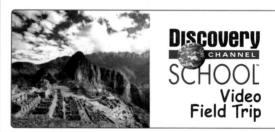

The Work of Scientists

Show the Video Field Trip to let students experience the work of scientists. Discussion question: **What two readings are necessary to determine longitude?** *(Latitude and the difference in time between where you are and the time at a fixed location)*

Independent Practice **L2**
All in One Teaching Resources
• Guided Reading and Study Worksheet: *Measurement—A Common Language*

⊙ Student Edition on Audio CD

Monitor Progress _____ **L2**

Oral Presentation Call on students to identify the system that scientists all over the world use and to explain why scientists use a standard measurement system.

Answers
Figure 1 100 times larger
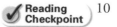 **Reading Checkpoint** 10

Length

Teach Key Concepts `L2`

The Meter

Focus Tell students that the SI unit of length is the meter.

Teach Ask: **What is length?** (*Length is the distance from one point to another.*) Have students turn back to Figure 1, the Common SI Prefixes. Explain that these prefixes can be combined with the word *meter* to form the names for the SI units of length. Ask: **What is the unit of length that equals 1,000 meters?** (*The kilometer*) Ask: **What does 1 meter equal in centimeters?** (*100 centimeters*)

Apply Ask: **What unit of length would you use to measure a piece of notebook paper?** (*The centimeter*) **The distance from Atlanta to Chicago?** (*The kilometer*) **learning modality: verbal**

 **Teaching Resources**

• Transparency P9

 **Build Inquiry** `L2`

Materials meter stick, metric ruler

Time 20 minutes

Focus Challenge students to create a metric measurement inventory of the classroom.

Teach Introduce students to the metric ruler and the meter stick. Explain the metric ruler is used to measure small objects and the meter stick is used to measure larger objects. Ask: **What measurements is a metric ruler divided into?** (*Centimeters and millimeters*) **Which instrument would you use to measure a paper clip?** (*Metric ruler*) Demonstrate how to use both.

Apply Give students 10 minutes to measure the length of any and every thing in the classroom. Ask them to keep a record of their measurements. Collect their records when the time is up, and ask volunteers to assemble the information into a large chart. **learning modality: kinesthetic**

Common Conversions for Length	
1 km	= 1,000 m
1 m	= 100 cm
1 m	= 1,000 mm
1 cm	= 10 mm

Length

How far can you throw a softball? Can you judge by eye how far the ball travels? A better way to find out would be to measure the distance, or length, that the ball travels. Length is the distance from one point to another. In the case of your softball throw, it would be from the point where you release the ball to the point where it first hits the ground.

Units of Length The basic unit of length in the SI system is the meter (m). One meter is about the distance from the floor to a doorknob. A softball throw would be measured in meters. So would your height. Most students your age are between 1.5 and 2 meters tall.

Science and **History**

Measurement Systems
Like so much else in science, systems of measurement developed gradually over time in different parts of the world.

640 B.C.
Standard Units of Weight
Merchants in the Middle East and Mediterranean used units of weight to be sure that they received the correct amount of gold and silver in trade and to check the purity of the metal. A *talent* was about 25 kilograms, and a *mina* was about 500 grams. The Lydians minted the first true coins to have standard weight and value.

1400 B.C.
A Simple Balance
The ancient Egyptians developed the first known weighing instrument, a simple balance with a pointer. Earlier, they had been the first to standardize a measure of length. The length, called a cubit, was originally defined as the distance between the elbow and the tip of the middle finger.

200 B.C.
Standard Measures
Shih Huang Ti, the first emperor of China, set standards for weight, length, and volume. He also improved travel conditions by setting standards for the widths of roads and for the distance between chariot wheels.

1500 B.C.	1000 B.C.	500 B.C.	A.D. 1

To measure objects smaller than a meter, scientists use units called the centimeter (cm) or the millimeter (mm). The prefix *centi-* means "one-hundredth," while the prefix *milli-* means one-thousandth. One meter, then, is equal to 100 centimeters or 1,000 millimeters. The length of a typical sheet of loose-leaf paper is 28 centimeters, which is equal to 280 millimeters.

What unit would you use to measure a long distance, such as the distance between two cities? For such measurements, scientists use a unit known as the kilometer (km). The prefix *kilo-* means one thousand. There are 1,000 meters in a kilometer. The distance from San Francisco to Boston is about 4,300 kilometers.

Science and History

Focus Ask: **How long is the period that the timeline shows?** (*3500 years, from 1500 B.C. to A.D. 2000*)

Teach Invite volunteers to read entries on the timeline. After the entire timeline has been read, ask: **When were the first standard units of measurement established?** (*In 640 B.C., merchants established standard units of weight.*) **Why do you think merchants established standard measurements?** (*Standard measurements would have been necessary for trade to flourish between countries and different peoples.*) **Is the reason why scientists use a standard system similar to why ancient merchants established standards?** (*Yes. Both merchants and scientists need to compare and communicate.*)

Writing in Science

Research and Write While scientists rely on SI units, people use different measurement units for other purposes. Research the units used in sailing, horse breeding, diamond cutting, farming, or another activity that interests you. Write a few paragraphs about your findings.

Writing in Science

Writing Mode Description
Scoring Rubric
4 Exceeds criteria; may have well-written directions and/or include illustrations
3 Meets all criteria
2 Meets some but not all criteria
1 Meets few criteria, with inaccurate information and/or brief descriptions

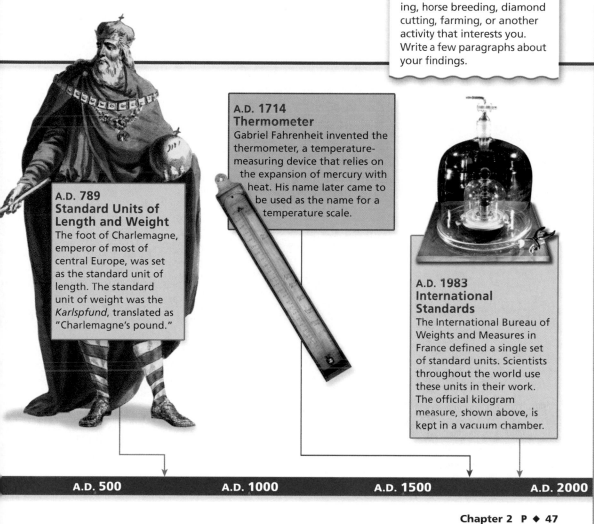

A.D. 789
Standard Units of Length and Weight
The foot of Charlemagne, emperor of most of central Europe, was set as the standard unit of length. The standard unit of weight was the *Karlspfund*, translated as "Charlemagne's pound."

A.D. 1714
Thermometer
Gabriel Fahrenheit invented the thermometer, a temperature-measuring device that relies on the expansion of mercury with heat. His name later came to be used as the name for a temperature scale.

A.D. 1983
International Standards
The International Bureau of Weights and Measures in France defined a single set of standard units. Scientists throughout the world use these units in their work. The official kilogram measure, shown above, is kept in a vacuum chamber.

| A.D. 500 | A.D. 1000 | A.D. 1500 | A.D. 2000 |

Chapter 2 P ◆ 47

Background

Facts and Figures The International System of Units (SI) was established by a conference in Paris, France, in 1960. The International Bureau of Weights and Measures (BIPM), located in a Paris suburb, has the responsibility of the worldwide standards of physical measurements. There are seven SI base units: meter, kilogram, second, ampere (unit of electric current), kelvin, mole (unit of amount of substance), and candela (unit of luminous intensity) All other units are derived from these seven. The kilogram is the only SI base unit still defined by a physical object. The object is a cylinder of platinum alloy, which is kept at the BIPM. The standard for the meter, adopted in 1983, is the distance traveled by light in a vacuum in 1/299,792,458 of a second.

Monitor Progress

Oral Presentation Ask volunteers to identify the basic unit of length in the SI system and explain what a centimeter and a millimeter are.

Using a Metric Ruler

Focus Explain that the metric ruler is the instrument students will be using most often to measure length.

Teach Ask: **What do the longer lines indicate on a metric ruler?** *(They are the centimeter markings.)* **What do the shorter lines indicate?** *(They are the millimeter markings.)* **In Figure 2, what is the back end of the shell lined up with on the ruler?** *(The zero mark)* **When the back end of the object is lined up with the zero mark, how do you determine the object's length?** *(Read the number at the other end of the object.)*

Apply Ask students to use their metric ruler to measure the length of a small paperclip. **How long is a paperclip?** *(Sample answer: 3.2 cm)* **learning modality: visual**

All in One Teaching Resources

• Transparency P10

Mass

Teach Key Concepts L2

The Kilogram

Focus Tell students that the basic SI unit of mass is the kilogram.

Teach Ask: **What is mass?** *(Mass is a measure of the amount of matter an object contains.)* **If the basic SI unit of mass is the kilogram, then what is a gram?** *(A gram is one-thousandth of a kilogram.)* **What is weight?** *(Weight is the measure of the force of gravity acting on an object.)* **Why doesn't gravity affect an object's mass?** *(Mass is a measure of the amount of matter, and gravity doesn't affect the amount of matter an object has.)* Explain that scientists do measure weight for various reasons, but when they do they usually use the SI unit of force, called the newton.

Apply Ask: **How many milligrams are there in a kilogram?** *(1 kg = 1,000,000 mg)* **learning modality: logical/mathematical**

FIGURE 2
Measuring Length
To measure the length of the turtle's shell, line up one end of the shell exactly with the zero mark on the ruler. Read the number at the other end of the shell to obtain its length.

Measuring Length A very common tool used to measure length is the metric ruler. As you can see in Figure 2, a metric ruler is divided into centimeters. The centimeter markings are the longer lines numbered 1, 2, 3, and so on. Each centimeter is then divided into 10 millimeters, which are marked by the shorter lines.

To use a metric ruler, line one end of the object up exactly with the zero mark. Then read the number at the other end of the object. The shell of the turtle in Figure 2 is 8.8 centimeters, or 88 millimeters, long.

Reading Checkpoint One centimeter is divided into how many millimeters?

Mass

Can you lift a bicycle with one finger? Probably not, unless the bicycle's frame is made of titanium, a strong but very light metal. Most bike racers use titanium frames because the bike's low mass allows them to ride faster. **Mass** is a measure of the amount of matter an object contains.

Units of Mass The basic unit of mass in the SI system is the **kilogram (kg)**. The kilogram is a useful unit when measuring the mass of objects such as bicycles, cars, or people. The mass of a wooden baseball bat is about 1 kilogram.

To measure the mass of smaller objects, you will use a unit known as the gram (g). As you can guess, there are 1,000 grams in a kilogram. A large paper clip has a mass of about 1 gram. Even smaller masses are measured in milligrams (mg). There are 1,000 milligrams in one gram.

Common Conversions for Mass	
1 kg	= 1,000 g
1 g	= 1,000 mg

Measuring Mass To find the mass of an object, you may use a balance like the one in Figure 3. This balance, known as a triple-beam balance, works by comparing the mass of the object you are measuring to a known mass. When you use a triple-beam balance, you first place the object on the pan. You then shift the riders on the beams until they balance the mass of the object. You can find step-by-step instructions for using a triple-beam balance in Appendix C.

The Difference Between Mass and Weight Mass is often confused with weight. But weight is not the same thing as mass. **Weight** is a measure of the force of gravity acting on an object. As you probably know, you can measure an object's weight using a scale. When you stand on a scale, gravity pulls you downward, compressing springs inside the scale. The more you weigh, the more the springs compress, and the higher the reading.

If, however, you were to weigh yourself on the moon, you would obtain a very different reading. Because the force of gravity is much weaker on the moon than on Earth, the springs inside the scale would compress much less. You would weigh less on the moon. But how would your mass compare? Because mass measures the amount of matter an object contains, it remains constant wherever an object may be. Your mass on the moon is the same as your mass on Earth. You can see why scientists prefer to use mass, rather than weight, when making measurements.

 Reading Checkpoint What is weight?

FIGURE 3
Measuring Mass
You can use a triple-beam balance to find the mass of small objects. To measure mass, place the object on the pan and shift the riders on each beam until the pointer stops at zero. **Observing** *What is the mass of this turtle?*

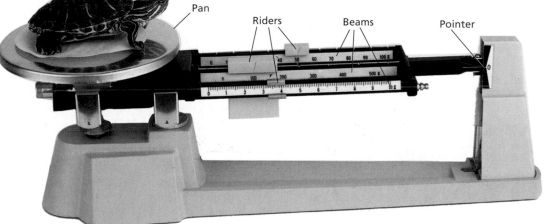

Pan   Riders   Beams   Pointer

Chapter 2 P ◆ 49

Volume

The Liter

Focus Tell students the basic unit of volume of liquids is the liter.

Teach Ask: **What is volume?** *(Volume is the amount of space an object takes up.)* Point out that volume is commonly considered a characteristic of liquids. Ask: **What is the volume of a large, plastic soft-drink bottle?** *(Two liters)* **How many milliliters of liquid does that bottle contain?** *(2,000 mL)* Then explain that scientists determine the volume of solid objects as well, because solid objects also take up space. **What unit of measure would you use for the volume of a small object?** *(The cubic centimeter, cm³)* **What unit would you use for the volume of a large object?** *(The cubic meter, m³)*

Apply Ask: **What unit of measure would you use for the volume of water in a bathtub?** *(The liter)* **What unit of measure would you use for the volume of a textbook?** *(The cubic centimeter, cm³)*
learning modality: verbal

All in One Teaching Resources
• Transparency P12

Use Visuals: Figure 4 **L2**

Measuring Volume

Focus Tell students that Figure 4 shows how to measure the volume of a liquid, a regular solid, and an irregular solid.

Teach Ask a student to read the annotation that explains how to measure the volume of a liquid. Ask: **What is a meniscus?** *(The curve of the top surface of a liquid in a graduated cylinder)* **When determining the volume of water in a graduated cylinder, how should you read the meniscus?** *(You should read the millimeter marking at the bottom of the curve.)* Have students read the annotations for calculating the volume of a regular solid and finding the volume of an irregular solid.

Apply Ask: **Which method would you use to find the volume of a book?** *(You would calculate the volume of a book by multiplying length × width × height.)* **learning modality: visual**

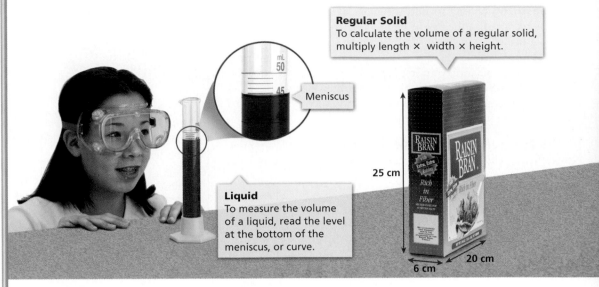

Regular Solid
To calculate the volume of a regular solid, multiply length × width × height.

Meniscus

25 cm

6 cm   20 cm

Liquid
To measure the volume of a liquid, read the level at the bottom of the meniscus, or curve.

FIGURE 4
Measuring Volume
Volume is the amount of space an object takes up. Measuring the volume of liquids, regular solids, and irregular solids requires different methods.
Observing *What is the proper way to read a meniscus?*

Common Conversions for Volume	
1 L	= 1,000 mL
1 L	= 1,000 cm³
1 mL	= 1 cm³

Volume

Do you drink milk or orange juice with breakfast? If so, how much do you have? You probably don't measure it out; you just pour it into a glass. You decide when to stop pouring by observing the amount of space it fills in the glass. **Volume** is the amount of space an object takes up.

Volume of Liquids To measure the volume of a liquid, scientists use a unit known as the liter (L). You have probably seen 1-liter and 2-liter bottles of beverages at the grocery store. You can measure smaller liquid volumes using milliliters (mL). There are 1,000 milliliters in a liter.

To measure the volume of a liquid, just pour it into a container with markings that show the volume. Scientists commonly use a graduated cylinder to measure liquid volumes. The graduated cylinder in Figure 4 is marked off in 1-milliliter segments. Notice that the top surface of the water in the graduated cylinder is curved. This curve is called the **meniscus.** To determine the volume of water, you should read the milliliter marking at the bottom of the curve.

Volume of Regular Solids How can you determine the volume of a solid object, such as a cereal box? The unit you would use is the cubic centimeter (cm³). A cubic centimeter is equal to the volume of a cube that measures 1 centimeter on each side. This is about the size of a sugar cube. One cubic centimeter is exactly equal to one milliliter.

35 mL · 41 mL

Irregular Solids

1 Record the volume of water in the graduated cylinder.

2 Carefully place the irregular solid into the water. Record the volume of the water plus the object.

3 Subtract the volume of the water alone from the volume of the water plus the object.

For solids with larger volumes, scientists use the SI unit known as the **cubic meter (m^3)**. A cubic meter is equal to the volume of a cube that measures 1 meter on each side.

You can calculate the volume of a regular solid using this formula:

Volume = Length × Width × Height

Suppose that a cereal box is 20 centimeters long, 6 centimeters wide, and 25 centimeters high. The volume of the box is

Volume = 20 cm × 6 cm × 25 cm = 3,000 cm^3

Notice that, when you calculate volume, in addition to multiplying the numbers (20 × 6 × 25 = 3,000), you also multiply the units (cm × cm × cm = cm^3). Therefore, you must be sure to use the same units for all measurements when calculating the volume of a regular solid.

Volume of Irregular Solids Suppose you wanted to measure the volume of a rock. Because of its irregular shape, you can't measure a rock's length, width, or height. How, then, could you find its volume? One method is to immerse the object in water, and measure how much the water level rises. This method is shown in Figure 4.

✓ **Reading Checkpoint** What is a cubic meter?

Go Online
PHSchool.com

For: More on measurement
Visit: PHSchool.com
Web Code: cgd-6021

Differentiated Instruction

English Learners/Beginning **L1**
Comprehension: Modified Cloze
Distribute a simplified paragraph about SI units and measurement, but leave some words blank. Model how to fill in the blank, using a sample sentence on the board. Provide students with the correct answers as choices. **learning modality: verbal**

English Learners/Intermediate **L2**
Comprehension: Modified Cloze
Distribute the same paragraph, but include some additional terms as incorrect answer choices. After students complete the paragraph, have them work together to write definitions for the answer choices not used. **learning modality: verbal**

Lab zone **Build Inquiry** **L2**

Materials small rock, shoe box, graduated cylinder, metric ruler

Time 20 minutes

Focus Tell students they will find the volume of a regular solid and an irregular solid.

Teach Ask: **What is the formula used to calculate the volume of a regular solid?** *(Volume = Length × Width × Height)* **What unit of measure would you use?** *(The cubic centimeter, cm^3)* **What process do you use to find the volume of an irregular solid?** *(Record the volume of water in a graduated cylinder. Place the irregular solid into the water, and record the volume of water plus the object. Subtract the volume of water alone from the volume of water plus the object.)* Explain that the result should be expressed in milliliters. Because the object is solid, a final step will be to convert the milliliter measure into cubic centimeters. Ask: **One milliliter equals how many cubic centimeters?** *(One milliliter equals one cubic centimeter.)*

Apply Divide the class into small groups, and give each group a shoe box and a small rock. Ask each group to determine the volume of each. **learning modality: kinesthetic**

Go Online
PHSchool.com

For: More on measurement
Visit: PHSchool.com
Web Code: cgd-6021

Students can review measurement in an online interactivity.

Monitor Progress _____ **L2**

Skills Check Have students make three flowcharts that describe how to determine the volume of a liquid, a regular solid, and an irregular solid. Students can keep their flowcharts in their portfolios.

Portfolio

Answers
Figure 4 You should read the milliliter marking at the bottom of the meniscus.

✓ **Reading Checkpoint** A cubic meter is equal to the volume of a cube that measures 1 meter on each side.

Density

Teach Key Concepts L2

Mass Over Volume

Focus Tell students that scientists identify materials by a physical characteristic called density.

Teach Ask: **What is density?** *(Density is a measure of how much mass is contained in a given volume.)* Show students two familiar objects about the same size, such as a CD and a round plastic top to a storage container. Ask: **How would you compare these in terms of volume?** *(Both have about the same volume.)* **Does either have more mass than the other?** *(The CD has more mass.)* Explain that because the CD has more mass in about the same amount of space, it has greater density. Ask: **What is the formula used to calculate density?** *(Density = Mass/Volume)* **What are two common units of density?** *(Two units are g/cm³ and g/mL.)*

Apply Ask: **Which object would have a greater density, a rock or a rubber ball the same size?** *(The rock)* **Why?** *(A rock has more mass in the same volume.)* **learning modality: logical/mathematical**

FIGURE 5
Density
Although the bowling ball and beach ball have the same volume, one contains much more mass than the other. **Inferring** *Which item has the greater density?*

Density

As you can see in Figure 5, two objects of the same size can have very different masses. This is because different materials have different densities. **Density** is a measure of how much mass is contained in a given volume. To calculate the density of an object, divide its mass by its volume.

$$\text{Density} = \frac{\text{Mass}}{\text{Volume}}$$

Units of Density Because density is actually made up of two other measurements—mass and volume—an object's density is expressed as a combination of two units. Two common units of density are grams per cubic centimeter (g/cm³) and grams per milliliter (g/mL). In each case, the numerator is a measure of mass while the denominator is a measure of volume.

Math ► Sample Problem

Calculating Density

Suppose that a metal object has a mass of 57 g and a volume of 21 cm³. Calculate its density.

1 Read and Understand
What information are you given?
Mass of metal object = **57 g**
Volume of metal object = **21 cm³**

2 Plan and Solve
What quantity are you trying to calculate?
The density of the metal object = ?

What formula contains the given quantities and the unknown quantity?

$$\text{Density} = \frac{\text{Mass}}{\text{Volume}}$$

Perform the calculation.

$$\text{Density} = \frac{\text{Mass}}{\text{Volume}} = \frac{57\ \text{g}}{21\ \text{cm}^3} = 2.7\ \text{g/cm}^3$$

3 Look Back and Check
Does your answer make sense?
The answer tells you that the metal object has a density of 2.7 g/cm³. The answer makes sense because it is the same as the density of a known metal—aluminum.

Math ► Sample Problem

Math Skills Calculating density

Focus Tell students that this problem involves using a formula to calculate the density of a metal object.

Teach Ask: **What is the mass of the metal object?** *(57 g)* **What is the volume of the metal object?** *(21 cm³)* Explain that in the Plan and Solve step of the problem, the given values for mass and volume are plugged into the formula used to calculate density. Have students work the problem with a calculator or pencil and paper. Ask: **What is the density of the object?** *(2.7 g/cm³)* Explain the answer is rounded to two figures according to rules they will learn later in the section. Direct students' attention to the table in Figure 6 to confirm that the metal object has the same density as aluminum.

All in One Teaching Resources
• Transparency P13

Math ► Practice

1. What is the density of a wood block with a volume of 125 cm³ and a mass of 57 g?

2. What is the density of a liquid with a mass of 45 g and a volume of 48 mL?

Math ► Practice

Math Skill Calculating density

Answers
1. 0.46 g/cm³
2. 0.94 g/mL

Densities of Common Substances The table in Figure 6 lists the densities of some common substances. The density of a substance is the same for all samples of that substance. For example, all samples of pure gold—no matter how large or small—have a density of 19.3 g/cm³.

Once you know an object's density, you can determine whether or not the object will float in a given liquid. An object will float if it is less dense than the surrounding liquid. For example, the density of water is 1 g/cm³. A piece of wood with a density of 0.8 g/cm³ will float in water. A ring made of pure silver, which has a density of 10.5 g/cm³, will sink.

 Reading Checkpoint Will an object with a density of 0.7 g/cm³ float or sink in water?

Time

The crowd cheers wildly as you near the finish line. You push your legs to run even faster in the final moments of the race. From the corner of your eye, you see your opponent catching up to you. At moments like this, just one second can mean the difference between winning and losing.

Units of Time The second (s) is the SI unit used to measure time. Your heart beats about once per second—when you are not running, that is! The second can easily be divided by multiples of 10, like the other SI units. For example, a millisecond (ms) is one-thousandth of a second. Longer periods of time are expressed in minutes or hours. There are 60 seconds in a minute, and 60 minutes in an hour.

Measuring Time Clocks and watches are used to measure time. Some clocks are more accurate than others. Some digital stopwatches, which are used to time races, can measure time accurately to one hundredth of a second.

 Reading Checkpoint How many milliseconds are in one second?

Densities of Some Common Substances	
Substance	**Density (g/cm³)**
Air	0.001
Ice	0.9
Water	1.0
Aluminum	2.7
Gold	19.3

FIGURE 6
The density of a substance stays the same no matter how large or small a sample of the substance is. **Applying Concepts** *How could you use density to determine whether a bar of metal is pure gold?*

FIGURE 7
Measuring Time
A stopwatch can be used to measure time.

Common Conversions for Time	
1 s	= 1,000 ms
1 min	= 60 s
1 h	= 60 min

Chapter 2 P ◆ 53

Time

Teach Key Concepts **L2**
The Second

Focus Tell students that the SI unit of measure for time is the familiar second.

Teach Ask: **Are the units used to measure time based on the number 10?** (*The units below the second are, but the units above the second—minutes, hours, days—are not.*) **How many milliseconds are there in a second?** (*1,000*)

Apply Recall for students that a folk measure of counting the passing of seconds is to count with the word *Mississippi*: "one Mississippi, two Mississippi, three Mississippi." Give pairs of students access to a watch or clock with a second hand, and have each pair test whether the folk "definition" of a second is accurate.
learning modality: verbal

Monitor Progress **L2**

Oral Presentation Call on volunteers to explain what density is, what the formula for finding density is, and how you can determine whether a substance will float in water.

Answers
Figure 5 The bowling ball
Figure 6 The density of a substance is the same for all samples of that substance. All samples of pure gold have a density of 19.3 g/cm³. Therefore, if the bar of metal has a density of 19.3 g/cm³, the metal is gold.

 Reading Checkpoint The object will float because it has a density less than the density of water, 1 g/cm³.

 Reading Checkpoint 1,000 ms

P ● 53

Temperature

Teach Key Concepts L2
The Celsius and Kelvin Scales

Focus Tell students that scientists use two scales to measure temperature.

Teach Ask: **What are the two scales scientists use to measure temperature?** *(The Celsius scale and the Kelvin scale)* **Why is the Celsius scale more like the SI units for length, mass, and volume than the Kelvin scale?** *(Because the difference between the freezing point and the boiling point of water in Celsius degrees is a multiple of 10)* **What is an instrument used to measure temperature?** *(A thermometer)*

Apply Mount a Celsius thermometer on the outside of the school building. Ask students to take a temperature reading once a day, and record their readings in a data table. At the end of a week, call on students to present the range of temperatures they recorded. **learning modality: visual**

All in One Teaching Resources
• Transparency P14

Converting Between Units

Teach Key Concepts L2
Conversion Factors

Focus Tell students that in science it is often necessary to convert one unit of measure into another.

Teach Ask: **What is a conversion factor?** *(An equation that shows how two units of measurement are related)* Ask students to turn back through the pages of this section and examine the small boxes of common conversions for length, mass, volume, time, and temperature. Ask: **How many milligrams equal 1 gram?** *(1,000)* **How many millimeters equals 1 meter?** *(1,000).*

Apply Tell students that in doing research a scientist finds that the mass of a substance is 2.3 grams. It would be more convenient for a report if that value were expressed in milligrams. Ask: **How many milligrams is 2.3 grams?** *(2,300 mg)* **learning modality: logical/mathematical**

All in One Teaching Resources
• Transparency P15

Common Conversions for Temperature		
0°C	=	273 K
100°C	=	373 K

Celsius (°C)   **Kelvin (K)**

Boiling Point of Water — 100 — 373

Freezing Point of Water — 0 — 273

Absolute Zero — −273 — 0

FIGURE 8
Measuring Temperature
Scientists use the Celsius and Kelvin scales to measure temperature. Units on both scales are the same size.
Observing *At what temperature on the Kelvin scale does water boil?*

Temperature

As you head out the door each morning, one of the first things you might notice is the temperature. Is it cold out this morning? How high will the temperature rise?

Units of Temperature Scientists commonly use the Celsius temperature scale. On the Celsius scale, water freezes at 0°C and boils at 100°C. There are exactly 100 degrees between the freezing point and boiling point of water. Normal human body temperature is about 37°C.

In addition to the Celsius scale, scientists sometimes use another temperature scale, called the Kelvin scale. In fact, the kelvin (K) is the official SI unit for temperature. Units on the Kelvin scale are the same size as those on the Celsius scale. Figure 8 compares these two temperature scales.

Zero on the Kelvin scale (0 K) is the temperature that scientists consider to be the coldest possible temperature. Nothing can get colder than this temperature, called absolute zero. Absolute zero is equal to −273°C on the Celsius scale. The Kelvin scale is useful because it does not have negative numbers to complicate calculations.

Measuring Temperature You can measure temperature using a thermometer. When you first place the thermometer in a substance, the liquid inside the thermometer will begin to move up or down. Wait until the level of the liquid stops changing. Then read the number next to the top of the liquid in the thermometer.

 Reading Checkpoint What is the official SI unit for temperature?

Converting Between Units

Do you have a jar where you keep all your pennies? Suppose you counted your penny collection and discovered that you had 236 pennies. How many dollars does that equal? With only a little thought, you could probably answer, "$2.36."

Just like converting between dollars and cents, it is often necessary to convert from one unit of measurement to another. **To convert one measurement to another, you need to know the appropriate conversion factor. A conversion factor is an equation that shows how two units of measurement are related.** For conversion factors, refer to the conversion tables included throughout this section.

Suppose you walk 1.5 kilometers to a friend's house. How many meters have you walked? To convert 1.5 kilometers to meters, follow these steps:

❶ Begin by writing down the measurement you want to convert.

❷ Find a conversion factor that relates the two units you are converting.

❸ Write the conversion factor as a fraction. Make sure to place the units you are converting from in the denominator.

❹ Multiply the measurement you are converting from by the fraction. When you do this, the units in the measurement will cancel out with the units in the denominator of the fraction. Your answer will then be in the units you are converting to.

By converting between units, you now know that you walked 1,500 meters to your friend's house.

Reading Checkpoint What is a conversion factor?

❶ 1.5 km = ? m

❷ 1 km = 1,000 m

❸ $\frac{1{,}000 \text{ m}}{1 \text{ km}}$

❹ $1.5 \text{ km} \times \frac{1{,}000 \text{ m}}{1 \text{ km}} = 1{,}500 \text{ m}$

1.5 km = 1,500 m

FIGURE 9
Converting Between Units
Using the appropriate conversion factor, you can easily convert one unit of measurement to another. This example shows how to convert 1.5 kilometers to meters.

Section 1 Assessment

Target Reading Skill

Comparing and Contrasting Use the information in your table about the different types of measurement to answer Question 2.

Reviewing Key Concepts

1. a. **Identifying** What is the standard measurement system used by scientists around the world?
   b. **Predicting** Suppose that two scientists use different measurement systems in their work. What problems might arise if they shared their data?
2. a. **Listing** What SI unit would you use to measure the length of a baseball bat? What SI unit would you use to measure the mass of a baseball?
   b. **Estimating** Estimate the length of a baseball bat and mass of a baseball. Be sure to use the appropriate SI units in your predictions. How could you determine how close your estimates are?
   c. **Problem Solving** Outline a step-by-step method for determining the density of a baseball.
3. a. **Reviewing** What is a conversion factor?
   b. **Identifying** What conversion factor would you use to convert between liters and milliliters?
   c. **Calculating** Your cat's bowl holds 0.25 liters of liquid. How many milliliters of water can you pour into the bowl?

Math Practice

Two solid cubes have the same mass. They each have a mass of 50 g.

4. **Calculating Density** Cube A has a volume of 2 cm × 2 cm × 2 cm. What is its density?
5. **Calculating Density** Cube B has a volume of 4 cm × 4 cm × 4 cm. What is its density?

Lab zone Chapter Project

Keep Students on Track Check to see that each student has a written plan that briefly describes how he or she will proceed with the project. Also check that the objects to be included in the model or the dimensions of the landmark are listed in the data table. Suggest that students proceed with converting the actual measurements to scale measurements. By this time, each student should have determined an appropriate scale.

Math Practice

Math Skill Calculating density

Answers

4. 6.25 g/cm^3 (6 to the correct significant figure)
5. 0.781 g/cm^3 (0.8 to the correct significant figure)

Monitor Progress L2

Answers

Figure 8 373 K

Reading Checkpoint The kelvin (K)

Reading Checkpoint An equation that shows how two units of measurement are related

Assess

Reviewing Key Concepts

1. a. The International System of Units (SI) **b.** Confusion might arise if the scientists didn't take into consideration the two systems. To avoid confusion, the scientists would have to convert one set of measurements into the other system.
2. a. Centimeters for the length of a baseball bat; grams for the mass of a baseball **b.** Sample answer: 76 cm for the length of a baseball bat; 145 g for the mass of a baseball. To determine how close these estimates are, you could measure the length of a bat and the mass of a baseball. **c.** To determine the density of a baseball, follow these steps: (1) Use a balance to measure the mass of the baseball. (2) To determine the volume, immerse the baseball in water, and measure how much the water level rises. (3) Divide the mass by the volume to calculate a baseball's density.
3. a. An equation that shows how two units of measurement are related **b.** 1 L = 1,000 mL **c.** 250 mL

Reteach L1

Write these terms on the board: *length, mass, volume, density, time, temperature.* Call on volunteers to identify the units of measure used for each and describe the processes used to determine a measurement for each.

Performance Assessment L2

Writing Have students describe how to find the length of a baseball bat, the mass of a shoe, the volume of water in a cup, the volume of a cereal box, and the density of a rock.

All in One Teaching Resources

- Section Summary: *Measurement—A Common Language*
- Review and Reinforcement: *Measurement—A Common Language*
- Enrich: *Measurement—A Common Language*

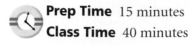

Backpack Basics

Prepare for Inquiry

Skills Objectives

After this lab, students will be able to:

- measure the mass and the dimensions of a regular object
- calculate the volume and density of a regular object

🕐 **Prep Time** 15 minutes
Class Time 40 minutes

Advance Planning

Most texts are too heavy for a standard laboratory balance. Make sure to have a bathroom scale handy. Tell students ahead of time to bring a backpack and three to five texts to class.

Safety

🏃 Students should use caution, when moving around meter sticks, so as not to hit others. Be sure that students do not lift heavy backpacks, beyond their capability.

All in One Teaching Resources

- Lab Worksheet: *Backpack Basics*

Guide Inquiry

Invitation

Studies show that many students carry a load in their backpacks in excess of safety guidelines. Ask: **Does your backpack feel too heavy? Do you know how much your backpack usually weighs? Do you know how much is safe to carry on your back? Do you think the amount you carry in your backpack is safe?** *(Accept all reasonable answers.)*

Introduce the Procedure

Ask: **How do you measure the volume of a backpack?** *(Measure length, width, and height of the main compartment with a meter stick and multiply.)* **A balance measures mass and a scale measures weight. What is the difference? Why can we convert weight to mass?** *(Mass is the amount of matter. Weight is the force of gravity on matter. Since gravity on Earth is constant, objects of the same mass have the same weight.)*

Lab zone Consumer Lab

Backpack Basics

Problem

Which backpack is a better choice for carrying the recommended safe load of books?

Skills Focus

measuring, calculating, drawing conclusions

Materials

- balance • 5–6 textbooks • meter stick
- 2 backpacks (one large and one small)

Procedure

PART 1 Determining Your Maximum Safe Load

1. To prevent back problems, experts recommend that the mass of the backpack you carry should be no greater than 15 percent of your body mass. Use the table below to find your "maximum safe load."

Determining Maximum Safe Load	
Body Mass kg (lbs)	**Maximum Safe Load (kg)**
30 (66)	4.5
35 (77)	5.3
40 (88)	6.0
45 (99)	6.8
50 (110)	7.5
55 (121)	8.3
60 (132)	9.0
65 (143)	9.8
70 (154)	10.5
75 (165)	11.3
80 (176)	12.0
85 (187)	12.8

2. To determine how many textbooks equal your maximum safe load, use a balance to find the mass of one textbook. Next, divide your maximum safe load by the mass of the textbook. Your answer is the number of textbooks (of that size) you can safely carry in a backpack.

PART 2 Comparing Backpacks

3. Your teacher will give you two backpacks—one large and one small. Load each backpack with the number of textbooks you calculated in Step 2. Carry each backpack on your back for one minute and note how it feels. Also, observe how empty or full each backpack is.

4. Using a meter stick, measure the length, width, and height in centimeters of each backpack. Your partner should stretch out the backpacks fully as you measure them. Record the dimensions in a data table like the one at the top of the next page.

5. Calculate the volume of each backpack using this formula:

Volume = Length × Width × Height

Record the volumes in your data table.

6. Calculate the approximate volume of the textbook you used in Part 1. Measure its length, width, and height in centimeters, and then multiply these measurements together.

Troubleshooting the Experiment

- Some students may feel uncomfortable about using their own weight for calculations. Be sensitive. Allow students to work in groups.
- Small paperbacks can be measured on a balance. Most texts are in excess of 600 g and will need to be placed on a bathroom scale.
- Books may be placed directly on the scale, or the student may step on the scale with the book and subtract his or her mass to determine the mass of the book. This is particularly useful if the scale is not responsive to small masses. If a kilogram scale is not available, pounds are converted to kilograms by dividing by 2.2.

Data Table						
Backpack	Length (cm)	Width (cm)	Height (cm)	Volume (cm³)	Total Number of Textbooks	Total Mass of Textbooks (kg)
1						
2						

7. Calculate the total number of textbooks that could fit into each backpack by dividing the volume of each backpack (from Step 5) by the volume of one textbook (from Step 6). Record the results for each backpack in your data table.

8. Calculate the total mass of textbooks that could fit into each backpack by multiplying the mass of one textbook (from Step 2) by the total number of textbooks that fit into each (from Step 7). Record the results in your data table.

Analyze and Conclude

1. **Observing** Is each backpack large enough to carry your maximum safe load? What differences did you notice between the two backpacks when carrying this load of books?

2. **Measuring** How do the two backpacks compare in volume? What is the total mass of books that each backpack could carry?

3. **Calculating** Calculate how many times your maximum safe load each backpack could carry. (*Hint:* Divide the total mass of books from Step 8 by your maximum safe load in Step 1.)

4. **Drawing Conclusions** Based on the calculations and observations you made in this lab, what are some of the pros and cons of each backpack?

5. **Communicating** Choose one of the backpacks and write an advertisement for it. In your advertisement, be sure to explain why it would be the best choice for students.

More to Explore

For a week, record the actual mass of the backpack you carry to school each day. Then calculate the average (mean) mass of your backpack. How does this compare to your recommended maximum safe load?

P ◆ 57

Expected Outcome

A large student backpack might have the following dimensions: 44 cm × 33 cm × 26 cm. Such a backpack has a capacity of about 37 L (L × W × H/1000). The average density of several textbooks is approximately 0.8 kg/L. This backpack filled to capacity would hold about 30 kg of books. The backpack itself has a mass of 0.7 kg for a total of about 31 kg. A 68 kg student (150 lb) cannot safely lift more than 10 kg (0.15 × 68) on his or her back.

Analyze and Conclude

1. Sample answer: Each backpack is large enough to carry the maximum safe load. The larger backpack carried the books more easily than the smaller backpack, but the smaller backpack felt more comfortable.

2. Sample answer: The larger backpack has three times the volume of the smaller backpack. The larger backpack could carry a total mass of 28.4 kg, while the smaller backpack could carry a total mass of only 9.0 kg.

3. Sample answer: The larger backpack could carry about four times my maximum safe load. The smaller backpack could carry about two times my maximum safe load.

4. Sample answer: The larger backpack could carry many more books, though it wouldn't be as comfortable. The smaller backpack couldn't carry as many books, but it could carry them more comfortably.

5. Students' advertisements should mention the comfort and the carrying capacity of the backpack chosen.

Extend Inquiry

More to Explore For five straight days, each student will use a balance to determine the mass of the backpack plus its contents carried that day. To find the mean, students will add the masses of each of the five days and then divide the sum by 5. Many students may find they will exceed the recommended maximum safe load for their body mass.

Sample Data Table

Backpack	Length (cm)	Width (cm)	Height (cm)	Volume (cm³)	Total Number of Textbooks	Total Mass of Textbooks (kg)
1	43.8	33.0	25.7	37,146	22	28.4
2	32.6	21.7	15.4	10,894	7	9.0

Science and Society

Should the United States Go Metric?

Key Concept

The English system of measurement is generally used throughout the United States. Almost all of the other countries in the world rely on the metric system. The question for Americans is whether the country should convert to the metric system.

Build Background Knowledge

Using the Metric System

Ask: **Why do scientists use a standard system of measurement?** (*Using a standard system allows scientist to compare data and communicate with one another about their results.*) Explain that business and industry might benefit in using a standard system for the same reasons. Yet, the United States is the only industrialized country in the world whose population and businesses generally don't use the metric system. Ask: **How might this cause difficulty in world trade?** (*U.S. products might be at a disadvantage because they aren't produced in metric dimensions.*) Explain that much of American industry has already converted to the metric system because of those problems, though most Americans still do not use metric measurements easily.

Introduce the Debate

Have students look at the map of the world shown in the feature. Ask: **What does this map tell you about measurement and the United States?** (*The United States is practically alone in the world in using the English system.*) Tell students that they will debate whether the United States should convert to the metric system or stay with the English system.

Should the United States Go Metric?

On a long car ride, have you ever asked, "Are we there yet?" If the driver answered, "We're 30 kilometers away," would you know whether you were close to your destination or far away?

As a U.S. resident, you probably have no trouble understanding English units, which include miles, feet, pounds, and gallons. Metric units, however, may be more unfamiliar. But most countries in the world use the metric system. Should the United States convert to metric or continue using the English system?

The Issues

Why Change?

People in the United States are comfortable with the English system of measurement. If the country converted to metric, citizens might have a hard time buying products or calculating distances. These problems may not disappear overnight.

Businesses in the United States rely on the English system. Many of the tools and machines that manufacture goods are based on the English system, as are the goods themselves. To go metric, the machines would have to be replaced and the goods repackaged. This could cost millions of dollars.

GAS Save on a 10 litre purchase!

CURRENT TEMPERATURE 21° C

CITY LIMITS 1 km

Welcome to The METRIC SYSTEM HIGHWAY

58 ◆ P

Facilitate the Debate

- Have students read the feature and answer the You Decide questions individually as a homework assignment. Allow a day for research about other countries that have gone metric. On the second day, divide the class into small groups for discussion. Have students consider these questions: What advantages for the United States would there be in converting to the metric system? How difficult would converting be for the average citizen? Would the cost of converting be worth the trouble involved?

- Divide the class into two groups. Arbitrarily assign one group to argue that the United States should go metric. Assign the other group to argue that going metric is unnecessary. Alternately call on students from each group to state its position or refute an idea someone from the other group has put forward.

Why Be Left Behind?

Supporters of the metric system point out how easy it is to learn. Because metric units are based on the number 10, converting from kilometers to meters, for example, is simple. In contrast, converting miles to feet, or gallons to ounces, is more complicated. Schoolchildren could master the metric system much more quickly than the English system.

Furthermore, conversion may help the United States stay competitive in foreign trade. Many U.S. businesses sell their products in other countries. But people worldwide prefer products labeled in units they know—in this case, metric units. They may avoid products that are not made to metric standards. In fact, by 2010, products sold in Europe must be labeled in metric units only.

Why Not Compromise?

The next time you drink a bottle of juice, look at its label. Most likely, it includes both English and metric units. Labels like these are a compromise. They allow users of both measurement systems to know exactly what they are buying.

Some people feel that such a compromise works well enough. People who need to use the metric system, such as those in science and industry, should be able to use it. However, those who prefer to use English units should be able to do so as well.

The countries in red currently use the English system of measurement.

You Decide

1. Identify the Problem
In your own words, state the advantages and disadvantages of converting to the metric system.

2. Analyze the Options
Do some research on countries that have recently gone metric. What problems did these countries face? How did they overcome the problems? Did the benefits of converting to the metric system outweigh the costs?

3. Find a Solution
Take a stance on this issue. Then engage in a class debate about whether or not the United States should convert to the metric system. Support your opinion with facts from this feature and from your research.

Go Online
PHSchool.com
For: More on going metric
Visit: PHSchool.com
Web Code: cgh-6020

P ◆ 59

Go Online
PHSchool.com
For: More on going metric
Visit: PHSchool.com
Web Code: cgh-6020

Students can research this issue on line.

You Decide

1. Sample answer: Advantages—The metric system is easy to use, since it is based on the number 10. The rest of the world uses the metric system, and converting would help companies in the United States in world trade. Disadvantages—Learning a new measurement system may be difficult for older Americans. The cost of converting machines and other devices may be great.

2. Students should discover in their research that most countries changed to the metric system long ago. The United Kingdom, for example, began the transition to the metric system in 1965. In Ireland, the conversion is still in process; road signs had to be converted from miles to kilometers in late 2004. Students may find that some citizens of countries that converted relatively recently reported having trouble learning the metric system.

3. Some students may support the conversion, while others may oppose it. Whatever the position taken, students should be prepared to support their stance with facts and well-reasoned arguments.

Extend

Encourage interested students to contact the U.S. Metric Association (USMA), which is headquartered in Northridge, California. This organization is a nonprofit advocate of U.S. conversion to the metric system. A first step might be to find this organization's Web page on the Internet.

Background

History of Science Before metric measurement, traditional measuring units often depended on the dimensions of the human body. In the late 1700s, the original metric measurements were more rationally defined. For example, the meter was defined as one ten-millionth of the distance from the Equator to the North Pole. The metric system was adopted by France in 1795, though it was not compulsory. In 1820, Belgium, the Netherlands, and Luxembourg became the first countries to require use. Between 1850 and 1900, the metric system was adopted throughout most of Europe and Latin America. In 1875, most industrialized countries—including the United States—signed the Treaty of the Meter, which established the International Bureau of Weights and Measures (BIPM).

Objectives

After this lesson, students will be able to

P.2.2.1 Describe what math skills scientists use in collecting data and making measurements.

P.2.2.2 Identify the math skills scientists use to analyze their data.

Target Reading Skill

Asking Questions Explain that changing a head into a question helps students anticipate the ideas, facts, and events they are about to read.

Answers

Sample questions and answers: **What is estimation?** *(Approximation of a number based on reasonable assumptions)* **What are accuracy and precision?** *(Accuracy refers to how close a measurement is to the true or accepted value, and precision refers to how close a group of measurements are to each other.)* **What are significant figures?** *(Significant figures refers to the digits in a measurement.)* **What is percent error?** *(Percent error is a calculation used to determine how accurate an experimental value really is.)* **What are mean, median, and mode?** *(They are ways to calculate an "average.")*

All in One Teaching Resources

• Transparency P16

Preteach

Build Background Knowledge L2

Using Math in Science Activities

Ask: **What mathematical operation do you use in finding the volume of a regular solid?** *(Multiplication)* **What mathematical operation do you use in determining the density of an object?** *(Division)* **Have you ever used math in carrying out a science experiment?** *(Sample answer: Many experiments require finding the average result.)*

Mathematics and Science

Reading Preview

Key Concepts

• What math skills do scientists use in collecting data and making measurements?

• What math skills help scientists analyze their data?

Key Terms

• estimate • accuracy
• precision • significant figures
• percent error • mean
• median • mode

Target Reading Skill

Asking Questions Before you read, preview the red headings. In a graphic organizer like the one below, ask a *what, how,* or *why* question for each heading. As you read, write the answers to your questions.

Mathematics and Science

Question	Answer
What does estimation have to do with science?	Scientists use estimation . . .

Lab zone Discover **Activity**

How Many Marbles Are There?

1. Your teacher will give you a jar full of marbles.

2. With a partner, come up with a way to determine the number of marbles in the jar without actually counting them.

3. Use your method to determine the number of marbles. Write down your answer.

4. Compare the method you used to that of another group.

Think About It

Predicting Which method do you think led to a more accurate answer? Why?

Here's a riddle for you. What do the following things have in common: microscopes, telescopes, thermometers, balances, and mathematics? Do you give up? The answer is that they are all tools that scientists use.

Does it surprise you that mathematics is included in this list? You probably think of mathematics as something that is separate from science. But it is not. In fact, mathematics is sometimes called the "language of science." Mathematics is essential for asking and answering questions about the natural world. From making measurements to collecting and analyzing data, scientists use math every day. This section focuses on some important math skills you will use in science class.

FIGURE 10
Estimation
Estimation is an important math skill that scientists use in their work. Estimating is a quick way to determine the large number of birds in this photo.

Lab zone Discover **Activity**

Skills Focus Predicting

Materials clear glass jar with top, marbles of different colors

Time 15 minutes

Tips You could have one jar of marbles displayed in a location where all students can examine it. When all groups have concluded their work, have a representative

from each group describe the method used and the result. Finally, have volunteers open the jar and count the marbles.

Think It Over Sample answer: The method that worked best was to count and estimate the marbles in the lower eighth of the jar, and then multiply the result by 8 to determine the number of marbles in the whole jar.

Estimation

Have you ever been on stage and wondered how many people there were in the audience? Maybe you counted the number of people in one row and multiplied by the number of rows. This would be one way to arrive at an estimate. An **estimate** is an approximation of a number based on reasonable assumptions. Estimating is not the same as guessing because an estimate is based on known information.

Scientists must sometimes rely on estimates when they cannot obtain exact numbers. Astronomers, for example, can't actually measure the distance between stars. Park rangers can't count the number of trees in large forests. Instead, scientists find ways to make reasonable estimates. An astronomer's estimate might be based on indirect measurements, calculations, and models. A park ranger's estimate might be based on a sample. The ranger could count the trees in a small area and then multiply to estimate the number in the entire forest.

 Reading Checkpoint What are estimates based on?

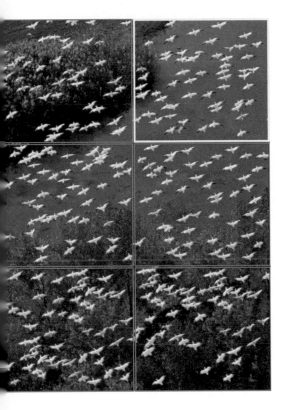

There are 58 birds in the highlighted area. The total area is nine times larger. Thus, you can estimate that there are 58 × 9, or 522 birds in total.

 Math Skills

Area

The area of a surface is the amount of space it covers. To find the area, multiply its length by its width. Remember to multiply the units as well.

$$Area = Length \times Width$$

Suppose the area highlighted in Figure 10 measures 12.0 m by 11.0 m.

$$Area = 12.0 \text{ m} \times 11.0 \text{ m}$$
$$= 132 \text{ m}^2$$

Practice Problems Calculate the area of the following objects.

1. A room 4.0 m long and 3.0 m wide
2. A ticket stub 5.1 mm long and 2.62 mm wide

Instruct

Estimation

Teach Key Concepts   L2
Approximation Based on Reason

Focus Explain that scientists have to estimate a measurement when they are not able to make an exact measurement.

Teach Ask: **What is an estimate?** (*An approximation of a number based on reasonable assumptions*) **How is making an estimate different from guessing?** (*Guessing isn't based on anything other than a feeling, but an estimate is based on known information.*)

Apply Ask: **How would you estimate the number of students in this school?** (*Count the number of students in one class, and multiply the number of students in one class by the number of classes in the school.*) **learning modality: logical/mathematical**

Math Skills

Math Skill Area

Focus Tell students that a common measurement scientists make is to find the area of an object.

Teach Ask: **What is the area of an object?** (*The amount of space the object covers*) **What is the formula used to find area?** (*Area = Length × Width*)

Answers
1. 4.0 m × 3.0 m = 12 m²
2. 5.1 mm × 2.62 − 13.4 mm² (13 to the correct significant figure)

All in One Teaching Resources
- Transparency P17

Independent Practice   L2
All in One Teaching Resources
- Guided Reading and Study Worksheet: *Mathematics and Science*

Student Edition on Audio CD

Monitor Progress _____   L2

Oral Presentation Call on students to explain what an estimate is, how an estimate is different from a guess, and why scientists sometimes have to estimate.

Answer
Reading Checkpoint Known information and reasonable assumptions

---

Differentiated Instruction

Gifted and Talented   L3
Communicating A triple-beam balance can easily be adjusted out of true by turning the adjusting screw. Have students who understand how to operate a balance prepare a demonstration for the class that shows how a scientific instrument can be accurate and precise as well as inaccurate and precise. **learning modality: visual**

Special Needs   L1
Interpreting Diagrams and Communicating Refer students to Figure 11. Tell them to use the figure as a guide and make their own drawings of the three examples of accuracy and precision. Students should label their drawings and write a brief annotation explaining why each example is classified as it is. **learning modality: visual**

 Chapter 2 P ◆ 61

P ● 61

Accuracy and Precision

Teach Key Concepts L2

Correctness and Closeness

Focus Tell students that there is a difference between accuracy and precision.

Teach Ask: **What is accuracy?** (*Accuracy refers to how close a measurement is to the true or accepted value.*) **If the air temperature were 30°C, what would an accurate thermometer read?** (*It would read 30°C.*) **What is precision?** (*Precision refers to how close a group of measurements are to each other.*)

Apply Ask: **If the air temperature is 30°C all afternoon and a thermometer shows at repeated readings that the temperature is 32°C, are the measurements accurate or precise?** (*They are not accurate, but they are precise.*) **learning modality: verbal**

All in One **Teaching Resources**
• Transparency P18

⚑ Address Misconceptions L1

Accuracy of Metric Units

Focus Many students may think that scientists use the metric system because metric units are more accurate than units of other systems.

Teach Ask: **Is a measurement with centimeters more accurate than a measurement with inches?** (*Some students may think that a centimeter measurement is more accurate.*) Point out that using a standard system allows scientists to compare data and communicate, not because metric measurements are more accurate.

Apply As students observe, measure the width of a book with a metric ruler three times, each time recording the measurement on the board. Then, repeat the procedure using an inch ruler. Ask: **What does measuring several times ensure?** (*Precision*) Have students convert the mode of the centimeter measurements to inches, and the mode of the inch measurements to centimeters. Ask: **Which is more accurate, the centimeter or the inch measurement?** (*They are equally accurate.*) **learning modality: visual**

Neither Precise nor Accurate

Precise but Not Accurate

Both Precise and Accurate

Accuracy and Precision

Suppose you were to meet a friend at 4:00 P.M. Your friend arrives at 4:15 and says, "But it's 4:00 according to all the clocks in my house." The problem is that your friend's clocks do not show the accurate, or correct, time. **Accuracy** refers to how close a measurement is to the true or accepted value. An accurate clock would read 4:00 P.M. However, if all of your friend's clocks are always 15 minutes late, they can be said to be precise. **Precision** refers to how close a group of measurements are to each other.

Accuracy Versus Precision As you can see from the clock example, accuracy and precision do not mean the same thing. To understand the difference, think about a game of darts. As Figure 11 shows, accurate throws land close to the bull's-eye. Precise throws, on the other hand, land close to one another.

Accuracy and Precision in Measurements Both accuracy and precision are important when you make measurements. For example, suppose your younger sister wants to find out how tall she has grown. When you measure her height, the measurement needs to be accurate, or close to her true height. The measurement also needs to be precise. This means that if you measured her height several times, you would get the same measurement again and again.

How can you be sure that a measurement you make is both accurate and precise? First, you need to use a high-quality measurement tool. Next, you need to make your measurement carefully. Finally, you need to repeat the measurement a few times. If you follow these steps and get the same measurement each time, then you can feel confident that your measurement is reliable.

 Reading Checkpoint What does an accurate measurement mean?

FIGURE 11
Accuracy and Precision
In a game of darts, it's easy to see the difference between accurate throws and precise throws. In order to hit the bull's-eye consistently, you need both accuracy and precision!

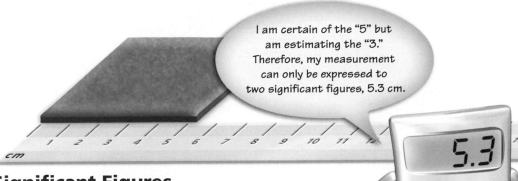
I am certain of the "5" but am estimating the "3." Therefore, my measurement can only be expressed to two significant figures, 5.3 cm.

Significant Figures

Whenever you measure something, you give meaning, or significance, to each digit in the measurement. In fact, scientists use the term **significant figures** to refer to the digits in a measurement. **The significant figures in a measurement include all of the digits that have been measured exactly, plus one digit whose value has been estimated.**

For example, you might estimate that the tile in Figure 12 is 5.3 centimeters long—you are certain of the 5, but you have estimated the 3 on the end. To find the number of significant figures in a measurement, count the number of digits that were accurately measured, plus the one estimated digit. Therefore, a measurement of 5.3 centimeters has two significant figures.

Adding or Subtracting Measurements When you add or subtract measurements, the answer can only have as many figures after the decimal point as the measurement with the fewest figures after the decimal. For example, suppose you add a tile that is 5.3 centimeters long to a row of tiles that is 21.94 centimeters long.

    5.3 cm (1 significant figure after decimal)
 + 21.94 cm (2 significant figures after decimal)
   27.24 cm = 27.2 cm (1 significant figure after decimal)

The answer, "27.2 centimeters," has only one significant figure after the decimal point because the measurement 5.3 centimeters has only one figure after the decimal point.

Why is it incorrect to express your answer as 27.24 centimeters? The reason is that your answer would appear to be more accurate than it really is. Remember that when you first measured the tile, you estimated the "3" in the tenths place. When you add that number to another, the number in the tenths place in the sum is still only an estimate. If you expressed your answer as "27.24" centimeters, the "2" in the tenths place would appear to be an exact measurement, rather than an estimate.

FIGURE 12
Significant Figures
A measurement should contain only those numbers that are significant—all of the digits that have been measured exactly plus one you have estimated.
Measuring *Why can you only report the length of the tile to two significant figures?*

Go Online
SciLINKS NSTA
For: Links on math and science
Visit: www.SciLinks.org
Web Code: scn-1622

Chapter 2 P ◆ 63

Percent Error

Teach Key Concepts L2

Calculating Percent Error

Focus Tell students that the accuracy of a measurement is expressed in a percentage called the percent error.

Teach Ask: **What are percent error calculations used to determine?** *(How accurate, or close to the true value, an experimental value really is)* Explain that determining percent error is one way to check on how accurately a measurement was made in an investigation. Ask: **What is the formula used to calculate percent error?** *(Percent error = Difference between experimental value and true value / True value × 100%)* **Why is the fraction in the formula multiplied by 100%?** *(Percent error is expressed in terms of the percentage of the true value that is in error.)*

Apply Give this scenario to students: A scientist uses a balance to determine the mass of a metal object. The scientist later learns that the true mass of the object is much different than the mass he determined, and the percent error is 35%. Ask: **What steps might that scientist take given the percent error was 35%?** *(He might check the accuracy of the balance he used, or he might be more careful in measuring mass in the future.)*
learning modality: verbal

Help Students Read

Monitoring Your Understanding Refer to the Content Refresher in this chapter, which provides the guidelines for the Monitoring Your Understanding strategy.

Have students read the subsection *Percent Error*. When they reach the end, have them stop and write down the main ideas of the subsection. Have them ask questions of themselves, such as "Did I have any trouble reading this passage? If so, why?" Then, have them come up with their own strategies to improve their understanding. Have them use their strategies as they continue reading.

The length "2.25 m" has three significant figures, while the width "3 m" has one. Therefore, my answer can only have one significant figure.

FIGURE 13
Multiplying Measurements
When you multiply measurements, your answer can only have the same number of significant figures as the measurement with the fewest significant figures.

For Good Measure

In this activity, you will practice the skills of estimating and measuring.

1. Estimate the following measurements without using any measurement tools. Be sure to use the correct units.
   a. the length of your desk
   b. the mass of a penny
   c. the volume of a shoe box
2. Determine the actual measurement for each item above. Be sure to express each measurement to the correct number of significant figures.

Measuring How close were your estimates to the actual measurements?

Multiplying or Dividing Measurements You need to follow a slightly different rule when you multiply or divide measurements. When multiplying or dividing, the answer can only have the same number of significant figures as the measurement with the fewest significant figures.

Suppose you need to tile a space that measures 2.25 meters by 3 meters. The area of the space would be calculated as follows:

$$2.25 \text{ m (3 signficant figures)}$$
$$\times \; 3 \text{ m (1 signficant figure)}$$
$$\overline{6.75 \text{ m}^2 \; = \; 7 \text{ m}^2 \text{ (1 significant figure)}}$$

The answer has one significant figure because the least precise measurement (3 meters) has one significant figure.

Reading Checkpoint What is the rule for multiplying or dividing measurements?

Percent Error

"Today, class, your job is to determine the density of this metal." With those words, your science teacher hands you a small piece of a shiny metal. You get to work, carefully measuring its mass and volume. When you divide the mass by the volume, you arrive at a density of 9.37 g/cm³. "That's pretty close," says your teacher, "but now you need to calculate your percent error. The correct value for the density of this metal is 8.92 g/cm³."

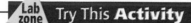

Skills Focus Measuring

Materials metric ruler, meter stick, balance, penny, shoe box

Time 15 minutes

Tips Remind students that when they measure, a measurement should include all the digits measured plus one estimated digit.

Expected Outcome Many students' estimates may be far different from the actual measurements, especially the mass of a penny and the volume of a shoe box.

Extend Have students estimate the area and the volume of the classroom. Then have students determine the actual measurements of the classroom. **learning modality: kinesthetic**

Percent error calculations are used to determine how accurate, or close to the true value, an experimental value really is. To calculate **percent error,** use the following formula:

$$\text{Percent error} = \frac{\text{Difference between experimental value and true value}}{\text{True value}} \times 100\%$$

A low percent error means that the result you obtained was very accurate. A high percent error means that your result was not very accurate. You may not have made your measurements carefully enough or your measurement tool may have been of poor quality.

 Reading Checkpoint What does a low percent error mean?

Math ▶ Sample Problem

Percent Error
You calculate the density of an object to be 9.37 g/cm^3. The density of the object is actually 8.92 g/cm^3. Calculate your percent error.

1 Read and Understand
What information are you given?
Experimental value = 9.37 g/cm^3
True value = 8.92 g/cm^3

2 Plan and Solve
What quantity are you trying to calculate?
Percent error = ?

What formula contains the given quantities and the unknown quantity?

$$\text{Percent Error} = \frac{\text{Difference between experimental value and true value}}{\text{True value}} \times 100\%$$

Perform the calculation.

$$\text{Percent error} = \frac{9.37 \text{ g/cm}^3 - 8.92 \text{ g/cm}^3}{8.92 \text{ g/cm}^3} \times 100\%$$

Percent error = 5.04%

3 Look Back and Check
Does your answer make sense?
The answer tells you that your percent error is about 5%. This answer makes sense because the experimental value and the true value were close to each other.

Math ▶ Practice

Tanya measured the mass of an object to be 187 g. Sam measured the object's mass to be 145 g. The object's actual mass was 170 g.

1. What is Tanya's percent error?
2. What is Sam's percent error?

Math ▶ Practice

Math Skill Percent error

Answer
1. Percent error = 10.0%
2. Percent error = 14.7%

Math ▶ Sample Problem

Math Skills Formulas and equations

Focus Ask: **What is the formula used to calculate percent error?** *(Percent error = Difference between experimental value and true value / True value × 100%)* Point out that sometimes the experimental value is more than the true value and sometimes it is less. Ask: **Should the experimental value be subtracted from the true value, or should the true value be subtracted from the experimental value?** *(If the true value is more than the experimental value, then the experimental value should be subtracted from the true value. If the experimental value is more than the true value, then the true value should be subtracted from the experimental value.)*

Teach Read aloud the problem. Remind students that the g/cm^3 is one of the common units used for density. Then, ask: **How many significant figures do these measurements have?** *(Three)* Have students work the problem with paper and pencil or with a calculator. Ask: **What is the difference between the experimental value and the true value?** *(0.45)* **When you divide that difference by the true value, what is the quotient?** *(0.0504484)* **What is the product when you multiply that by 100%?** *(5.04484%)* **Why, then, does the Sample Problem show that the Percent error is 5.04%?** *(The measurements have 3 significant figures, and therefore the percent error should also have 3 significant figures.)*

All in One Teaching Resources
• Transparency P21

Monitor Progress _____ L2

Writing Have students write step-by-step instructions for how to determine percent error.

Answers

 Reading Checkpoint When multiplying or dividing, the answer can have only the same number of significant figures as the measurement with the fewest significant figures.

Reading Checkpoint The result is very accurate.

Mean, Median, and Mode

Teach Key Concepts
L2

Calculating an "Average"

Focus Tell students that an "average" in science can indicate one of three different values.

Teach Ask: **What do you mean when you say to a friend that something is "average"?** *(Sample answer: It is not out of the ordinary and about in the middle.)* Explain that in math, an average can mean one of three particular values. Ask: **What is the mean of a list of numbers?** *(The numerical average)* **What is the formula for calculating mean?** *(Mean = Sum of values / Total number of values)* **What is the median of a list of numbers?** *(The middle number)* **If a list of numbers has an even number of entries, how do you determine the median?** *(Add the two middle numbers together and divide by two)* **What is the mode of a group of numbers?** *(The number that appears most often in the list)*

Apply Have students determine the mean, median, and mode for each of the following lists of numbers.
1. 15 16 17 17 18 19 20 *(Mean = 17; median = 17; mode = 17)*
2. 35 44 31 35 38 35 44 *(Mean = 37; median =35; mode = 35)*
3. 88 72 75 83 88 76 71 82 *(Mean = 79; median = 79; mode = 88)*
learning modality: logical/mathematical

All in One Teaching Resources
• Transparency P22

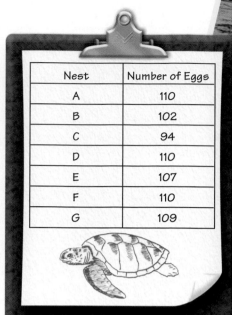

Nest	Number of Eggs
A	110
B	102
C	94
D	110
E	107
F	110
G	109

To Find the Mean

Add the numbers together and divide by the total number of items on the list.

$$
\begin{array}{r}
110 \\
102 \\
94 \\
110 \\
107 \\
110 \\
+\ 109 \\
\hline
\text{Total} \quad 742 \\
\end{array}
$$

$$\text{Mean} = \frac{742 \text{ eggs}}{7} = 106 \text{ eggs}$$

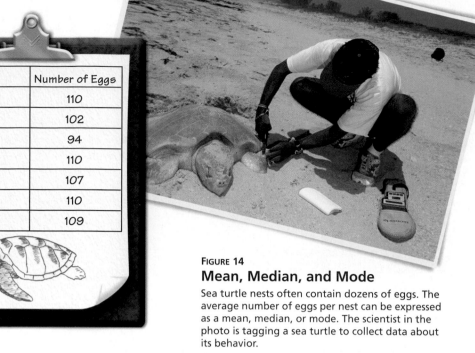

FIGURE 14
Mean, Median, and Mode
Sea turtle nests often contain dozens of eggs. The average number of eggs per nest can be expressed as a mean, median, or mode. The scientist in the photo is tagging a sea turtle to collect data about its behavior.

Mean, Median, and Mode

Walking along a beach one summer night, you spot a sea turtle. The turtle has laid its eggs in the warm sand. How many eggs does a sea turtle lay? Suppose you count the eggs and find that there are 107. Do all sea turtles lay 107 eggs? To find out, you would have to study many more turtle nests.

Figure 14 shows data from a survey of sea turtle nests. Notice that the number of eggs ranges from 94 to 110. How can you use this data to determine the "average" number of eggs? **There are several ways to calculate an "average." They include the mean, median, and mode.**

Mean One type of average is called the mean. The **mean,** or numerical average, is calculated by adding up all of the numbers and then dividing by the total number of items in the list.

$$\text{Mean} = \frac{\text{Sum of values}}{\text{Total number of values}}$$

Median Sometimes it may be more useful to know the **median,** or the middle number in a set of data. To find the median, place all the numbers in order from smallest to largest. If the ordered list has an odd number of entries, the median is the middle entry in the list. If a list has an even number of entries, you can find the median by adding the two middle numbers together and dividing by two.

Mode A third way to represent an average is called the mode. The **mode** is the number that appears most often in a list of numbers. The mode is particularly useful when a list contains many numbers that are the same.

 Reading Checkpoint What is the median number in a list that has an odd number of entries?

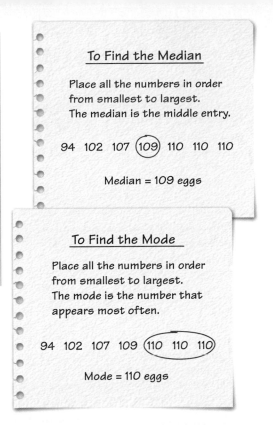

To Find the Median

Place all the numbers in order from smallest to largest. The median is the middle entry.

94 102 107 (109) 110 110 110

Median = 109 eggs

To Find the Mode

Place all the numbers in order from smallest to largest. The mode is the number that appears most often.

94 102 107 109 (110 110 110)

Mode = 110 eggs

Section 2 Assessment

Target Reading Skill Asking Questions Work with a partner to check the answers about the section headings in your graphic organizer.

Reviewing Key Concepts

1. a. **Identifying** What math skill do scientists rely on when they cannot obtain exact numbers?
   b. **Explaining** Why is it important to obtain measurements that are both accurate and precise?
   c. **Interpreting Data** A friend measures the length of her room to be 3.7 meters. How many digits can you be certain of? Explain.
2. a. **Listing** What are three ways of calculating an "average"?
   b. **Problem Solving** Use all three ways to determine a student's "average" grade on eight exams: 88, 100, 92, 74, 90, 90, 84, 94.
   c. **Calculating** Suppose the student determined that his mean grade was 93. Calculate his percent error.

Math Practice

1. **Area** To win a prize at a fair, you must throw a coin into a space that is 7.0 cm long and 4.0 cm wide. What is the area of the space you are aiming for?
2. **Percent Error** You measured the cafeteria line to be 10.5 m long. The line is actually 6.2 m long. Calculate your percent error.

Chapter 2 P ◆ 67

Math Practice

Math Skill Area, percent error
Answers
1. 28 cm²
2. 69%

Chapter Project

Keep Students on Track By this point, all students should have completed their sketches for the Chapter 2 Project. Check to see that all have. Also, briefly question each student about the kinds of materials he or she will be using to construct his or her model.

Monitor Progress _____ L2

Skills Check Have students make a table that contains definitions and formulas for finding the mean, median, and mode for a list of numbers.
Students can keep their tables in their portfolios.

Answer

✓ **Reading Checkpoint** The middle entry in the list

Assess

Reviewing Key Concepts

1. a. Estimation **b.** It is important to be accurate because an accurate measurement is close to the true or accepted value. It is important to be precise because a precise measurement is one that is the same every time if measured repeatedly. **c.** You could be certain of the first digit. The second digit is an estimate.
2. a. Calculating the mean, the median, and the mode **b.** Mean—89; median—82; mode—90 **c.** Percent error = 93 − 89 / 89 × 100% = 4.5%

Reteach L1

Use Figure 11 to reteach the concepts of accuracy and precision.

Performance Assessment L2

Writing Ask students to write a description of a scientist carrying out an activity in which the scientist measures and estimates. In this description, students should describe the accuracy and precision of the scientist's work, explain the significant numbers used for the results, and state the percent error of one of the scientist's results. Have students also describe how the scientist determines the mean, median, and mode of a list of measurements in preparing a report.

All in One Teaching Resources

- Section Summary: *Mathematics and Science*
- Review and Reinforcement: *Mathematics and Science*
- Enrich: *Mathematics and Science*

Objectives

After this lesson, students will be able to

P.2.3.1 Explain what type of data line graphs can display.

P.2.3.2 Describe how you determine a line of best fit or the slope of a graph.

P.2.3.3 Explain why line graphs are powerful tools in science.

Target Reading Skill

Building Vocabulary Explain that knowing the definitions of key-concept words helps students understand what they read.

Answers

Sample answer: **Graph** (*A graph is a picture of data that reveals patterns or trends.*) **horizontal axis** (*The horizontal axis is the graph line that runs from left to right.*) **vertical axis** (*The vertical axis is the graph line that runs up and down.*) **origin** (*The origin of a graph is the point where the horizontal and vertical axes meet.*) **coordinate** (*A coordinate is a point on a graph that is determined by a pair of numbers.*) **data point** (*A data point on a graph is where an imaginary line from the horizontal axis would meet an imaginary line from the vertical axis.*) **line of best fit** (*The line of best fit on a graph is a smooth line between points that reflects the general pattern of the points.*) **linear graph** (*A linear graph is a straight-line graph.*) **slope** (*The slope of a graph line is how steep the line is.*) **nonlinear graph** (*A nonlinear graph is a graph on which the data points do not fall on a straight line.*)

Preteach

Build Background Knowledge **L2**

Experience With Graphs

Ask: **What is a graph?** (*Sample answer: A graph is a drawing that displays information in the form of a line or with different-sized bars.*) **For what have you most often seen graphs used?** (*Sample answer: In a newspaper, temperatures over a period or rainfall through a week or month are sometimes shown in the form of a graph.*)

Section
3 Graphs in Science

Reading Preview

Key Concepts
- What type of data can line graphs display?
- How do you determine a line of best fit or the slope of a graph?
- Why are line graphs powerful tools in science?

Key Terms
- graph • horizontal axis
- vertical axis • origin
- coordinate • data point
- line of best fit • linear graph
- slope • nonlinear graph

Target Reading Skill

Building Vocabulary A definition states the meaning of a word or phrase by telling about its most important feature or function. After you read this section, reread the paragraphs that contain definitions of Key Terms. Use all the information you have learned to write a definition of each Key Term in your own words.

Lab zone Discover **Activity**

What's in a Picture?

1. Read over the information written below.
2. At age 1, Sarah was 75 cm tall. By the time she turned 2, Sarah had grown 10 cm. By age 3, she had grown another 10 cm. At age 4, Sarah was 100 cm tall.
3. Look at the "picture" to the right.

Think It Over
Inferring What are the advantages of showing information in a visual way, rather than with words in paragraph form?

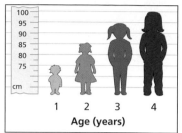

It's been a long day and all you can think about is food. You toss down your gym bag and head into the kitchen. Now for some pasta! You set a pot of water on the stove, turn on the heat, and wait eagerly for the water to boil.

Several minutes later, you are still waiting for the first sign of bubbles. Could the saying "A watched pot never boils" really be true? Or is the water taking longer to boil today because you filled the pot more than usual? Is the volume of water related to boiling time? You could do an experiment and collect some data to find out.

Lab zone Discover **Activity**

Skills Focus Inferring

Time 10 minutes

Expected Outcome Students will be able to observe that a graph can visually show relationships between two variables better than data given in paragraph form.

Think It Over Sample answer: Showing information in a visual manner provides an observer with a much better understanding of how data are related and how change has occurred. Showing information with words in paragraph form can be more confusing.

The Importance of Graphs

In Chapter 1, you learned why it is important to organize the data you collect in an experiment. Creating a data table is one way to organize experimental data. Another way to show data is in the form of a graph. You can think of a **graph** as a "picture" of your data. Have you ever heard the saying "A picture is worth a thousand words"? This is exactly why graphs are such useful tools. Because of their visual nature, graphs can reveal patterns or trends that words and data tables cannot.

The three types of graphs that scientists commonly use are bar graphs, circle graphs, and line graphs. You can learn about these graphs in the Skills Handbook. This section focuses specifically on line graphs—how to create them and how to interpret the patterns they reveal.

Why Are Line Graphs Useful? Suppose you set up the experiment in Figure 15. You record in a data table the time it takes each pot of water to boil. From your data table, you can tell that as the volume of water increases, the boiling time seems to increase as well. But a line graph could reveal more clearly how these two variables are related.

Line graphs are used to display data to show how one variable (the responding variable) changes in response to another variable (the manipulated variable). In the water-boiling experiment, the responding variable is the time it takes for the water to boil. The manipulated variable is the volume of water in the pot.

FIGURE 15
Collecting Data
How long does it take different volumes of water to boil? You can collect data and plot a line graph to see the relationship between volume and boiling time.
Inferring *Why might a line graph be more useful than a data table?*

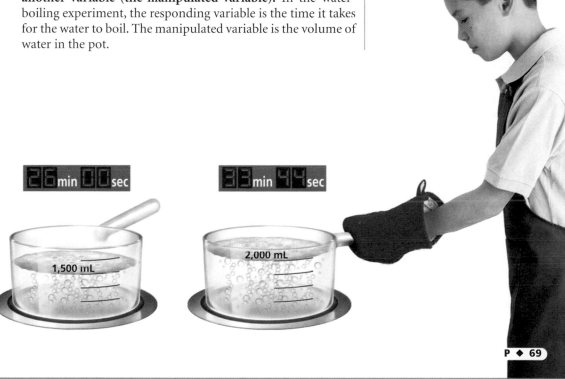

P ◆ 69

Use Visuals: Figure 16 L1
Plotting a Line Graph

Focus Tell students that Figure 16 presents a step-by-step process they can use when plotting a line graph to determine the relationship between two variables.

Teach Explain that the figure is made up of six illustrations labeled 1 through 6. Each illustration shows a step in the process of plotting a graph. Point out that each step of the figure relates to the numbered steps in the text. For each step in turn, ask a volunteer to read the text explanation of that step. Then, focus students' attention on the corresponding step in the figure. As students work through the process, ask questions to make sure they understand how to plot a graph. For instance, for Step 2 ask: **What is the manipulated variable, and what is the responding variable for the experiment being graphed?** (*The manipulated variable is volume of water, and the responding variable is boiling time.*) **What units of measurement are used for each variable?** (*Minutes for boiling time, and milliliters for volume of water*)

Apply Explain to students that air pressure affects the boiling time of water, and therefore an experiment on another day may result in different times. Make a data table on the board similar to the table for Figure 16, but vary the boiling time for each volume: 500 mL (8.1 min), 1,000 mL (16.8 min), 1,500 mL (26.2 min), 2,000 mL (34.1 min). Provide graph paper, and ask students to plot a graph using that data. **learning modality: logical/mathematical**

All in One Teaching Resources
• Transparency P23

FIGURE 16
Plotting a Line Graph
You can obtain a picture of your experimental data by following these six steps.

1 Draw the Axes

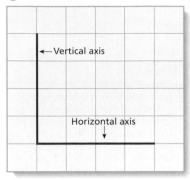

2 Label the Axes

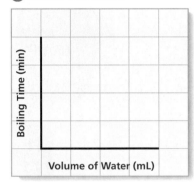

3 Create a Scale

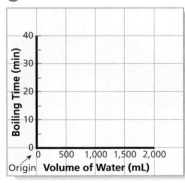

Plotting a Line Graph When is it appropriate to plot a line graph? The answer is, when your manipulated variable is *continuous*, meaning when there are other points between the ones that you tested. For example, in the water-boiling experiment, volumes of 501 milliliters, 502 milliliters, and so on exist between 500 milliliters and 1,000 milliliters. Time, temperature, and mass are other examples of continuous variables.

To plot a line graph of your data, follow these steps.

1 **On graph paper, draw a horizontal axis (or *x*-axis) and a vertical axis (or *y*-axis).** The **horizontal axis** or *x*-axis, is the graph line that runs left to right. The **vertical axis,** or *y*-axis, is the graph line that runs up and down.

2 **Label the graph's axes.** Label the horizontal axis with the name of the manipulated variable. Label the vertical axis with the name of the responding variable. Be sure to include units of measurement on each axis.

3 **Create a scale on each axis that covers the range of the data collected.** In other words, your scale needs to span from the smallest value to the largest value you will show. Determine the space you have available on each axis, and mark off equally spaced intervals. Both scales should begin at zero when possible. The point where the *x*-axis and *y*-axis cross is called the **origin** of the graph. On this graph, the origin has coordinates of (0, 0), which represents "0 milliliters and 0 minutes." A **coordinate** is a pair of numbers used to determine the position of a point on a graph.

Data Table	
Volume of Water (mL)	Boiling Time
500	7 min 48 s (7.8 min)
1,000	16 min 37 s (16.6 min)
1,500	26 min 00 s (26.0 min)
2,000	33 min 44 s (33.7 min)

❹ **Plot a point on the graph for each piece of data.** The dotted lines show you how to plot the first piece of data (500 milliliters and 7.8 minutes). Draw an imaginary vertical line extending up from the 500 milliliters mark on the horizontal axis. Then draw an imaginary horizontal line extending across from the vertical axis at 7.8 minutes. Plot a point where these two lines intersect, or cross. The point showing the location of that intersection is called a **data point.**

❺ **Draw a "line of best fit" to reflect the general trend of the data.** After you have plotted all the data points, your first instinct might be simply to connect all the dots. The correct approach to drawing a line graph, however, is not to connect the dots automatically. Rather, you should first stop and look at the points you plotted to identify a general pattern in the data. Then draw a smooth line between the points to reflect that general pattern. This graph line, called the **line of best fit,** may touch very few or none of the points. In such cases, try to have about the same number of points above the line as there are below.

Notice that the resulting line of best fit for this graph is a straight line. A line graph in which the data points yield a straight line is called a **linear graph.**

❻ **Add a title that identifies the variables or relationship shown in the graph.**

Reading Checkpoint What is a data point?

❹ **Plot the Data**

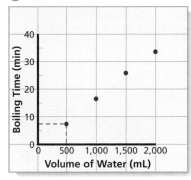

❺ **Draw a Line of Best Fit**

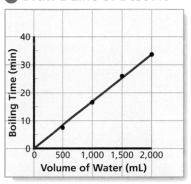

❻ **Add a Title**

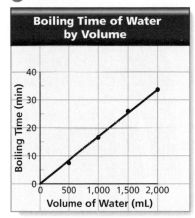

Boiling Time of Water by Volume

Chapter 2   P ◆ 71

Address Misconceptions L2

Graphs Don't Make Data Accurate

Focus Many students may mistakenly think that a graph in some way ensures the accuracy of the data that has been graphed. Tell students that a graph can be as inaccurate as any other method of displaying data.

Teach Ask: **When a scientist plots a line graph, where does the data come from?** *(The data could come from any source, including observations in the field or experimental results.)* **What would you have to know to be sure that the data plotted were accurate?** *(You would have to know how the scientists gathered the data.)* Point out that the data scientists gather are not always accurate.

Apply Ask volunteers for their estimates for the high temperature on each of the last five days. Write these estimates incorrectly on the board, and ask students to make a graph of the data you have collected. When they have made their graphs, ask: **Does the line graph you've made accurately display the high temperatures for the last five days?** *(No, because the temperatures obviously are wrong)* **Can you tell simply by looking at your finished graphs that the data are inaccurate?** *(There is no way to tell just by looking at the graphs.)* **learning modality: visual**

Monitor Progress _____ L2

Skills Check Have students make a flowchart that includes the six steps for plotting a graph. For the steps in their flowcharts, they can use the highlighted sentences under the subsection Plotting a Graph.

Students can place their flowcharts in their portfolios. **Portfolio**

Answer

Reading Checkpoint The point showing the location of the intersection of an imaginary vertical line drawn from the horizontal axis and an imaginary horizontal line drawn from the vertical axis

P ● 71

Why Draw a Line of Best Fit?

Teach Key Concepts L2
Emphasizing the Overall Trend

Focus Explain to students that drawing a line of best fit on a graph can emphasize a trend in the data.

Teach Ask: **What is a line of best fit?** (*A smooth line between data points that is drawn to reflect the general pattern of the data*) **What does a line of best fit emphasize?** (*The overall trend shown by all the data taken as a whole*) Explain that you don't always draw a line of best fit on a graph. You draw a line of best fit only when the data points seem to be following along a straight line, with only small variations.

Apply Have students look through a science magazine such as *Science* or *Scientific American* to find a graph that has a line of best fit. **learning modality: logical/mathematical**

All in One Teaching Resources
• Transparency P24

Slope

Teach Key Concepts L2
Steepness of the Graph Line

Focus Tell students that the steepness of a graph can provide information about how a responding variable—the *y*—changes in response to changes in the manipulated variable—the *x*.

Teach Ask: **What is the rise of a graph line?** (*Vertical change*) **What is the run of a graph line?** (*Horizontal change*) Tell students that how much *y* changes is another way of saying vertical change, or the rise. How much *x* changes is another way of saying horizontal change, or the run. Ask: **What is the formula used to determine the slope of a line?** ($Slope = Rise / Run = Y_2 - Y_1 \div X_2 - X_2$)

Apply Have students look at the graph in Figure 19, and explain that the first data point after (0, 0) is (10, 5), and the fourth data point is (40, 20). Have students use those two points to calculate the slope of the graph. **learning modality: logical/ mathematical**

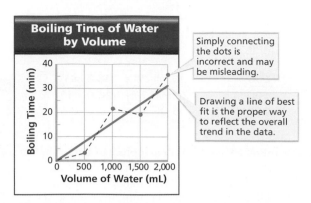

FIGURE 17
Line of Best Fit
Connecting the dots in this graph would yield a zigzag line. However, a line going upwards from left to right is a more accurate reflection of the data.
Relating Cause and Effect *What factors might explain why the data points don't fall perfectly along a straight line?*

Simply connecting the dots is incorrect and may be misleading.

Drawing a line of best fit is the proper way to reflect the overall trend in the data.

Why Draw a Line of Best Fit?

You may be wondering why you cannot simply connect all your data points with a line to create a line graph. To understand why this is the case, consider the following situation. Suppose your friend performs the same water-boiling experiment as you did and plots the graph shown in Figure 17.

Notice that your friend's graph shows the same general trend as yours—points going upwards from left to right. However, if your friend simply connects the dots, the line would be a zigzag, rather than a straight line.

Why don't your friend's data points fall perfectly along a straight line? It is because whenever data is collected, small measurement errors and inaccuracies can be introduced. By simply connecting the dots, you would place too much importance on each individual data point in determining the overall shape of the line. **A line of best fit emphasizes the overall trend shown by all the data taken as a whole.**

Reading Checkpoint Why shouldn't you automatically "connect the dots" when creating a line graph?

Tips for Drawing a Line of Best Fit

• If the data points seem to follow along a straight line, draw a straight line.

• Include as many data points as possible directly on the line.

• For data points that don't easily fit on the line, try to have the same number of points above the line as below the line.

FIGURE 18
Drawing a Line of Best Fit
These tips will help you determine the overall trend shown by your experimental data.

Differentiated Instruction

Less Proficient Readers L1
Answering Questions Select a passage from the text, such as the subsection *Why Draw a Line of Best Fit?* Read the passage aloud to students as they follow along in their books. After reading, ask some questions about the passage. If they don't know the answers, challenge them to find the answers in the passage. **learning modality: verbal**

Slope

When a line graph is linear, you can determine a value called slope. One way to define **slope** is the steepness of the graph line. **The slope of a graph line tells you how much y changes for every change in x.** Thus, another definition of slope is the ratio of the vertical change (the "rise") to the horizontal change (the "run"). Slope is calculated using this formula:

$$\text{Slope} = \frac{\text{Rise}}{\text{Run}} = \frac{Y_2 - Y_1}{X_2 - X_1}$$

To calculate slope, pick any two points on the line and write down the coordinates. In Figure 19, suppose you chose the points $(20, 10)$ and $(50, 25)$.

$$\text{Slope} = \frac{25 - 10}{50 - 20} = \frac{15}{30} = 0.5$$

In the case of Figure 19, the slope represents the distance the car travels per unit of time, or its speed. A slope of 0.5 tells you that the car has a speed of 0.5 km/min.

 Reading Checkpoint What are two ways to define slope?

FIGURE 19
Slope
The slope of a line indicates how much y changes for every change in x. **Calculating** *What is the slope of this line?*

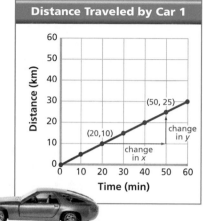

Distance Traveled by Car 1

Math Analyzing Data

Car Travel

The graph shows the distance a car travels in a one-hour period. Use the graph to answer the questions below.

1. **Reading Graphs** What variable is plotted on the horizontal axis? What variable is plotted on the vertical axis?

2. **Interpreting Data** How far does the car travel in the first 10 minutes? In 40 minutes?

3. **Predicting** Use the graph to predict how far the car would travel in 120 minutes. Assume the car continues to travel at the same speed.

4. **Calculating** Calculate the slope of the graph. What information does the slope provide about the speed of Car 2?

5. **Drawing Conclusions** Compare this graph to the one for Car 1 in Figure 19. What is the relationship between the steepness of the graph lines and the speed of the cars?

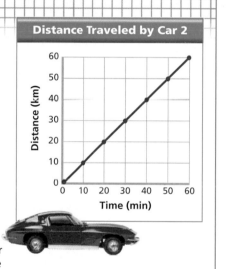

Distance Traveled by Car 2

All in One Teaching Resources
• Transparency P25

Math Analyzing Data

Math Skill Making and interpreting graphs

Focus Tell students that the slope of a graph provides information about how much the responding variable (y) changes for every change in the manipulated variable (x).

Teach Have students examine the graph and compare it to the graph in Figure 19. Ask: **How are the two graphs the same and how are they different?** *(The x and the y and the scales are the same. The only difference is the line plotted on each graph. The line in Figure 19 represents the speed of Car 1, and the line in Math Analyzing Data represents the speed of Car 2.)*

Answers

1. Time (min), the manipulated variable, is plotted on the horizontal axis. Distance (km), the responding variable, is plotted on the vertical axis.

2. The car travels 10 km in 10 min and 40 km in 40 min.

3. The car is traveling 1 km per min. It would travel 120 km in 120 min.

4. The slope is 1. The slope provides information about the car's average speed.

5. The slope of the graph for Car 1 is 0.5. Because the distance and time values are marked the same on the two graphs, a steeper line represents a greater speed. Car 2 is traveling twice as fast as Car 1.

Monitor Progress _____ L2

Writing Have students answer the question Why Draw a Line of Best Fit?

Answers
Figure 17 Whenever data are collected, errors and inaccuracies can be introduced.

Figure 19 The slope is 0.5.

Reading Checkpoint The line would be a zigzag line, rather than a straight line and would not yield information about general trends.

Reading Checkpoint One way to define slope is the steepness of the graph line. Another way is the ratio of the vertical change (the "rise") to the horizontal change (the "run").

Using Graphs to Identify Trends

Teach Key Concepts L2

Identify Trends and Make Predictions

Focus Tell students that scientists often display data in graphs because scientists can identify trends in the data and make predictions.

Teach Ask: **What is a nonlinear graph?** (*A line graph in which the data points do not fall along a straight line*) **What kind of graph reveals trends in the data, linear graphs or nonlinear graphs?** (*Both reveal trends.*)

Apply Have students look at Graph A in Figure 20, and ask: **What prediction can you make about how many baskets a player would make shooting the ball from 6 m?** (*The player would make fewer baskets than shooting closer to the hoop. A good prediction would be that the player wouldn't make any baskets.*) **learning modality: visual**

All in One Teaching Resources
• Transparency P26

Use Visuals: Figure 20 L2

Interpreting a Nonlinear Graph

Focus Tell students that scientists use graphs to help identify trends in data.

Teach Direct students' attention to Graph B in Figure 20, and ask: **What data have been plotted in this graph?** (*The growth of the population of bacteria over time*) **What is the time period shown in the graph for bacterial growth?** (*120 minutes, or 2 hours*) Ask: **If bacterial cells divide in two every 20 minutes and there is 1 bacterial cell at the origin of the graph, then how many bacterial cells does the graph show at the end of each 20-minute period?** (*2 at 20 min, 4 at 40 min, 8 at 60 min, 16 at 80 min, 32 at 100 min, 64 at 120 min—twice as many as at the end of the previous 20-min period*) **Why, then, does the graph show a steep curve?** (*Every 20 minutes, the population doubles*)

Apply Ask: **How many bacterial cells do you predict there would be after 140 minutes?** (*Two times 64, or 128*) **Would the curve of the line become steeper or less steep?** (*Steeper*) **learning modality: visual**

FIGURE 20

Trends in Graphs

Data may yield one of the trends shown in these graphs.
Reading Graphs *Which graph shows no relationship between the two variables?*

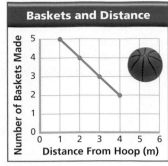

A **Linear Trend** As the distance from the hoop increases, the number of baskets made decreases. The graph line descends to the right.

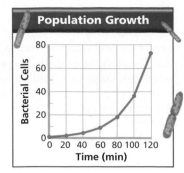

B **Nonlinear Trend** Bacteria reproduce by dividing in two every 20 minutes. The number of bacterial cells increases sharply. The graph is a steep curve.

Using Graphs to Identify Trends

Your data won't always give you a graph with a straight line. A line graph in which the data points do not fall along a straight line is called a **nonlinear graph.**

Whether a graph is linear or nonlinear, the information it contains is very useful. **Line graphs are powerful tools in science because they allow you to identify trends and make predictions.**

Linear Trends When a graph is linear, you can easily see how two variables are related. For instance, Graph A in Figure 20 shows that the farther one student stands from a basketball hoop, the fewer baskets she can make.

You can also use the graph to make predictions. For example, how many baskets can she make at a distance of 5 meters? If you extend the graph line, you can see that your prediction would be one basket.

Nonlinear Trends There are several kinds of nonlinear graphs. In some nonlinear graphs, the data points may fall along a curve. A curve may be shallow, or it may be steep, as in Graph B.

Other nonlinear graphs show different trends. A graph may rise and then level off, as in Graph C. Or, a graph may show a repeating pattern, as in Graph D. Because each of these graphs reveals a trend in the data, they are useful in understanding how the variables are related.

Distance Biked

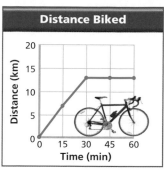
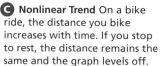

C **Nonlinear Trend** On a bike ride, the distance you bike increases with time. If you stop to rest, the distance remains the same and the graph levels off.

Seasonal Rainfall

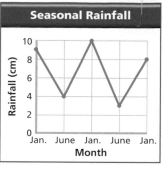

D **Nonlinear Trend** In many places, rainfall varies with the seasons. The graph shows a repeating, or cyclical, pattern.

Hours of TV per Day

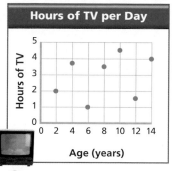

E **No Trend** There is no relationship between the amount of television these children watch and their age. The data points are scattered, and the graph shows no recognizable pattern.

No Trend In other nonlinear graphs, the data points may be scattered about in no recognizable pattern, as in Graph E. Would you be surprised to learn that even such graphs are useful? When there are no identifiable trends in a graph, it most likely means that there is no relationship between the two variables.

 Reading Checkpoint What is a nonlinear graph?

Section 3 Assessment

Target Reading Skill Building Vocabulary Use your definitions to help answer the questions below.

Reviewing Key Concepts

1. a. Reviewing What can graphs reveal that data tables cannot?
 b. Describing What can a line graph tell you about the relationship between the variables in an experiment?
 c. Interpreting Data Could you use a line graph to show data about how body mass (the responding variable) changes with height (the manipulated variable)? Explain.
2. a. Defining What is a line of best fit?
 b. Explaining What does calculating the slope of a graph line tell you about the data?
 c. Comparing and Contrasting How does a graph line with a steeper slope compare to one with a shallower slope?

3. a. Listing List two things that line graphs allow scientists to do.
 b. Reading Graphs Describe how Graph D in Figure 20 allows scientists to do these two things.

Lab zone At-Home **Activity**

Which Line Is Best? Show a family member how to "draw" a line of best fit by plotting the data points from Figure 17 onto a piece of graph paper. Tape the graph paper onto a thick piece of cardboard. Insert a pushpin into each data point. Then arrange a piece of string so that it best reflects the data. Once you have determined the line of best fit, tape the string to the graph. Explain why a line of best fit need not go through each data point.

Chapter 2 P ◆ 75

Lab zone At Home **Activity**

Demonstrate how to tape graph paper onto cardboard, mount pushpins at each data point, and arrange the string. Encourage students to carry out the activity at home. They can explain to family members that a line of best fit shows the general trend of the data rather than emphasizing inconsistencies or normal variations in the data.

Lab zone Chapter **Project**

Keep Students on Track By now, each student should have begun to construct a model. If students are constructing the models at home, ask such questions as these to get an idea of a student's progress: What is the largest part or object in your model? How big is the object in reality and in your model? Are you experiencing any difficulties? Inquire whether students have had to change materials or modify the model in any way.

Density Graphs

Prepare for Inquiry

Key Concept
The slope of a graph with volume measurements on the horizontal axis and mass measurements on the vertical axis provides information about the density of a liquid.

Skills Objectives
After this lab, students will be able to
- graph data related to the mass and volume of a liquid
- calculate the slope of the resulting graph line

Prep Time 10 minutes
Class Time 40 minutes

Advance Planning
For each group of students, pour a different volume of a liquid into each of three graduated cylinders. Virtually any liquid will work, though a liquid colored with food coloring may be easy to read. Avoid viscous liquids, such as honey.

Safety
 Make sure students wear goggles during the lab. Tell students where to dispose of the liquids. Review the safety guidelines in Appendix A.

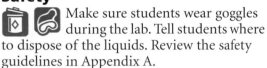 **Teaching Resources**
- Lab Worksheet: *Density Graphs*

Guide Inquiry

Introduce the Procedure
Review with students how to determine volume by reading the bottom of a meniscus, as shown in Section 1. Also review how to draw a line of best fit and how to calculate slope.

Expected Outcome
Students will draw the conclusion that the slope of the line represents the density of the liquid.

Density Graphs

Problem
How can you determine the density of a liquid?

Skills Focus
graphing, calculating

Materials
- graduated cylinder
- balance
- graph paper
- 3 samples of a liquid

Procedure
1. Measure the mass of an empty graduated cylinder. Record the mass in a data table.
2. Pour one of the liquid samples into the graduated cylinder. Measure and record the mass of the graduated cylinder plus the liquid.
3. Calculate the mass of the liquid alone by subtracting the mass of the empty graduated cylinder from the mass in Step 2.
4. Determine the volume of the liquid by reading the level at the bottom of the meniscus.
5. Repeat Steps 2–4 with the two other samples.

Analyze and Conclude
1. **Graphing** Use the data in your data table to create a graph. Graph volume on the horizontal axis and mass on the vertical axis.
2. **Interpreting Data** Look at the points you plotted to identify a general trend in the data. Then draw a line of best fit that reflects the trend in the data.

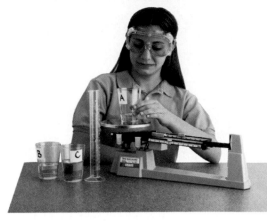

3. **Calculating** Select two points along the graph line and use them to calculate the slope of the line. Use this formula:

$$\text{Slope} = \frac{\text{Rise}}{\text{Run}} = \frac{Y_2 - Y_1}{X_2 - X_1}$$

4. **Drawing Conclusions** Explain why the slope represents the density of the liquid.
5. **Communicating** In a paragraph, explain why mass and volume measurements for any sample of the liquid should fall along the graph line.

Design an Experiment
Propose a plan to determine which is denser—a marble or the liquid you used in this lab. *Obtain your teacher's permission before carrying out your investigation.*

Data Table				
Sample	Mass of Empty Graduated Cylinder	Mass of Liquid and Graduated Cylinder	Mass of Liquid Alone	Volume of Liquid
1				
2				
3				

Analyze and Conclude
1. The graph that results should be linear.
2. Slopes will vary depending on the liquid used.
3. The slope represents the density of the liquid because density equals mass over volume and slope equals rise over run. In this graph, the rise represents the mass of the liquid and the run represents the volume.
4. Students should mention that the density of a substance is the same for all samples.

Extend Inquiry

Design an Experiment Students' experiments should be similar to this Skills Lab. They will plan to find the mass of a marble, make a graph, and calculate the slope of a graph line, which represents the density of the marble. Then they will compare the densities of the marble and the liquid to determine which is denser.

Safety in the Science Laboratory

Reading Preview

Key Concepts
- Why is preparation important when carrying out scientific investigations in the lab and in the field?
- What should you do if an accident occurs?

Target Reading Skill
Outlining As you read, make an outline about science safety that you can use for review. Use the red headings for the main ideas and the blue headings for supporting ideas.

Safety in the Science Laboratory
I. Safety in the lab
A. Preparing for the lab
B.
C.
II. Safety in the field

Lab zone Discover **Activity**

Where Is the Safety Equipment in Your School?

1. Look around your classroom or school for any safety-related equipment.
2. Draw a floor plan of the room or building and clearly label where each item is located.

Think It Over
Predicting Why is it important to know where safety equipment is located?

After hiking for a few hours, your group finally reaches a beautiful campsite by a lake. Your first task is to set up tents. Eager to explore the area, you toss aside the tent directions, thinking to yourself, "How hard could it be?" You begin to put all the pieces together, guessing as you go. When you have finished, you step back to survey your work. You notice that the tent is quite lopsided. Deciding that it will do, you run off with your friends to explore.

Later that night, as you settle into your sleeping bag, heavy rain starts to fall. Water begins to pour in through the lopsided part of the tent. You look for a flashlight so you can investigate. But then you realize that you forgot to pack one.

You have probably heard the motto, "Be prepared." Obviously, following that advice would have been helpful in this situation. Proper preparation for the camping trip should have included reading the tent directions and packing the proper supplies. The result would probably have been a more enjoyable camping experience.

◄ **Proper preparation is important for a camping trip.**

Chapter 2 P ◆ 77

Lab zone Discover **Activity**

Skills Focus Predicting

Time 15 minutes

Tips Allow pairs of students to search the school for safety-related equipment. After students have completed their search, discuss as a class what they have found. Then direct students to make their floor plans.

Expected Outcome Students will learn where safety-related equipment is kept in the classroom and in the school building, and they will be better able to access such equipment in an emergency.

Think It Over Sample answer: It is important to know where safety equipment is located because in an emergency there may not be time to ask a teacher or search for the equipment.

Objectives
After this lesson, students will be able to
P.2.4.1 Explain why preparation is important when carrying out scientific investigations in the lab and in the field.
P.2.4.2 Describe what you should do if an accident occurs.

Target Reading Skill

Outlining Explain that using an outline format helps students organize information by main topic, subtopic, and details.

Answers
Safety in the Science Laboratory
I. Safety in the Lab
    A. Preparing for the Lab
    B. Performing the Lab
    C. End-of-Lab Procedures
II. Safety in the Field
III. In Case of an Accident

All in One Teaching Resources
- Transparency P27

Preteach

Build Background Knowledge   L2

What To Do?
To emphasize the importance of learning safe practices in the science laboratory, give students this fictional scenario: A student is working alone in the science laboratory, and a material used in an experiment catches on fire. Ask: **Can you say whether the student violated any safety rules?** *(Sample answer: Yes, the student violated a rule that says no one should ever work in the science lab alone.)* **If the student hadn't been working alone, what is the first thing the student should do?** *(Sample answer: Tell the teacher.)*

Safety in the Lab

Teach Key Concepts L2
Staying Safe in the Laboratory

Focus Tell students that the laboratory can be a dangerous place, and scientists take steps to ensure safety.

Teach Ask: **Why does good preparation help you stay safe in the lab?** *(If you prepare well, you know what equipment you will be using and the procedures you will be following. With that knowledge, you can take the proper precautions.)* **What should you do if you don't understand something you read that you're supposed to do in a lab?** *(Ask the teacher before beginning the lab.)* **What is the most important safety rule in performing a lab?** *(Always follow your teacher's instructions and the textbook directions exactly.)* **What is the last thing you should do at the end of a lab?** *(Wash your hands)*

Apply Ask: **Why is it important to dispose of waste materials properly at the end of a lab?** *(You may be using harmful chemicals or some other substance that can't just be thrown away or poured down a drain, because they might do harm to people or other living things.)* **learning modality: verbal**

 **Teaching Resources**

• Transparency P28

For: Links on laboratory safety
Visit: www.SciLinks.org
Web Code: scn-1624

Download a worksheet that will guide students' review of Internet resources on laboratory safety.

Independent Practice L2

All in One Teaching Resources

• Guided Reading and Study Worksheet: *Safety in the Science Laboratory*

◉ **Student Edition on Audio CD**

For: Links on laboratory safety
Visit: www.SciLinks.org
Web Code: scn-1624

FIGURE 20
Safety in the Lab
Good preparation for an experiment helps you stay safe in the laboratory. **Observing** *List three precautions each student is taking while performing the labs.*

Safety in the Lab

Just as when you go camping, you have to be prepared before you begin any scientific investigation. **Good preparation helps you stay safe when doing science activities in the laboratory.**

Thermometers, balances, and glassware—these are some of the equipment you will use in science labs. Do you know how to use these items? What should you do if something goes wrong? Thinking about these questions ahead of time is an important part of being prepared.

Preparing for the Lab Preparing for a lab should begin the day before you will perform the lab. It is important to read through the procedure carefully and make sure you understand all the directions. Also, review the general safety guidelines in Appendix A, including those related to the specific equipment you will use. If anything is unclear, be prepared to ask your teacher about it before you begin the lab.

Wear safety goggles to protect your eyes from chemical splashes, glass breakage, and sharp objects.

Wear an apron to protect yourself and your clothes from chemicals.

Wear heat-resistant gloves when handling hot objects.

Keep your work area clean and uncluttered.

Make sure electric cords are untangled and out of the way.

Wear closed-toe shoes when working in the laboratory.

78 ◆ P

Differentiated Instruction

Less Proficient Readers L1
Communicating Have students use sketches, photographs, and short captions to create a visual display about safety in the laboratory and in the field. Tell students to draw ideas from the photograph in Figure 21 as well as from the information they've learned about the safety symbols. **learning modality: visual**

Gifted and Talented L3
Researching Safe Practices Encourage interested students to visit a science laboratory at a local college or university and inquire about the safe practices that laboratory personnel take. Students can ask for a copy of their safety guidelines. Ask these students to prepare a presentation to the class. **learning modality: verbal**

Performing the Lab Whenever you perform a science lab, your chief concern must be the safety of yourself, your classmates, and your teacher. The most important safety rule is simple: Always follow your teacher's instructions and the textbook directions exactly. You should never try anything on your own without asking your teacher first.

Labs and activities in this textbook series include safety symbols such as those at right. These symbols alert you to possible dangers in performing the lab and remind you to work carefully. They also identify any safety equipment that you should use to protect yourself from potential hazards. The symbols are explained in detail in Appendix A. Make sure you are familiar with each safety symbol and what it means.

Other things you can do to make your lab experience safe and successful include keeping your work area clean and organized. Also, do not rush through any of the steps. Finally, always show respect and courtesy to your teacher and classmates.

Safety Symbols	
	Safety Goggles
	Lab Apron
	Breakage
	Heat-Resistant Gloves
	Plastic Gloves
	Heating
	Flames
	No Flames
	Corrosive Chemical
	Poison
	Fumes
	Sharp Object
	Animal Safety
	Plant Safety
	Electric Shock
	Physical Safety
	Disposal
	Hand Washing
	General Safety Awareness

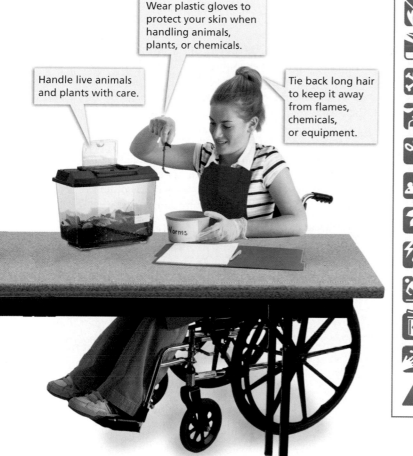

Wear plastic gloves to protect your skin when handling animals, plants, or chemicals.

Handle live animals and plants with care.

Tie back long hair to keep it away from flames, chemicals, or equipment.

Use Visuals: Figure 21 L2
Safety Symbols

Focus Tell students that in carrying out science investigations, they will see safety symbols that caution them about each investigation.

Teach Have students examine the safety symbols listed in Figure 21. Then ask them to turn to laboratory investigations in this and other chapters to see the symbols that are used. Ask: **Where are the symbols explained in detail?** *(In Appendix A)* Have students turn to Appendix A and become familiar with what each symbol stands for.

Apply Ask: **What does the "skull and crossbones" symbol mean when you see it in a laboratory procedure?** *(Caution, poison being used)* **What steps should you take to avoid injury?** *(Do not let any poisonous chemical come in contact with your skin, and do not inhale vapors. Wash your hands when you are finished with the activity.)* **learning modality: verbal**

All in One Teaching Resources
• Transparency P29

Monitor Progress L2

Oral Presentation Call on students at random to explain what a student should do to prepare for a lab and during a lab to stay safe.

Answer
Figure 21 Wearing goggles, wearing heat-resistant gloves, making sure electric cords are untangled and out of the way, wearing an apron, keeping work area clean and uncluttered, wearing closed-toe shoes, handling live animals and plants with care, wearing plastic gloves, tying back long hair

Safety in the Field

Teach Key Concepts
Staying Safe in the Field

Focus Explain to students that many scientific investigations are done in the field, where there may be many hazards.

Teach Ask: **What does it mean to do an investigation in the "field"?** (*The field can be any outdoor area, such as the schoolyard, a forest, a park, or a beach.*) **Why should you never carry out a field investigation alone?** (*Hazards in the field are hard to plan for, and something might happen that could cause injury. If a person is alone, there is no one to help or go for help in case of an accident or injury.*)

Apply Describe a student who decides to collect water samples from a mountain stream. She sets out for the field alone, without informing the teacher. While collecting the water, the wind picks up and quickly a thunderstorm arrives. She ends up soaked, shivering, and scared. Ask: **What did this student do wrong?** (*She didn't tell a teacher or another adult where she was going, she went alone, and she failed to prepare for conditions that might arise in the field.*) **learning modality: verbal**

In Case of an Accident

Teach Key Concepts
Notify Your Teacher Immediately

Focus Tell students that accidents can occur in the laboratory, and they should know what to do if they are involved in a lab accident.

Teach Ask: **What is the first thing you should do if you are involved in an accident in the laboratory?** (*Notify the teacher immediately*) Explain that substances and devices used in a laboratory can cause serious injuries, but taking the proper actions can prevent or lesson harm. A teacher has been trained in taking the correct actions in an emergency.

Apply Ask: **What would you do if in preparing a liquid mixture in a beaker you splashed some liquid on your skin?** (*Notify the teacher immediately*) **What action would you and your teacher then take to try to prevent injury?** (*Flush the skin with large amounts of water*) **learning modality: verbal**

Figure 22
Safety in the Field
These are just some of the items that might come in handy while you are out in the field.
Applying Concepts *What other items might be useful on a field trip to a beach?*

▲ Flashlight

▲ Bug spray   ▲ Sunscreen

▲ Hiking shoes

▲ Bandages

▲ Compass

80 ◆ P

End-of-Lab Procedures Your lab work does not end when you reach the last step in the procedure. There are important things you need to do at the end of every lab.

When you have completed a lab, be sure to clean up your work area. Turn off and unplug any equipment and return it to its proper place. It is very important that you dispose of any waste materials properly. Some wastes should not be thrown in the trash or poured down the drain. Follow your teacher's instructions about proper disposal. Finally, be sure to wash your hands thoroughly after working in the laboratory.

Reading Checkpoint How should lab wastes be disposed of?

Safety in the Field

The laboratory is not the only place where you will conduct scientific investigations. Some investigations will be done in the "field." The field can be any outdoor area, such as a schoolyard, a forest, a park, or a beach. **Just as in the laboratory, good preparation helps you stay safe when doing science activities in the field.**

There can be many potential safety hazards outdoors. For example, you could encounter severe weather, traffic, wild animals, or poisonous plants. Advance planning may help you avoid some potential hazards. For example, you can listen to the weather forecast and plan your trip accordingly. Other hazards may be impossible to anticipate.

Whenever you do field work, always tell an adult where you will be. Never carry out a field investigation alone. Ask an adult or a classmate to accompany you. Dress appropriately for the weather and other conditions you will encounter. Use common sense to avoid any potentially dangerous situations.

Reading Checkpoint What are some potential outdoor hazards?

In Case of an Accident

Good preparation and careful work habits can go a long way toward making your lab experiences safe ones. But, at some point, an accident may occur. A classmate might accidentally knock over a beaker or a chemical might spill on your sleeve. Would you know what to do?

When any accident occurs, no matter how minor, notify your teacher immediately. Then, listen to your teacher's directions and carry them out quickly. Make sure you know the location and proper use of all the emergency equipment in your lab room. Knowing safety and first aid procedures beforehand will prepare you to handle accidents properly. Figure 23 lists some first-aid procedures you should know.

Reading Checkpoint What should you do when an accident occurs?

In Case of Emergency
ALWAYS NOTIFY YOUR TEACHER IMMEDIATELY

Injury	What to Do
Burns	Immerse burns in cold water.
Cuts	Cover cuts with a clean dressing. Apply direct pressure to the wound to stop bleeding.
Spills on Skin	Flush the skin with large amounts of water.
Foreign Object in Eye	Flush the eye with large amounts of water. Seek medical attention.

FIGURE 23
In Case of an Accident
These first-aid tips can help guide your actions during emergency situations. Remember, always notify your teacher immediately if an accident occurs.

Section 4 Assessment

Target Reading Skill Outlining Use the information in your outline about science safety to help you answer the questions below.

Reviewing Key Concepts

1. **a. Listing** List two things you should do ahead of time to prepare for a lab.
   b. Interpreting Diagrams Suppose a lab included the safety symbols below. What do these symbols mean? What precautions should you take?

   c. Making Generalizations Why is it more difficult to prepare for a lab activity in the field than for one in a laboratory?

2. **a. Reviewing** Suppose during a lab activity you get a cut and start to bleed. What is the first thing you should do?
   b. Sequencing Outline in order the next steps you would take to deal with your injury.
   c. Making Judgments Some people feel that most accidents that occur really could have been prevented with better preparation or safer behaviors. Do you agree or disagree with this viewpoint? Explain your reasoning.

Writing in Science

Safety Poster Make a poster of one of the safety rules in Appendix A to post in your lab. Be sure to include the safety symbol, clear directions, and additional illustrations.

Chapter 2 P ◆ 81

Lab zone Chapter Project

Keep Students on Track At the beginning of the last week of the project, ask a few volunteers to display their models and give their oral presentations. This will give students having trouble with the project some idea of what they should focus on to complete their projects. Also, check to see that students who are still working on their projects are in the final phases.

Writing in Science

Writing Mode Persuasion
Scoring Rubric
4 Exceeds criteria; may have well-written directions and/or superior illustrations
3 Meets all criteria
2 Meets some but not all criteria
1 Meets few criteria, with only brief and/or inaccurate information and/or few illustrations

---

Monitor Progress [L2]

Answers

Figure 22 Sample answer: lip balm, safe drinking water, wading shoes, towel

Reading Checkpoint Lab wastes should be disposed of following your teacher's instructions about proper disposal.

Reading Checkpoint Sample answer: Lightning, wind, sun exposure, cold, heat, insect and snake bites, cuts, sprains

Reading Checkpoint Notify your teacher immediately, and then listen to your teacher's directions and carry them out quickly.

Assess

Reviewing Key Concepts

1. **a.** Read through the procedure to make sure you understand all the directions, and review the safety guidelines in Appendix A. **b.** Sharp object: Always direct a sharp edge or point away from yourself and others. Electric shock: Never use electrical equipment around water, or when the equipment is wet or your hands are wet. Be sure cords are untangled and cannot trip anyone. Unplug equipment when not in use. Disposal: Chemicals and other laboratory materials used in the activity must be disposed of safely. Follow the instructions from your teacher. **c.** Some hazards in the field may be impossible to anticipate.
2. **a.** Notify your teacher immediately. **b.** Cover the cut with a clean dressing. Apply direct pressure to the wound to stop bleeding. **c.** Sample answer: Yes. Good preparation and safe behaviors can help people avoid many of the circumstances and situations that are the cause of accidents.

Reteach [L1]

Use Figure 21 to question students about the variety of dangers in doing laboratory investigations.

Performance Assessment [L2]

Writing Ask students to write a tale of two students, one who follows safety guidelines in the lab and one who doesn't.

All in One Teaching Resources

- Section Summary: *Safety in the Science Laboratory*
- Review and Reinforcement: *Safety in the Science Laboratory*
- Enrich: *Safety in the Science Laboratory*

Study Guide

- Complete student edition
- Section and chapter self-assessments
- Assessment reports for teachers

Help Students Read

Building Vocabulary

Word Origin Have students look up the origin of the word *meniscus*. They will discover that the word comes from the Greek word *meniskos,* which means "crescent moon." Ask students how a meniscus is like a crescent moon. *(A crescent moon has a curved shape, and a meniscus is the curved top surface of water in a graduated cylinder.)*

Word/Part Analysis Have students analyze the words and word parts in the terms *linear graph* and *nonlinear graph*. Explain that *linear* is an adjective form of the word *line,* and the word *linear* implies a straight line. Therefore, a linear graph is a graph with a straight line. Tell students that *non* is a word part that means "not." Ask students to explain what a nonlinear graph is. *(A graph that does not have a straight line)*

Connecting Concepts

Concept Maps Help students develop one way to show how the information in this chapter is related. The work of scientists involves making measurements of several characteristics of matter, and scientists use specific instruments and units of measure for each of these characteristics. Scientists also use mathematics in collecting and analyzing data. Among the ways scientists show data is in the form of a graph. The work of scientists also involves keeping safe in the laboratory and in the field. Have students brainstorm to identify the key concepts, key terms, details, and examples. Then write each one on a self-sticking note and attach it at random on chart paper or on the board.

① Measurement—A Common Language

Key Concepts

- Using SI as the standard system of measurement allows scientists to compare data and communicate with each other about their results.
- SI units of measure include the meter (length), kilogram (mass), cubic meter (volume), kilograms per cubic meter (density), second (time), and Kelvin (temperature).

$$Volume = Length \times Width \times Height$$

$$Density = \frac{Mass}{Volume}$$

- To convert one measurement to another, you need to know the appropriate conversion factor. A conversion factor is an equation that shows how two units of measurement are related.

Key Terms

metric system	weight	density
SI	volume	
mass	meniscus	

② Mathematics and Science

Key Concepts

- In collecting data and making measurements, scientists use math skills involving estimation, accuracy and precision, and significant figures.
- When analyzing data, scientists use math skills involving percent error, mean, median, and mode.

$$Percent\ error = \frac{Difference\ between\ experimental\ value\ and\ true\ value}{True\ value} \times 100\%$$

$$Mean = \frac{Sum\ of\ values}{Total\ number\ of\ values}$$

Key Terms

estimate	percent error
accuracy	mean
precision	median
significant figures	mode

③ Graphs in Science

Key Concepts

- Line graphs are used to display data to see how one variable (the responding variable) changes in response to another variable (the manipulated variable).
- A line of best fit emphasizes the overall trend shown by all the data taken as a whole.
- The slope of a graph line tells you how much y changes for every change in x.

$$Slope = \frac{Rise}{Run} = \frac{Y_2 - Y_1}{X_2 - X_1}$$

- Line graphs are powerful tools in science because they allow you to identify trends and make predictions.

Key Terms

graph
horizontal axis
vertical axis
origin
coordinate
data point
line of best fit
linear graph
slope
nonlinear graph

④ Safety in the Science Laboratory

Key Concepts

- Good preparation helps you stay safe when doing science activities in the laboratory.
- Just as in the laboratory, good preparation helps you stay safe when doing science activities in the field.
- When any accident occurs, no matter how minor, notify your teacher immediately. Then, listen to your teacher's directions and carry them out quickly.

Tell students that this concept map will be organized in hierarchical order and to begin at the top with key concepts. Ask students these questions to guide them in categorizing the information on the self-sticking notes: **What is the standard measurement system scientists use? What math skills do scientists use in analyzing data? Why are line graphs powerful tools in science? Why is preparation important in carrying out investigations?**

Prompt students by using connecting words or phrases, such as "involves," "use," and "includes," to indicate the basis for the organization of the map. The phrases should form a sentence between or among a set of concepts.

Answer

Accept logical presentations by students.

All in One Teaching Resources

- Key Terms Review: *The Work of Scientists*
- Transparency P30

Review and Assessment

Organizing Information

Concept Mapping Copy the concept map about averages onto a separate sheet of paper. Then complete it and add a title. (For more on Concept Mapping, see the Skills Handbook.)

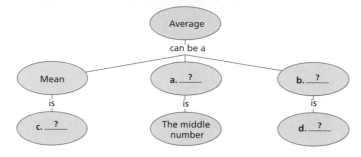

Average
can be a

Mean
a. __?__
b. __?__

is
is
is

c. __?__
The middle number
d. __?__

Reviewing Key Terms

Choose the letter of the best answer.

1. The amount of matter an object contains is its
   a. length.
   b. mass.
   c. weight.
   d. volume.

2. The significant figures in a measurement
   a. include only the first two digits.
   b. include only the estimated digits.
   c. include only the digits that have been measured exactly.
   d. include all of the digits that have been measured exactly, plus one digit.

3. Percent error calculations are used to determine
   a. the distance from one point to another.
   b. how accurate an experimental value is.
   c. how precise an experimental value is.
   d. the steepness of a graph line.

4. The median of a set of numbers is
   a. an estimate.
   b. the middle number.
   c. the numerical average.
   d. the number that appears most often.

5. The point where the x axis and the y-axis cross on a graph is called the
   a. origin.
   b. coordinate.
   c. meniscus.
   d. variable.

If the statement is true, write _true_. If it is false, change the underlined word or words to make the statement true.

6. The basic SI unit of length is the <u>gram</u>.

7. A common unit of <u>volume</u> is g/cm^3.

8. <u>Precision</u> refers to how close a measurement is to the true or accepted value.

9. The horizontal axis on a graph is also known as the <u>x-axis</u>.

10. The <u>slope</u> of a graph line tells you how much y changes for every change in x.

Writing in Science

Interview You are a sports reporter interviewing an Olympic swimmer who lost the silver medal by a few hundredths of a second. Write a one page interview in which you discuss the meaning of time and the advanced instruments used to measure time.

Discovery CHANNEL SCHOOL

The Work of Scientists
Video Preview
Video Field Trip
▶ Video Assessment

Review and Assessment

Organizing Information
a. Median
b. Mode
c. The numerical average
d. The number that appears most often in a list of numbers

Reviewing Key Terms
1. b 2. d 3. b 4. b 5. a
6. meter
7. density
8. Accuracy
9. true
10. true

Writing in Science

Writing Mode Description
Scoring Rubric
4 Exceeds criteria; may have an engaging story and/or superior descriptions of time and the instruments used to measure time
3 Meets all criteria
2 Meets some but not all criteria
1 Meets few criteria, with only brief and/or inaccurate information

Discovery CHANNEL SCHOOL
Video Assessment

The Work of Scientists

Show the Video Assessment to review chapter content and as a prompt for the writing assignment. Discussion question: **What's the difference between accuracy and precision?** (*Sample answer: Accuracy refers to how close a measurement is the true or accepted value, while precision refers to how close a group of measurements are to each other.*)

Go Online
PHSchool.com
For: Self-Assessment
Visit: PHschool.com
Web Code: cga-6020

Students can take a practice test online that is automatically scored.

All in One Teaching Resources
- Transparency P31
- Chapter Test
- Performance Assessment Teacher Notes
- Performance Assessment Student Worksheet
- Performance Assessment Scoring Rubric

ExamView® Computer Test Bank CD-ROM

Checking Concepts

11. Standard units of measure serve to minimize confusion in scientists throughout the world.

12. Sample answer: Mass is a measure of how much matter an object contains and is the same anywhere in the universe. Weight is a measure of force of gravity acting on an object. Therefore, weight varies throughout the universe and at different distances from the center of Earth.

13. Sample answer: Mathematics provides a way for scientists to record and communicate their data and findings, express relationships among variables, and calculate answers.

14. Sample answer: Only when measurements are accurate and precise can you be sure that they are close to the true, or correct, values and were made carefully using high-quality measuring tools.

15. Sample answer: A smooth line is most likely to show the general trend of the data. Connecting the dots may not show the trend and may even make inconsistencies or normal variations in the data appear too important.

16. Sample answer: You should read through the procedure, review safety guidelines, and ask your teacher about anything that is unclear.

Thinking Critically

17. Object B has a greater volume (64 cm³) than object A (48 cm³).

18. Sample answer: If water expands when it freezes, ice must be less dense than water. Therefore, ice cubes float in water because they are less dense than water.

19. Sample answer: Because we hurried, we may have made mistakes in performing some procedures and taken measurements that were imprecise and inaccurate.

20. Sample answer: Food or drink could become health hazards by being contaminated with materials in the lab, and food or drink might contaminate materials to be used in experiments.

Math Practice
21. 2.5 g/cm³
22. 204 cm²
23. Percent error = 12.8%

Checking Concepts

11. Why must scientists use standard units of measure in their experiments?

12. In your own words, describe the difference between mass and weight.

13. In what ways do scientists rely on mathematics in their work?

14. Why is it important to be both accurate and precise when you make measurements?

15. When graphing, why should you draw a smooth line that reflects the general pattern, rather than automatically connect the data points?

16. List three things you can do to prepare for a lab experiment.

Thinking Critically

17. **Comparing and Contrasting** Which of the objects below has a greater volume? Explain.

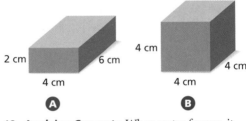

A   B

18. **Applying Concepts** When water freezes, it expands. Use this statement and your knowledge of density to explain why ice cubes float in water.

19. **Relating Cause and Effect** In a lab activity that involves many measurements and calculations, you and your lab partner rush through the procedures. In the end, you obtain a percent error of 50 percent. Explain what may have led to such a high percent error.

20. **Making Judgments** Why do you think that, as a general precaution, you should never bring food or drink into a laboratory?

Math Practice

21. **Calculating Density** A 12.5 g marble displaces 5 mL of water. What is its density?

22. **Area** Calculate the area of a picture frame that measures 17 cm × 12 cm.

23. **Percent Error** You measure the mass of a mystery object to be 658 g. The actual mass of the object is 755 g. What is your percent error?

Applying Skills

Use the graph to answer Questions 24–26.

A scientist measured the distance a lava stream flowed over 5-minutes.

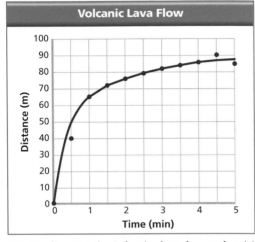

Volcanic Lava Flow

24. **Reading Graphs** What is plotted on each axis?

25. **Interpreting Data** Did the stream travel the same distance every minute? Explain.

26. **Predicting** Predict the movement of the stream between 5 and 6 minutes.

Lab zone Chapter **Project**

Performance Assessment Display your model and explain how you chose its scale. What was the most difficult thing about creating your model to scale? How could you improve your model?

Lab zone Chapter **Project**

Performance Assessment Allow each student or group of students 3 to 5 minutes to talk about their models or their contribution to the model. Instruct each student in a group to participate somehow in the presentation. If time permits, allow members of the class to pose a question or two about the model to each student or group.

In assessing their models, students should reflect on the materials they used and the difficulties they had in making their models to scale. They should describe what they learned from the process, how their models compare with others made by classmates, and how they could have improved their models.

Standardized Test Prep

Choose the letter of the best answer.

1. A student grows tomatoes for an experiment. Which piece of equipment will he need to determine the mass of the tomatoes?
  A graduated cylinder
  B meter stick
  C bathroom scale
  D triple-beam balance

2. Ranida measured the length of a string several times and obtained these measurements: 21.5 cm, 21.3 cm, 21.7 cm, and 21.6 cm. The actual length of the string is 25.5 cm. Which of the following statements best describes Ranida's measurements?
  F The measurements were accurate.
  G The measurements were not accurate, but they were precise.
  H The measurements were both accurate and precise.
  J The measurements were neither accurate nor precise.

3. Ellis measured the mass of five samples of quartz. His results were 39.75 g, 38.91 g, 37.66 g, 39.75 g, and 39.55 g. What was the mean mass of the samples?
  A 39.55 g   **B** 39.75 g
  C 38.91 g   **D** 39.12 g

The graph below shows the masses of five different volumes of liquid. Use the graph and your knowledge of science to answer Questions 4–5.

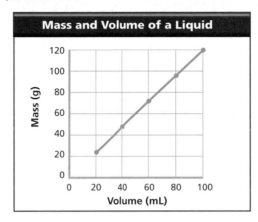

Mass and Volume of a Liquid

4. What is the general trend in the data?
  F There is no trend in the data.
  G There is a linear trend in the data.
  H There is a nonlinear trend in the data.
  J The trend is linear at first but then becomes nonlinear.

5. What is the slope of the graph line?
  A –1.0 g/mL   **B** 1.0 g/mL
  C 1.2 mL/g   **D** 1.2 g/mL

Constructed Response

6. Two students arrive at science class before anyone else. They want to finish the day's lab early and decide to begin the experiment. The first step involves heating a beaker of water. The students set up a hot plate near the sink to be close to the water. They fill the beaker with water and set the wet beaker onto the hot plate. Identify all the things the students did wrong and why.

Applying Skills

24. Distance (m) on the vertical axis; Time (min) on the horizontal axis

25. No. For the first minute, the stream traveled about 65 m. For the second minute, the stream traveled only about 10 m. The stream traveled fewer meters for each additional minute.

26. Sample answer: The stream will barely travel any distance.

Standardized Test Prep

1. D   **2.** G   **3.** D   **4.** G   **5.** D
6. Sample answer: The students' actions were inappropriate because a student should never try anything on his or her own without asking the teacher first. In addition, the students violated safety precautions about using electrical equipment, which should never be used around water or when the equipment is wet or hands are wet.

Chapter at a Glance

PRENTICE HALL
TeacherEXPRESS™
Plan • Teach • Assess

 Chapter Project *Design and Build a Chair*

| **Technology** | **Local Standards** |

Video Preview

All in One Teaching Resources
• Chapter Project Teacher Notes, pp. 175–176
• Chapter Project Student Introduction, pp. 177–178
• Chapter Project Student Worksheets 1–2, pp. 179-180
• Chapter Project Scoring Rubric, p. 181

Section 1

3–4 periods
1 1/2–2
blocks

Understanding Technology

P.3.1.1 Describe the goal of technology.
P.3.1.2 Explain how technology differs from science.
P.3.1.3 Identify factors that cause technology to progress.
P.3.1.4 Describe the components of a technological system.

Section 2

3–4 periods
1 1/2–2
blocks

Technology Design Skills

P.3.2.1 Describe what is involved in each step of the technology design process.
P.3.2.2 Explain what patents are.

Video Field Trip

Section 3

2–3 periods
1–1 1/2
blocks

Technology and Society

P.3.3.1 Describe how technology is tied to history.
P.3.3.2 Explain how technology affects people in both positive and negative ways.
P.3.3.3 Explain how analyzing risks and benefits can help people make decisions about technology.

PHSchool.com

| **Review and Assessment** | **Test Preparation** |

All in One Teaching Resources
• Key Terms Review, p. 212
• Transparency P38
• Performance Assessment Teacher Notes, p. 218
• Performance Assessment Scoring Rubric, p. 219
• Performance Assessment Student Worksheet, p. 220

PHSchool.com

Video Assessment

Test Preparation Blackline Masters
• Diagnostic test
• Benchmark test

Chapter Activities Planner

For more activities

LAB ZONE
Easy Planner
CD-ROM

Student Edition	Inquiry	Time	Materials	Skills	Resources
Chapter Project	Open-Ended	2–3 weeks	All in One Teaching Resources See p. 175		Lab zone Easy Planner All in One Teaching Resources Support pp. 175-176
Section 1					
Discover Activity, p. 88	Guided	15 minutes		Forming operational definitions	Lab zone Easy Planner
Skills Activity, p. 90	Guided	10 minutes		Classifying	Lab zone Easy Planner
Try This Activity, p. 93	Directed	15 minutes		Predicting	Lab zone Easy Planner
At-Home Activity, p. 95		15 minutes		Communicating	Lab zone Easy Planner
Skills Lab, p. 96	Guided	30 minutes	Retractable pen, plastic cups, paper	Observing, inferring, predicting	Lab zone Easy Planner Lab Activity Video All in One Teaching Resources Skills Lab: *Investigating a Technological System*
Section 2					
Discover Activity, p. 97	Guided	5–10 minutes	Aluminum foil, pennies	Problem solving	Lab zone Easy Planner
Try This Activity, p. 101	Guided	10–15 minutes		Predicting	Lab zone Easy Planner
Technology Lab, pp. 106–107	Guided	40 minutes	Raw eggs, plastic bags, meter stick, various packaging materials, tape, scissors, modeling clay	Evaluating the design, troubleshooting	Lab zone Easy Planner Lab Activity Video All in One Teaching Resources Technology Lab: *Design and Build "Egg-ceptional" Packaging*
Section 3					
Discover Activity, p. 108	Guided	10–15 minutes		Inferring	Lab zone Easy Planner

Section 1 Understanding Technology

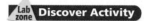 *3–4 periods, 1 1/2–2 blocks*

ABILITY LEVELS
L1 Basic to Average
L2 For All Students
L3 Average to Advanced

Objectives

P.3.1.1 Describe the goal of technology.

P.3.1.2 Explain how technology differs from science.

P.3.1.3 Identify factors that cause technology to progress.

P.3.1.4 Describe the components of a technological system.

Local Standards

Key Terms

• technology • obsolete • system • goal • input • process • output • feedback

---

Preteach

Build Background Knowledge

Students classify objects according to whether they are examples of technology or not.

Lab zone **Discover Activity** *What Are Some Examples of Technology?*

Targeted Print and Technology Resources

All in One **Teaching Resources**

L2 Reading Strategy Transparency P32: *Previewing Visuals*

 **Presentation-Pro CD-ROM**

Transparency P32

Instruct

What Is Technology? Use the definition of *technology* to help students understand what technology is.

How Does Technology Relate to Science? Use examples shown in Figure 3 to clarify how technology relates to science.

How Technology Progresses Call on volunteers to explain what obsolete, current, emerging, and coexisting technologies are.

Technology as a System Ask volunteers to explain what the components of a system are.

Lab zone **Skills Lab** *Investigating a Technological System*

Targeted Print and Technology Resources

All in One **Teaching Resources**

L2 Guided Reading, pp. 184–187

L2 Transparencies P33, P34

L2 Skills Lab: *Investigating a Technological System,* pp. 190-192

Lab Activity Video/DVD
Skills Lab: *Investigating a Technological System*

www.SciLinks.org
Web Code: scn.1631

 **Student Edition on Audio CD**

Transparencies P33, P34

Assess

Section Assessment Questions

Have students use their completed graphic organizers of Previewing Visuals to answer the questions.

Reteach

Use the example of the oven in Figure 5 to review the components of a system.

Targeted Print and Technology Resources

All in One **Teaching Resources**

• Section Summary, p. 183

L1 Review and Reinforce, p. 188

L3 Enrich, p. 189

Section 2 Technology Design Skills

 3–4 periods, 1 1/2–2 blocks

ABILITY LEVELS
L1 Basic to Average
L2 For All Students
L3 Average to Advanced

Objectives

P.3.2.1 Describe what is involved in each step of the technology design process.

P.3.2.2 Explain what patents are.

Key Terms

• engineer • brainstorming • constraint • trade-off • prototype
• troubleshooting • patent

Local Standards

Preteach

Build Background Knowledge

Students describe experiences with fixing a problem with a model they have built.

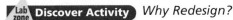 **Discover Activity** *Why Redesign?*

Targeted Print and Technology Resources

 **Teaching Resources**
L2 Reading Strategy Transparency P35: *Sequencing*

 Presentation-Pro CD-ROM

Transparency P35

Instruct

Identifying a Need Ask leading questions for a discussion on the technology design process.

Researching the Problem Lead a discussion on how to research a problem related to technology design.

Designing a Solution Write the headings *Brainstorming*, *Constraints*, and *Making Trade-offs* on the board, and have students relate these activities to the design of the computer mouse.

Building a Prototype Ask leading questions for a discussion about building a prototype.

Troubleshooting and Redesigning Lead a discussion about what is involved in troubleshooting and redesigning.

Communicating the Solution Ask students about what engineers had to communicate to consumers about the newly designed mouse.

Patents Give students a fictional scenario to evaluate the protection provided by a patent.

 **Technology Lab** *Design and Build "Egg-ceptional" Packaging*

Targeted Print and Technology Resources

 Teaching Resources
L2 Guided Reading, pp. 195-198
L2 Transparency P36
L2 Technology Lab: *Design and Build "Egg-ceptional" Packaging*, pp. 201-204

Lab Activity Video/DVD
Technology Lab: *Design and Build "Egg-ceptional" Packaging*

www.PHSchool.com Web Code: cgp-6032

DISCOVERY CHANNEL SCHOOL
Video Field Trip

 Student Edition on Audio CD

Transparency P36

Assess

Section Assessment Questions

 Have students use their completed graphic organizers of Sequencing to answer the questions.

Reteach

Have students make a flowchart of the technology design process using Figures 8, 9, 10, 11, and 12 for reference.

Targeted Print and Technology Resources

 Teaching Resources
• Section Summary, p. 194
L1 Review and Reinforce, p. 199
L3 Enrich, p. 200

Section 3 Technology and Society

2–3 periods, 1–1 1/2 blocks

Objectives

P.3.3.1 Describe how technology is tied to history.

P.3.3.2 Explain how technology affects people in both positive and negative ways.

P.3.3.3 Explain how analyzing risks and benefits can help people make decisions about technology.

Key Term

• risk-benefit analysis

Local Standards

Preteach

Build Background Knowledge

Students analyze the advantages and disadvantages of using automobiles for transportation.

Lab zone Discover Activity *How Does Technology Affect Your Life?*

Targeted Print and Technology Resources

All in One Teaching Resources

L2 Reading Strategy Transparency P37: *Relating Cause and Effect*

○ Presentation-Pro CD-ROM

Transparency P37

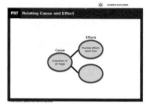

Instruct

Technology's Impact on Society Use the example of changes in loom technology to teach students about technology's impact on society.

Impacts of Technology—Good and Bad Bring students together for a round-table discussion of the impacts of technology.

Analyzing Risks and Benefits Ask leading questions for a discussion of risk-benefit analysis and trade-offs.

Targeted Print and Technology Resources

All in One Teaching Resources

L2 Guided Reading, pp. 207-209

www.SciLinks.org Web Code: scn-1633

www.PHSchool.com Web Code: cgh-6030

○ Student Edition on Audio CD

Assess

Section Assessment Questions

Have students use their completed graphic organizers of Relating Cause and Effect to answer the questions.

Reteach

Use the example of different bicycle helmets to review risk-benefit analysis, making trade-offs, and using technology wisely.

Targeted Print and Technology Resources

All in One Teaching Resources

• Section Summary, p. 206

L1 Review and Reinforce, p. 210

L3 Enrich, p. 211

Go Online

NSTA-PDLINKS

For: Professional development support
Visit: www.SciLinks.org/PDLinks
Web Code: scf-1630

Professional Development

Section 1 Understanding Technology

A Common Technological System   One of the most common and understandable technological systems is a home heating system. The system's goal is to provide warmth to the home. The input is the fuel, usually natural gas or heating oil. The process is the burning of the fuel, a chemical reaction that produces heat energy. The output is that heat energy, which is distributed through the home by a blower fan. The feedback is provided by the thermostat, which switches off the furnace when a certain air temperature is attained.

Address Misconceptions

Students may think that all examples of technology are machinelike or complicated in some way. This misconception is addressed in Section 1, *Understanding Technology.*

Section 2 Technology Design Skills

Mouse Function   The computer mouse was invented in 1963 by Douglas Engelbart at the Stanford Research Institute. The first mouse was made of wood. The purpose of inventing this device was to free the computer user from the complicated keyboard.

The most recent mouse technology is the optical mouse, which operates by bouncing a light on the surface below the mouse. Sensors in the mouse send images to a processor in the computer. The processor detects how patterns in the images change as the mouse moves. These changes are converted into the movement of the arrow on the screen. The optical mouse has no moving parts to fail or wear out. It also can be used on any surface, not just a mouse pad.

Section 3 Technology and Society

Everyday Technology   People take most of the technological devices they use every day for granted, as if those devices had always been there. Yet, each had an inventor, and many devices were invented in the fairly recent past. The German inventor Baron Karl Drais von Sauerbronn invented the first bicycle in 1817. Walter Hunt, a New York mechanic, invented the safety pin in 1849. The first rubber-soled sports shoes, invented in the late 1800s, were called "plimsolls." The first mass-marketed canvas-top sports shoes were sold under the Keds® name in 1917. Toothpaste in a collapsible tube was invented by Washington Sheffield of Connecticut in 1891. The ice cream cone was first sold by several stands at the 1904 St. Louis World's Fair. In 1917, Gideon Sundback, a Canadian, received a patent for his "separable fastener," now called a zipper. The Swiss inventor George de Mestral invented hook and loop fasteners in 1948, and he founded Velcro Industries to manufacture the invention.

Help Students Read

Identifying Main Ideas
Paragraph and Subheading Organization

Strategy   Help students become aware of text organization and use it to identify the main idea and supporting details under each subhead. Assign students to read the paragraphs under the heading *How Technology Progresses* in Section 1.

Example
1. Main Idea of a Paragraph   Review with students that most paragraphs have a topic sentence expressing the main idea, while the other sentences provide supporting details.
2. Main Idea of a Subheading   Guide students to make the connection that just as a paragraph has a main idea and supporting details, the text under each subheading has a main idea with supporting details carried within the paragraphs.
3. Practice   Have students read through a section noting each of the subheads they read.

Chapter **Project**

Objectives
Students will design and build a chair made entirely of cardboard. After completing this Chapter Project, students will be able to
- identify the need of building a chair
- design a solution by brainstorming and evaluating constraints
- build a prototype of the chair by sketching the chair design
- troubleshoot and redesign the finished chair
- communicate your solution to the class

Skills Focus
Identifying a need, designing a solution, building a prototype, troubleshooting, redesigning

Project Time Line 2–3 weeks

All in One Teaching Resources
- Chapter Project Teacher Notes
- Chapter Project Worksheet 1
- Chapter Project Worksheet 2
- Chapter Project Scoring Rubric

Safety
Review the safety guidelines in Appendix A.

Developing a Plan
Students can individually make their chairs or work in small groups. Students should first identify the need of building a chair

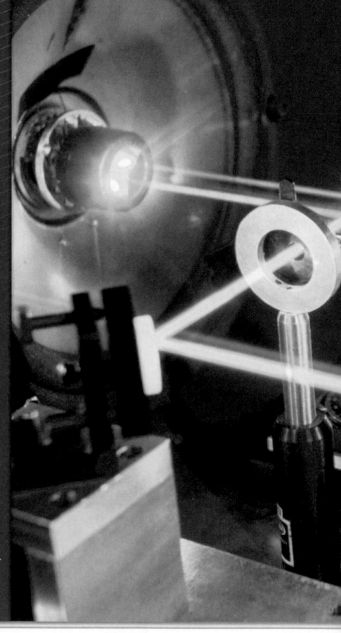

Chapter 3

Technology and Engineering

Chapter Preview

❶ Understanding Technology
Discover *What Are Some Examples of Technology?*
Skills Activity *Classifying*
Try This *Progress Report*
At-Home Activity *Technology Hunt*
Skills Lab *Investigating a Technological System*

❷ Technology Design Skills
Discover *Why Redesign?*
Active Art *The Technology Design Process*
Try This *Watch Ideas Take Off*
Technology Lab *Design and Build "Egg-ceptional" Packaging*

❸ Technology and Society
Discover *How Does Technology Affect Your Life?*
Analyzing Data *Working on the Farm*
Tech & Design in History *Everyday Technology*
Technology and Society *The Internet*

Lasers are used in many technology products, ▶ from supermarket scanners to audio equipment.

entirely of cardboard, without using tape or staples to hold the chair together. The next step is designing a solution by brainstorming and evaluating the constraints on the construction of the chair. They next build a prototype of the chair by sketching the chair design. After reviewing the prototype with you, students can troubleshoot and redesign and then proceed to building the chair. The final step is communicating the solution to the class by presenting the finished chair.

Possible Materials
The chairs should be constructed of corrugated cardboard 5/32-in. thick, with an edge crush test (ECT) rating of 32 lb/in. Single-wall boxes are usually made from 200-pound per-square-inch (psi) burst-strength cardboard, which translates to a 32 psi ECT rating. The cardboard should not span large flat horizontal areas unsupported. Cardboard that has a crease or fold has had its strength compromised. Unused

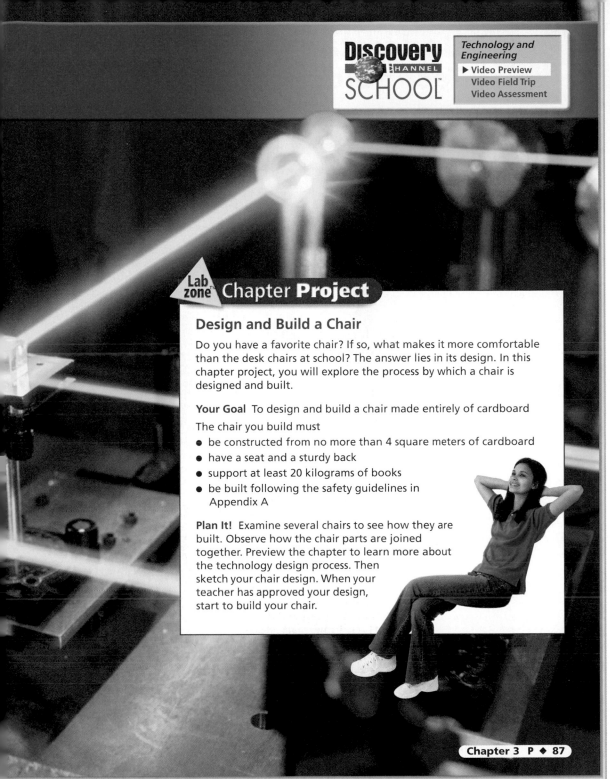

Lab zone Chapter **Project**

Design and Build a Chair

Do you have a favorite chair? If so, what makes it more comfortable than the desk chairs at school? The answer lies in its design. In this chapter project, you will explore the process by which a chair is designed and built.

Your Goal To design and build a chair made entirely of cardboard

The chair you build must

● be constructed from no more than 4 square meters of cardboard
● have a seat and a sturdy back
● support at least 20 kilograms of books
● be built following the safety guidelines in Appendix A

Plan It! Examine several chairs to see how they are built. Observe how the chair parts are joined together. Preview the chapter to learn more about the technology design process. Then sketch your chair design. When your teacher has approved your design, start to build your chair.

Chapter 3 P ◆ 87

Discovery CHANNEL SCHOOL Video Preview

Technology and Engineering

Show the Video Preview to introduce the chapter content. Discussion question: **What is reverse engineering?** (*Analyzing an object—or parts or photographs of an object—in order to duplicate it*)

Performance Assessment

The Chapter Project Scoring Rubric will help you evaluate how well students complete their Chapter Project. You may want to share the rubric with your students so that they will know what is expected. Students will be assessed on

● how well they make a chair that supports at least 20 kilograms of books
● how well the chair corresponds to the instructions, with a strong back support
● whether they use cardboard only or hold the chair together with tape or staples
● how well they communicate their design to the class
● how well they participate in their groups

Students can keep their design solutions and prototypes in their portfolios.

Portfolio

cardboard is available from an art supply stores. Students should consider constructing their chairs with a series of interlocking cardboard pieces forming the base.

Possible Shortcuts

● You could have the students focus on creating drawings of their chairs from different perspectives. Students would not proceed to the construction of the chair.

Launching the Project

Ask students to think about different shapes and styles of chairs they have used or seen. Display photos of various kinds of chairs, including Victorian, Shaker, and Eames chairs. After students have examined the photos, ask: **How are chairs designed differently based on their intended use?** (*Sample answer: A desk chair is often designed with no arms so that it can be placed in the opening of a desk. An easy chair for a home is designed to be comforting and restful.*)

Objectives

After this lesson, students will be able to

P.3.1.1 Describe the goal of technology.

P.3.1.2 Explain how technology differs from science.

P.3.1.3 Identify factors that cause technology to progress.

P.3.1.4 Describe the components of a technological system.

Target Reading Skill 🎯

Previewing Visuals Explain that looking at the visuals before they read helps students activate prior knowledge and predict what they are about to read.

Answers

Sample answers:

Q. What does technology have to do with science?

A. Advances in technology contribute to advances in science.

Q. How does science affect technology?

A. Advances in science contribute to advances in technology.

All in One Teaching Resources

• Transparency P32

Preteach

Build Background Knowledge L2

Science and Technology

Ask: **What is technology?** (*Sample answer: Technology is something complicated or electronic, such as a computer.*) **Is a saw an example of technology?** (*Sample answer: An electric saw may be considered as technology, but a hand saw may not be.*) Explain that students will learn that both an electric saw and a hand saw are examples of technology. **What does science have to do with technology?** (*Sample answer: People who make technology use knowledge of science in their designs.*) **Does technology ever affect science?** (*Yes, by providing advanced instruments scientists use to do their research*)

Reading Preview

Key Concepts

• What is the goal of technology?

• How does technology differ from science?

• What factors cause technology to progress?

• What are the components of a technological system?

Key Terms

• technology • obsolete
• system • goal • input
• process • output • feedback

🎯 Target Reading Skill

Previewing Visuals When you preview, you look ahead at the material to be read. Preview Figure 3. Then write two questions you have about the diagram in a graphic organizer like the one below. As you read, answer your questions.

Science and Technology

Q.	What does technology have to do with science?
A.	
Q.	

Lab zone — Discover Activity

What Are Some Examples of Technology?

1. Look at the objects in the photographs.

2. With a partner, discuss whether or not each object is an example of technology. Write your reasons for each decision.

Think It Over

Forming Operational Definitions On what basis did you and your partner decide whether an object was an example of technology? What is your definition of *technology*?

The year is 1900, and you are going to visit your aunt and uncle in a distant city. You awaken before dawn and get dressed by the flickering light of an oil lamp. Then you and your family hurry to the train station. The train ride is quite an experience. You never imagined anything could move so fast.

Your aunt and uncle greet you with hot soup prepared on their shiny, black, coal-burning stove. After the meal, you help with the cleanup. As you wash the bowls and spoons, you are amazed by the water faucet. To get water at home, you must go outside and pump it by hand.

FIGURE 1
Technology Through the Decades
The products featured in these ads are all examples of technology. Although they may seem outdated to you today, they were quite the sensation in their time!

Phonograph: 1900s ▶

Lab zone — Discover Activity

Skills Focus Forming operational definitions

Time 10 minutes

Tips Pair students of differing abilities.

Expected Outcome Many students will classify the computer and the camera as examples of technology, but not the other three objects. Students who classified all the objects as examples of technology are correct.

Think It Over Sample answer: The basis on which an object is judged to be an example of technology is whether that object is used to meet a person's need or solve a practical problem. Technology is the practical application of scientific concepts to meet practical needs.

What Is Technology?

Trains, coal-burning stoves, and water faucets all made life easier for people living in 1900. So did oil lamps and water pumps, even though they may seem old-fashioned. All of these items are examples of technology. In fact, even bowls and spoons are forms of technology. But what does *technology* mean?

Meanings of Technology When you see or hear the word *technology*, you may think of things such as computers, CD players, and cellphones. But technology includes more than modern inventions. Ancient inventions, such as stone tools, the wheel, and the compass, are examples of technology, too. Technology has been around since people started to make things to suit their needs.

In addition to things that people make, technology can also refer to the knowledge and processes needed to produce those objects. Put simply, **technology** is how people change the world around them to meet their needs or to solve practical problems.

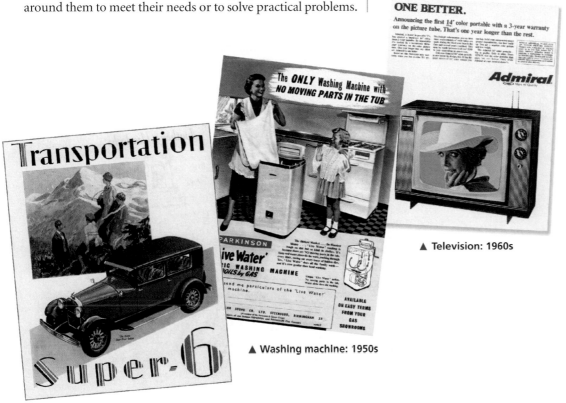

▲ Automobile: 1920s

▲ Washing machine: 1950s

▲ Television: 1960s

What Is Technology?

Teach Key Concepts L2
How People Change the World

Focus Tell students that almost every human activity in modern society involves the use of technology.

Teach Write the definition of technology on the board, and discuss how different examples of technology meet human needs or solve practical problems. Ask: **Why can a bowl be considered an example of technology?** (*A bowl is an object made by humans to meet the human need for a container to hold food.*) **What human need does a CD player meet?** (*It meets the need of a device to play recorded music, and hearing music is a pleasure to people.*) Emphasize that the knowledge and processes needed to produce a bowl or a CD player are also considered to be examples of technology.

Apply Have students look at the photo of the antique automobile on the page, and ask: **Is an antique car an example of technology, or can only a new car be considered as such?** (*An antique car is an example of technology because it was built to meet a human need.*) **Comparing this car to a car made today, what can you say about the knowledge and processes needed to produce cars?** (*The knowledge and processes have advanced over time.*) **learning modality: visual**

Independent Practice L2

All in One Teaching Resources

• Guided Reading and Study Worksheet: *Understanding Technology*

◉ **Student Edition on Audio CD**

Differentiated Instruction

Less Proficient Readers L1
Communicating Have students use sketches, photographs, and short captions to create a visual display about examples of technology from the six major areas of technology. Tell students to draw ideas from the illustrations in the chapter.
learning modality: visual

Gifted and Talented L3
Classifying Ask students to choose one of the six major areas of technology and then focus on a specific kind of technology within that area. For example, a student might focus on radio technology within the area of communication technology. Have students research this technology to find examples of obsolete, current, emerging, and coexisting technologies within the focused area. **learning modality: verbal**

Monitor Progress L2

Oral Presentation Ask students to point out and describe examples of technology in the classroom.

► Address Misconceptions L1

Simple Forms of Technology

Focus Many students have trouble understanding that technology includes not only engines, machines, and complicated "high tech" products but also the simplest of tools.

Teach Show students a picture from a history or archaeology textbook of a primitive tool made of a stone or bone fragment. Explain what early people used the tool for, and ask: **Can this object be considered an example of technology?** (*Yes, because people used the tool to meet their needs or to solve a practical problem*)

Apply Have students name simple tools they use at home. Ask them to decide whether to classify these tools as examples of technology or not. **learning modality: visual**

Use Visuals: Figure 2 L2

Six Areas of Technology

Focus Tell students that the figure shows the six major areas of technology.

Teach Call on volunteers to identify the example of each kind of technology shown in the photos. For example, ask: **What is shown that is manufacturing technology?** (*The camper's tent*) For each example identified, ask the student to name another item that would also be classified in that area of technology.

Apply Ask: **Do you think there is any communication technology in this car?** (*Yes. The car probably has a radio and a CD player. It may even have a GPS map display.*) Point out that the whole vehicle could be classified as transportation technology, or, because it is a manufactured product, the whole car could be considered a manufacturing technology. **learning modality: visual**

FIGURE 2
Areas of Technology
Technology can be classified into six major areas. If you've ever gone camping, you've probably relied on products from all six areas. In fact, almost everything you do involves products from the different areas of technology.

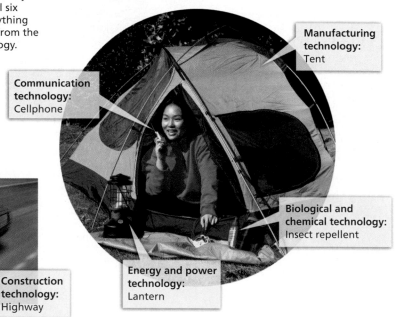

Manufacturing technology:
Tent

Communication technology:
Cellphone

Transportation technology:
Car

Biological and chemical technology:
Insect repellent

Construction technology:
Highway

Energy and power technology:
Lantern

The Goal of Technology What is the purpose of technology? **The goal of technology is to improve the way people live.** Think about the many ways that technology has improved people's lives. Medicines help you recover from sickness. Eyeglasses and binoculars extend your ability to see. The Internet makes it easier for you to obtain information.

Areas of Technology The products of technology can be classified into six major areas, which are shown in Figure 2. You probably use technology products from each of these areas every day.

Although the six areas of technology may seem distinct, they are not separate. For example, think about all the technologies involved in bringing a box of cereal to your breakfast table. Trains (transportation) carry grain from farms to factories (construction). There, vitamins and minerals (biological and chemical) are added to the grain. The cereal is baked in an oven (energy and power) and then packaged in plastic bags and cardboard boxes (manufacturing). Trucks transport the boxes to supermarkets, while the cereal company advertises the product on TV (communication). Finally, you buy the cereal and enjoy it for breakfast.

✓ **Reading Checkpoint** What is an example of transportation technology?

Lab zone Skills **Activity**

Skills Focus Classifying

Time 15 minutes

Tips Tell students they can list examples of technology they see within the classroom and know about in and around the school.

Expected Outcome Sample answer: Communication—cell phone; manufacturing—desk; biological and chemical—cleaning fluid; energy and power—electricity; transportation—automobile; construction—school building. Students might classify a computer as a communication technology or a manufacturing technology. **learning modality: logical/mathematical**

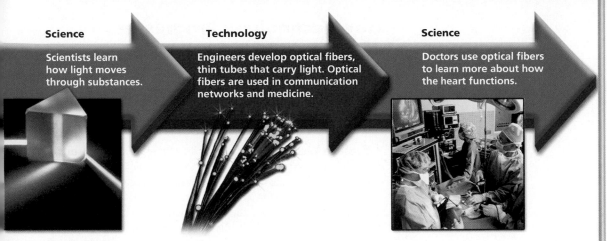

Science

Scientists learn how light moves through substances.

Technology

Engineers develop optical fibers, thin tubes that carry light. Optical fibers are used in communication networks and medicine.

Science

Doctors use optical fibers to learn more about how the heart functions.

How Does Technology Relate to Science?

You might wonder why you are learning about technology in a science book. Are science and technology the same thing? The answer is no. In fact, the purposes of science and technology are quite different. **Science is the study of the natural world to understand how it functions. Technology, on the other hand, changes, or modifies, the natural world to meet human needs or solve problems.**

To make the difference clear, contrast how scientists and technologists might view air currents, or winds. A scientist might study how air currents develop and how they affect weather conditions. A technologist, in contrast, might study how wind can be harnessed to produce electricity. In other words, a scientist studies something to learn about the topic itself. A technologist studies a topic to learn how people can apply that knowledge to solve problems.

Often, advances in science and technology depend on one another, as shown in Figure 3. Endoscopes are tiny medical instruments that allow doctors to view organs within the human body. Endoscopes transmit light using long, thin strands of glass called optical fibers. The design of these fibers would not have been possible without the work of scientists. Once scientists understood how light travels through substances, technologists were able to use this knowledge to design optical fibers and endoscopes. Endoscopes, in turn, have helped scientists learn more about the human body.

 Reading Checkpoint What might a scientist study about air currents? What might a technologist study about air currents?

FIGURE 3
Science and Technology
Advances in science contribute to advances in technology, which in turn contribute to science. Understanding the physics of light (science) led to the development of optical fibers and endoscopes (technology).
Relating Cause and Effect *How might endoscopes help scientists learn more about the human body?*

Chapter 3 P ◆ 91

How Does Technology Relate to Science?

Teach Key Concepts L2
Study vs. Doing

Focus Tell students that the difference between science and technology is the difference between studying the natural world to gain understanding and using knowledge about the natural world to do something to meet a human need.

Teach Ask: **What is the purpose of science?** (*To study the natural world to understand how it functions*) **What is the purpose of technology?** (*To change or modify the natural world to meet human needs or solve problems*) Review the example shown in Figure 3, in which advances in physical science lead to advances in the technology of optical fibers, which lead to advances in life science.

Apply Ask: **How might a scientist view the saltwater of the ocean, and how might a technologist view that same saltwater?** (*Sample Answer: A scientist might study how the salt became concentrated in ocean water, while a technologist might study how to remove the salt from ocean water to produce drinkable water.*) **learning modality: logical/mathematical**

All in One Teaching Resources
• Transparency P33

Monitor Progress L2

Skills Check Have each student make a table with two column heads: *Science* and *Technology*. Ask them to think about what they observed on the way to school this morning. Under the heading *Science*, they can write questions about the things they saw that might be answered by a scientist. Under the heading *Technology*, they can write questions about the things they saw that might be answered by a technologist. Students can keep their tables in their portfolios. **Portfolio**

Answers
Figure 3 Endoscopes enable doctors to view organs within the human body.

 Reading Checkpoint Sample answer: Trains

Reading Checkpoint Sample answer: A scientist might study the causes of air currents. A technologist might study how air currents can be used to produce electricity.

P ● 91

How Technology Progresses

Teach Key Concepts
Changing Technologies

Focus Tell students that technologies change over time, as knowledge increases and new needs have to be met.

Teach To help students understand how technologies change and progress, call on volunteers to explain what obsolete, current, emerging, and coexisting technologies are. Use the illustrations in Figure 4 to provide an example for each of the classifications of technology.

Apply Ask: **How would you classify a wind-up mantle clock?** *(A wind-up clock is an old technology, but it still fulfills people's needs for both appearance and utility. Therefore, a wind-up mantle clock is a coexisting technology.)* **learning modality: verbal**

Build Inquiry L2

Processing Words

Materials computer, typewriter, pen and paper, clock
Time 15 minutes

Focus Tell students that technologies for word processing have changed over time and they will continue to change.

Teach Divide the class into small groups, and provide each group with a printed paragraph of several sentences. Ask that each group designate different students to rewrite the paragraph on a computer, with a typewriter, and with pen and paper. Another group member should use a clock to record the time it takes each student to rewrite the paragraph.

Apply When all groups are done, ask: **Which student took the shortest time to rewrite the paragraph?** *(The student who used the computer)* **Why did the typewriter become obsolete?** *(It takes more trouble and a longer time to use the typewriter compared with a computer.)* **Why haven't pens also become obsolete?** *(Computers aren't always available, and pens can be carried everywhere.)* **learning modality: kinesthetic**

FIGURE 4
The Progress of Technology
Today, manual typewriters are obsolete and have been replaced by computers with word processing programs. At the same time, voice recognition software is an emerging, new technology. Pens and pencils coexist with these newer technologies.
Making Judgments *Do you think that pens and pencils will ever become obsolete? Why or why not?*

How Technology Progresses

Technology is always changing. Suppose a technological product, such as your CD player, breaks and you shop for a new one. Chances are good that you will find a new system that is better than your old one. Perhaps it will be smaller or easier to use. **Technology progresses as people's knowledge increases and as new needs can be satisfied.**

Obsolete Technologies A product may become **obsolete,** or no longer used. A technology becomes obsolete if it no longer meets people's needs as well as newer products do. Consider manual typewriters, for instance. Manual typewriters were quite useful in their time, but they had disadvantages. For example, they were noisy, and it was difficult to make changes to the typed document. Eventually, manual typewriters were replaced by electronic versions. Typewriters still exist today, but most people use computers with word processing programs instead.

Current Technologies Word processing programs are one example of a current technology. Current technologies are those in use at the present time. Word processing programs meet human needs because they perform more functions than typewriters, such as saving documents. In addition, they are easier to use. Reorganizing text, for example, is much easier with word processed documents than with typed documents.

Obsolete Technology   **Current Technology**

92 ◆ P

Differentiated Instruction

English Learners/Beginning L1
Vocabulary: Link to Visual Explain and clarify what obsolete, current, emerging, and coexisting technologies are by discussing the examples in Figure 4. Then show pictures of a dial phone, cordless phone, cellphone, and cord phone. Have students identify each as one of the four classifications of technology. **learning modality: visual**

English Learners/Intermediate L2
Vocabulary: Link to Visual Students can do the Beginning activity. Then, they can write sentences using the terms *obsolete technology, current technology, emerging technology,* and *coexisting technology* to describe another technology of their choosing. **learning modality: verbal**

Emerging Technologies Imagine writing an essay just by speaking into a microphone. As you speak, the words show up on your computer screen. Computer software that can recognize and process human voices is an emerging technology. Emerging technologies are those that are just beginning to become widely available. People commonly refer to complex emerging technologies as high technology, or "high tech."

Because emerging technologies are so new, they may be expensive and may not yet work perfectly. For example, voice recognition software may not be able to distinguish between words that sound alike, such as *choose* and *chews*.

Over time, emerging technologies usually improve and become less expensive. Technologies that are new and revolutionary today may be a normal part of life in a few years. When this happens, they become current technologies.

Coexisting Technologies Not all old technologies become obsolete and get replaced by emerging technologies. Some old technologies, such as pens and pencils, coexist along with current ones because they still fulfill people's needs. An older, simpler form of a technology may be more useful in certain situations than a current product. On a camping trip, for example, a hand-operated can opener is more useful than an electric one!

 Reading Checkpoint What is meant by "emerging technology"?

Lab zone Try This **Activity**

Progress Report

In this activity, you will learn how a certain technology has changed over time.

1. Talk with an older adult about the technologies they used to listen to music in the past.
2. Create a "timeline" similar to the one in Figure 4 identifying music technologies that are obsolete, current, emerging, and coexisting.

Predicting How do you think music technology will change during your lifetime?

Emerging Technology

Coexisting Technology

P ◆ 93

Lab zone Try This **Activity**

Skills Focus Predicting

Time 15 minutes

Tips Review how to make a timeline.

Expected Outcome Sample answer: Students will make a timeline that may include these technologies, in this order: 78-rpm record players (obsolete), reel-to-reel tape recorders (coexisting), LP record players (obsolete), 8-track tape recorders (obsolete), cassette tape recorders (current), CD players (current), computer media players (current), MP3 players (current), and various small-disc players (emerging). Students will predict that all but computer-based technologies will become obsolete. **learning modality: visual**

Help Students Read

Identifying Main Ideas Refer to the Content Refresher in this chapter, which provides the guidelines for using paragraph and subheading organization in the Identifying Main Ideas strategy.

Have students read the text under the heading *How Technology Progresses*. Ask: **What is the main idea of the first paragraph under the main heading?** *(Technology progresses as people's knowledge increases and as new needs can be satisfied.)* **What are the subheadings under the main heading?** *(Obsolete Technologies, Current Technologies, Emerging Technologies, and Coexisting Technologies)* **What is the main idea under the subheading Emerging Technologies?** *(Emerging technologies are those that are just beginning to become widely available.)*

Monitor Progress _____ L2

Oral Presentation Have students classify kinds of clothes as obsolete, current, emerging, or coexisting technologies.

Answers

Figure 4 Sample answer: Pens may become obsolete if a new product meets the same need better.

Reading Checkpoint An emerging technology is a technology that is just beginning to become widely available.

Technology as a System

Teach Key Concepts L2

Parts That Work Together

Focus Tell students that many familiar technologies have parts that work together. Such technologies are thought of as technological systems.

Teach Read aloud the definition of a technological system. Then ask volunteers to explain what each of the components of a system is. Ask: **What is the input of a technological system?** *(Something that is put into the system in order to reach the system's goal)*

Apply Ask: **Why is a home furnace considered to be a technological system?** *(It has many parts that work together.)* Sketch a home furnace system on the board, and ask students to identify the components of the system. **learning modality: visual**

All in One Teaching Resources

• Transparency P34

Use Visuals: Figure 5 L2

The Oven as a System

Focus Tell students that an oven is a technological system that includes a goal, inputs, processes, outputs, and feedback.

Teach Have students read the caption and annotations of Figure 5. Then call on volunteers to describe each of the components of the system.

Apply Ask: **How would you classify this oven in terms of whether it is obsolete, current, emerging, or coexisting technology?** *(Students may have different opinions on the classification of this oven. Some may argue that it is current technology, since it is used in almost every home. Others may argue that it is old technology that is still in use, and thus it should be classified as a coexisting technology.)* **learning modality: visual**

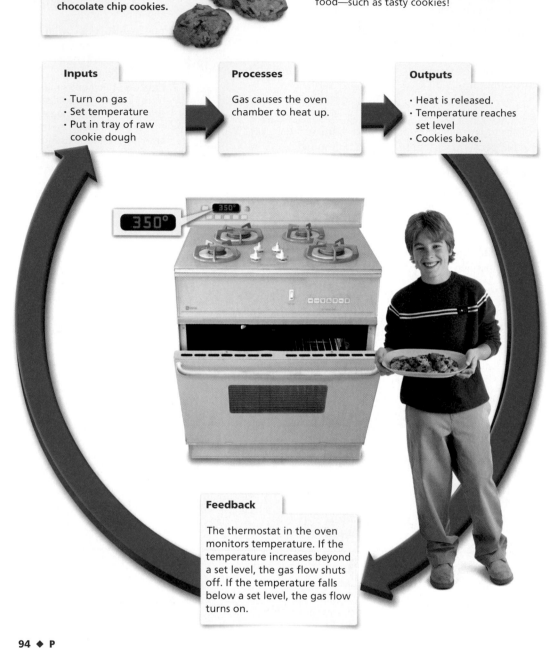

FIGURE 5
The Oven as a System
An oven is a technological system. Input, process, output, and feedback are all involved in achieving the goal of cooking food—such as tasty cookies!

Goal

Bake a tray of chocolate chip cookies.

Inputs
• Turn on gas
• Set temperature
• Put in tray of raw cookie dough

Processes

Gas causes the oven chamber to heat up.

Outputs
• Heat is released.
• Temperature reaches set level
• Cookies bake.

350°

Feedback

The thermostat in the oven monitors temperature. If the temperature increases beyond a set level, the gas flow shuts off. If the temperature falls below a set level, the gas flow turns on.

94 ◆ P

Go Online
SciLINKS NSTA

For: Links on technology
Visit: www.SciLinks.org
Web Code: scn-1631

Download a worksheet that will guide students' review of Internet resources on technology.

Technology as a System

When you hear the word *system*, what comes to mind? Maybe you think of your school system or the circulatory system in your body. All **systems** have one thing in common: They are made of parts that work together. The parts of your school system include buildings, books, and teachers. All of these parts are involved in educating the students in your community.

Technology products can be thought of as systems, too. **A technological system includes a goal, inputs, processes, outputs, and, in some cases, feedback.** Figure 5 describes these components in one familiar technological system—an oven.

Technological systems are designed to achieve a particular **goal**, or purpose. An **input** is something that is put into a system in order to reach that goal. The **process** is a sequence of actions that the system undergoes. An **output** is a result or product. If the system works correctly, the output should match the goal. Some technological systems have an additional component, called feedback. **Feedback** is information a system uses to monitor the input, process, and output so that the system can adjust itself to meet the goal.

 Reading Checkpoint What do all systems have in common?

Go Online
SciLINKS NSTA

For: Links on technology
Visit: www.SciLinks.org
Web Code: scn-1631

Section 1 Assessment

Target Reading Skill Previewing Visuals Refer to your questions and answers about Figure 3 to help you answer Question 2 below.

Reviewing Key Concepts

1. **a. Reviewing** What is technology?
   b. Applying Concepts How does a telephone fulfill the definition of technology?
2. **a. Identifying** Which field—science or technology—modifies the world to meet human needs?
   b. Comparing and Contrasting Compare and contrast science and technology.
   c. Making Judgments Do you think that the development of a new, powerful telescope could be possible without a knowledge of science? How could the new telescope help advance science?
3. **a. Explaining** Explain why technology is always changing.

b. **Sequencing** Place these technologies in the correct order: emerging technology, obsolete technology, current technology.
   c. **Developing Hypotheses** Why do you think computers become obsolete so quickly?
4. **a. Reviewing** What four components do all technological systems include? What fifth component do some systems also have?
   b. **Applying Concepts** An alarm clock is a technological system. Identify each component in this system.

Lab zone At-Home Activity

Technology Hunt With a family member, look around your home for ten examples of technology. In a table, list each item and the area of technology it represents. Describe how each item extends your abilities and how your life might be different without it.

Lab zone At Home Activity

Technology Hunt Students' answers will depend on the items and how they and their family members use them. Sample answer of one entry in the table: Microwave oven; energy and power technology; I can heat a cup of water for tea quickly and easily; It would take me five minutes longer to put water in a teakettle, heat the teakettle and water on the stove, and pour the hot water into a cup.

Lab zone Chapter Project

Keep Students on Track By this point, students should have brainstormed possible designs for the chair and evaluated the constraints spelled out in the instructions for constructing the chair. Talk with students about their ideas, and encourage them to begin working on their prototypes.

Monitor Progress L2
Answer

Reading Checkpoint They are made of parts that work together.

Assess

Reviewing Key Concepts

1. a. Technology is how people change the world around them to meet their needs or to solve practical problems. **b.** The telephone enables people to communicate over long distances using their voices.

2. a. Technology **b.** Science is the study of the natural world to understand how it functions. Technology changes the natural world to meet human needs or solve problems. **c.** Sample answer: A new powerful telescope could not be possible without a knowledge of light, lenses, mirrors, and computers. A new telescope could change scientists' understanding of the universe.

3. a. As knowledge increases, people seek to satisfy new needs. **b.** Obsolete technology, current technology, emerging technology **c.** Sample answer: Computer products change rapidly as scientists learn more and technologies apply the new knowledge to improving hardware and software.

4. a. Goals, inputs, processes, and outputs; in some cases, feedback **b.** Goal—wake up on time; input—energy; process—clock runs; output—alarm sounds; feedback—person awakens and stops alarm

Reteach L1
Use the example of the oven in Figure 5 to review the components of a system.

Performance Assessment L2
Oral Presentation Call on students to name one of the six major areas of technology and then give an example of a current and an obsolete technology in that area.

All in One Teaching Resources
- Section Summary: *Understanding Technology*
- Review and Reinforcement: *Understanding Technology*
- Enrich: *Understanding Technology*

Investigating a Technological System

Prepare for Inquiry

Key Concept
A system is a group of related parts that work together.

Skills Objectives
After this lab, students will be able to:
- observe the parts of a pen system
- infer the input, process, and output of a pen system
- predict whether most retractable pens work in a similar way to the one observed

 **Prep Time** 15 minutes

Class Time 30 minutes

Advance Planning
Collect the appropriate number of retractable pens. Use pens that have several parts that easily disassemble.

All in One Teaching Resources
- Lab Worksheet: *Investigating a Technological System*

Guide Inquiry

Invitation
Ask: **Is a pen an example of technology?**
(*Yes. A pen is an object used to meet the need of having an instrument to write on paper.*)
Lead a discussion about why a retractable pen is useful and how students think it works.

Introduce the Procedure
Ask: **If you consider the pen a system, what do you think the feedback of the system is?**
(*The feedback is the strength and clarity of the ink mark the pen makes.*)

Expected Outcome
Students will take apart a retractable pen and observe 4–7 parts, including a hollow barrel that screws apart in the middle, an ink cartridge, and a spring inside the forward section. The back half of the barrel will include a plunger that generally cannot be removed from the barrel. Students should be able to reassemble the pen to working order.

Investigating a Technological System

Problem
How do the parts of a pen work together as a system?

Skills Focus
observing, inferring, predicting

Materials
- retractable pen
- small tray to hold the pen parts
- paper

Procedure
1. Examine the retractable pen that your teacher gives you. Predict how many parts make up the pen.

2. Disassemble the pen completely. Be careful not to break or lose any of the parts. In your notebook, draw each part and describe what function it might serve.

3. Reassemble the pen. Click the pen on and off a few times, and then write with it. As you perform these actions, think about the sequence of events taking place inside the pen. Draw one or more diagrams to explain the process that takes place.

4. Think about how the pen functions as a technological system. In your notebook, describe the goal of the pen as a system. In addition, identify the inputs, process, and outputs of the system. Does the pen system include feedback?

5. Identify any of the pen parts that might not be essential for meeting the system's goal. Then take the pen apart again and remove those parts. Reassemble the pen without them and test whether or not the pen functions.

Analyze and Conclude
1. **Observing** How many parts make up the pen system? Of those parts, how many are essential to the pen's function? What purpose do the nonessential parts serve?

2. **Inferring** What kind of input do you need to provide to make the pen work? Describe the process and output that result from the input you provide.

3. **Predicting** Do you think that most retractable pens function in a similar manner to the one you observed? Why or why not?

4. **Forming Operational Definitions** Based on what you learned in this investigation, describe in your own words what is meant by the term *technological system*.

5. **Communicating** Suppose that you had never used or even seen a retractable pen before today. Write a letter to a friend about this remarkable device and how it works.

More to Explore
Choose another everyday device, such as a paper punch, a kitchen tool, or a child's toy. Observe the device closely to learn how it functions as a system. Then identify the system's goal, inputs, process, outputs, and feedback.

Analyze and Conclude
1. Answers will vary with the type of pen. Generally, there will be 4–7 parts, all but 1 or 2 of which are essential. Nonessential parts usually help make the pen look good.

2. The input includes depressing the plunger to extend the ink cartridge and holding the barrel of the pen. The process includes touching the pen tip on a surface and then moving the pen across the surface. The output is the ink mark.

3. All retractable pens are very similar.

4. Sample answer: A technological system is a collection of parts working together to produce a desired output.

5. The best letters will clearly list the parts of the pen and the function of each part.

Extend Inquiry

More to Explore Look for answers that clearly identify goal, input, process, output, and feedback.

Reading Preview

Key Concepts
- What are the steps in the technology design process, and what is involved in each step?
- What are patents?

Key Terms
- engineer • brainstorming
- constraint • trade-off
- prototype • troubleshooting
- patent

⊙ Target Reading Skill
Sequencing A sequence is the order in which a series of events occurs. As you read, make a flowchart that shows the steps in the technology design process. Put the steps of the process in separate boxes in the flowchart in the order in which they typically occur.

The Technology Design Process

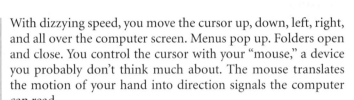

Lab zone Discover **Activity**

Why Redesign?

1. Use the materials your teacher gives you to design and construct a boat out of aluminum foil. Your goal is to make a boat that will float and carry as many pennies as possible.

2. Test your aluminum-foil boat against those of two other students to see how well your design works.

3. Based on your observations in Step 2, change the design of your boat, if necessary. Build a new boat and test it again.

Think It Over
Problem Solving What problems did you identify by testing your boat? How did you improve upon your original boat's design?

With dizzying speed, you move the cursor up, down, left, right, and all over the computer screen. Menus pop up. Folders open and close. You control the cursor with your "mouse," a device you probably don't think much about. The mouse translates the motion of your hand into direction signals the computer can read.

Have you ever wondered about the mouse's design—what it is made of and how its parts function together? The design of the mouse is the key to its success as a technology.

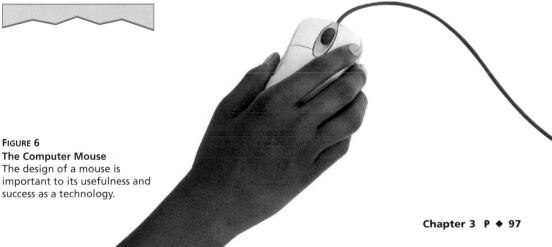

FIGURE 6
The Computer Mouse
The design of a mouse is important to its usefulness and success as a technology.

Chapter 3 P ◆ 97

Objectives

After this lesson, students will be able to
P.3.2.1 Describe what is involved in each step of the technology design process.
P.3.2.2 Explain what patents are.

Target Reading Skill ⊙

Sequencing Explain that organizing information from beginning to end helps students understand a step-by-step process.

Answers

The Technology Design Process
Identify the need.
Research the problem.
Design a solution.
Build a prototype.
Troubleshoot and redesign.
Communicate the solution.

All in One Teaching Resources
- Transparency P35

Preteach

Build Background Knowledge   L2

Experience With Designing a Solution
Ask: **Have you ever designed and made a model for a school science project?** *(Sample answer: Yes, in a previous year, I made a volcano that erupted.)* **Did everything work out right when you first made the model?** *(Sample answer: No, something was wrong with the model volcano, and it would not erupt.)* **What did you do when you saw that something was wrong?** *(Sample answer: I studied the model to find out what was wrong. When I discovered the problem, I fixed it.)* Tell students that this process is similar to what technologists use in designing technology.

Lab zone Discover **Activity**

Skills Focus Problem solving

Materials aluminum foil, pennies

Time 15 minutes

Tips Cut a large sheet of aluminum foil for each student. Set up a large container filled with water that students can use to test their designs. Adding one penny every 5 seconds is a good rule.

Expected Outcome Boats that are deep in the middle with high sides likely will float when several pennies are added.

Think It Over Sample answer: The boat sank with the addition of pennies. Deepening the inside of the boat improved the design.

Instruct

Identifying a Need

Teach Key Concepts **L2**

Engineers Use a Design Process

Focus Tell students that those who design and build technology follow a process that has several steps.

Teach Ask: **What is the technology design process?** (*A method by which an idea for a new technology is developed into a final process*) **What is the first step in the technology design process?** (*Identifying a need, and thus clearly defining a problem to be solved*)

Apply Ask: **What is the need that the computer mouse was originally designed to meet?** (*Sample answer: The need was a simple and easy way to control the function of a computer.*) **learning modality: verbal**

Teacher **Demo**

A Computer Mouse

Materials modern computer mouse

Time 5 minutes

Focus Explain that before the mouse was invented, early computers were controlled with keystrokes on the keyboard.

Teach Ask: **Why was the mouse needed?** (*It's a lot easier and faster to control the computer with a mouse than with the keyboard.*) Have students examine the views of the original mouse in the figure. Then, pass around a modern mouse for students to examine.

Apply Ask: **How does moving the mouse affect the cursor on the screen?** (*Moving the mouse signals the cursor to move on the screen*) Show students this effect on a computer monitor. **learning modality: visual**

Independent Practice **L2**

All in One Teaching Resources

- Guided Reading and Study Worksheet: *Technology Design Skills*

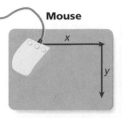

Mouse

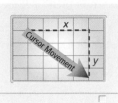

Computer Screen

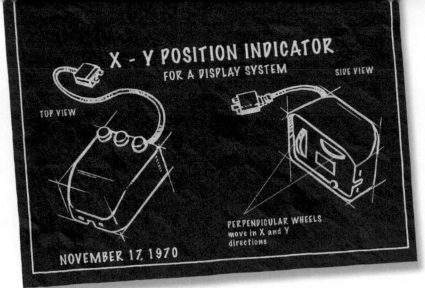

FIGURE 7
The Original Mouse
The original mouse was known as an X-Y position indicator. Moving the mouse signaled the cursor to move on the screen. Today's mouse works in a similar way.
Comparing and Contrasting *What differences do you notice between the original mouse and the ones in use today?*

Identifying a Need

The mouse was originally designed for use with large, complex computers. Early versions, such as the one in Figure 7, had several problems. For one thing, they were expensive. In addition, dirt easily became trapped in the mechanism, preventing the mouse from working. Also, the mouse often "slipped," meaning that the cursor didn't move when the mouse moved.

How did the modern mouse develop from the clunky one of the past? The modern mouse was the result of a technology design process. The technology design process is a method by which an idea for a new technology is developed into a final product. This process is sometimes called the engineering design process because it often involves the work of engineers. An **engineer** is a person who is trained to use both technological and scientific knowledge to solve practical problems.

Imagine that you are an engineer on the team that is redesigning the original mouse. What is the first thing your team should do? As your first step, you must decide exactly what need you are trying to meet. **When engineers identify a need, they clearly define the problem they are trying to solve.**

The overall need that the engineering team identified was for a reliable device that would be easy for anybody to use. In addition, the device should not cost too much and should be easy to manufacture. And, of course, the mouse must be safe, work well, and last a long time.

Reading Checkpoint What problems did the early mouse have?

98 ◆ P

Differentiated Instruction

Student Edition on Audio CD

Gifted and Talented **L3**
Classifying Engineers There are many different branches of engineering. Ask students to research the educational requirements and the focus of each of the following kinds of engineers. A civil engineer designs and supervises the construction of roads, bridges, airports, and other structures. An electrical engineer designs and supervises the manufacture of electrical equipment. A chemical engineer works in the production of chemicals and chemical products. An aerospace engineer designs and works in the manufacture of aircraft, missiles, and spacecraft. Nuclear engineers conduct research on nuclear energy and work in nuclear power plants. **learning modality: verbal**

Researching the Problem

What is the next stage for the engineering team? **After defining a problem, engineers need to research it fully. When engineers research a problem, they gather information that will help them in their tasks.**

There are many ways that engineers obtain information related to the product they are designing. The engineers may read books and articles about the topic. They may also attend conferences, where they can share ideas with other researchers. Engineers usually perform experiments related to the technology they are designing. In addition, engineers often talk to people like you to find out what customers want.

In gathering information about the mouse, the engineers conducted many tests. They discovered that the ball inside the mouse was held in place by a complex system of sensitive, costly parts. Because the parts were so sensitive, too much pressure on the ball made it slip frequently. Any bit of dirt or dust would jam up the system. This problem caused the mouse to stop working about once a week. To fix it, the entire mouse had to be taken apart, and each part had to be cleaned separately.

 Reading Checkpoint What does researching a problem involve?

Go Online
active art

For: Technology Design Process activity
Visit: PHSchool.com
Web Code: cgp-6032

FIGURE 8
The Technology Design Process
In designing a new piece of technology, engineers must first identify needs that the technology must meet. They then research the problem to gather information that may help them design a solution.

P ◆ 99

Researching the Problem

Teach Key Concepts L2
Gathering Information About a Problem

Focus Explain that gathering information is the next step in the technology design process.

Teach Ask: **Why do engineers spend time researching a problem when designing technology?** (*Information in articles and from other engineers may help them design the right solution to the problem.*) **What did the research that engineers working on the design of the computer mouse involve other than reading?** (*They conducted many tests and observed the causes of mouse problems.*)

Apply Ask: **What solution might you have proposed if you had been a researcher on the mouse and observed that moving parts slipped and became dirty?** (*Sample answer: To solve that problem would involve eliminating as many moving parts as possible.*)
learning modality: verbal

All in One Teaching Resources
• Transparency P36

Go Online
active art

For: Technology Design Process activity
Visit: PHSchool.com
Web Code: cgp-6032

Students can interact with the art of the technology design process online.

Monitor Progress L2

Writing Have students write a paragraph that describes how they would research a problem associated with designing a computer mouse.

Answers
Figure 7 Sample answer: Today's mouse is rounder, has two and not three buttons, has one ball instead of two wheels.

Reading Checkpoint It cost a lot, dirt quickly became trapped in the mechanism, and it often "slipped."

Reading Checkpoint Reading books and articles about a topic, attending conferences, performing experiments, and talking to customers

Designing a Solution

Teach Key Concepts L2
The Process of Design

Focus Tell students the next stage in the technology design process is designing a solution to the design problem.

Teach Write the following headings on the board: *Brainstorming, Evaluating Constraints, Making Trade-offs.* Call on volunteers to explain what each activity involves, and write brief descriptions on the board under each heading. Then have students analyze the specific models, constraints, and trade-offs that were involved in the design of the computer mouse.

Apply Give students this fictional scenario: A robot has landed on Venus and has sent back amazing images to Earth. But suddenly, the images stop arriving, though a signal from the robot indicates that it is still functional. Ask: **How would engineers go about designing a solution to that problem?** *(They might begin with brainstorming. Many engineers would propose a variety of creative solutions. They could then proceed to making computer-generated models.)* **learning modality: verbal**

Help Students Read

Identifying Main Ideas Refer to the Content Refresher in this chapter, which provides the guidelines for using paragraph and subheading organization in the Identifying Main Ideas strategy.

Have students read the text under the heading *Designing a Solution.* Ask: **What is the main idea of the first paragraph under the main heading?** *(The solution stage of the technology design process involves coming up with ideas or thinking about different ways to solve the problem.)* **What is the main idea under the subheading Evaluating Constraints?** *(To answer questions, engineers must evaluate the constraints of each possible design.)*

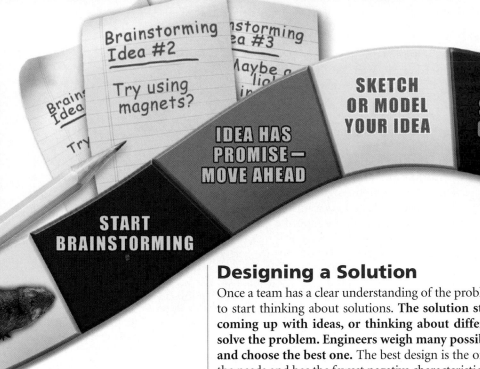

FIGURE 9
Designing a Solution
Brainstorming leads to several possible design solutions. Sketching and modeling help engineers visualize different designs. In choosing the best design, engineers must evaluate constraints and make trade-offs. Notice that engineers sometimes need to go back and repeat one or more steps.
Relating Cause and Effect *Why might a design team need to rethink their ideas?*

Designing a Solution

Once a team has a clear understanding of the problem, it is time to start thinking about solutions. **The solution stage involves coming up with ideas, or thinking about different ways to solve the problem. Engineers weigh many possible solutions and choose the best one.** The best design is the one that meets the needs and has the fewest negative characteristics.

Generating Ideas An important activity that helps generate ideas is called brainstorming. **Brainstorming** is a process in which group members freely suggest any creative solutions that come to mind. Some ideas come in a flash of inspiration. When the mouse engineers brainstormed, they proposed solutions that involved magnets, lights, and other creative ideas.

After brainstorming, engineers may refine their ideas by making sketches or constructing models. The models may be three-dimensional or computer-generated. Playing with a model can spark even more ideas. Many ideas for the mouse actually came from a model an engineer built—using a butter dish and the ball from a container of roll-on deodorant!

Evaluating Constraints Can a design idea actually work? If so, how well? To answer the questions, engineers must evaluate the constraints of each possible design. A **constraint** is any factor that limits or restricts a design. For example, one physical characteristic that may affect how well a mouse functions is friction. Friction is the force created when two surfaces rub against each other. What do you suppose would happen if the ball inside the mouse were made of a smooth material with too little "grip"? It would likely slip.

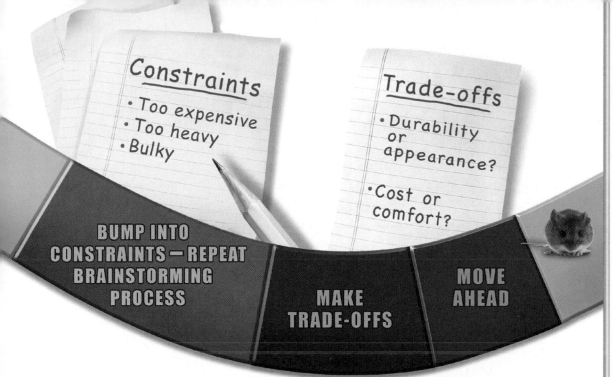

Constraints
• Too expensive
• Too heavy
• Bulky

Trade-offs
• Durability or appearance?
• Cost or comfort?

BUMP INTO CONSTRAINTS — REPEAT BRAINSTORMING PROCESS

MAKE TRADE-OFFS

MOVE AHEAD

Another physical constraint that engineers must consider is the strength of the materials they use. For example, they must think about how well the parts will stand up to repeated use. They must also consider whether the product would be likely to break and cause injuries.

Additional constraints might relate to how much money the finished product can cost and the overall size and appearance of the product. The amount of time needed to manufacture a product can be an additional constraint that engineers must consider.

Making Trade-Offs A team must sometimes make trade-offs on some features of the design. A **trade-off** is an exchange in which one benefit is given up in order to obtain another. For example, one material may be sturdy but look ugly. Another material may be more attractive but may be weaker. The design team may decide to use the more attractive material so that the product will appeal to customers. In this case, the team would be trading off strength for appearance.

 Reading Checkpoint What are two examples of constraints that engineers might need to consider?

Lab zone Try This Activity

Watch Ideas Take Off

In this activity, you will model some stages of the design process.

1. With a team of three or four classmates, brainstorm some ideas for a new product that would keep shoelaces from constantly untying.

2. Evaluate each idea, and discuss the constraints and trade-offs you might have to make.

3. Sketch the design solution the team has agreed on.

Predicting What do you think is the next step your team should take, after selecting a design solution?

Lab zone Try This Activity

Skills Focus Predicting

Time 20 minutes

Tips Discuss the problems of keeping shoes tied, and have students compare different types of laces for whether they stay tied.

Expected Outcome Groups might brainstorm a variety of ideas. Sample

design: Shoelaces could be manufactured with an outer coating of sticky material that would hold tied laces in place. Constraints might include ugly appearance. Trade-off: Using various colors would make the laces less ugly, though it would increase the cost of manufacture. **learning modality: logical/mathematical**

Lab zone Build Inquiry L2

Designing a Solution

Materials student backpack

Time 20 minutes

Focus Tell students that engineers probably designed their backpacks, and maybe they could design a better one.

Teach Divide the class into small groups, and ask each group to use their technology design skills in an evaluation of a backpack. Ask: **What are the first three stages in the technology design process?** *(Identify the needs, research the problem, and design a solution)* Tell students that they should first identify problems students have with their backpacks. Then they should research the problem by putting the backpack through some tests. Next, they should work together to design a solution, which will involve brainstorming, evaluating, constraints, and sketching a model.

Apply Have groups present their ideas and sketches to the class. After students respond to these ideas, groups can form again and rework their designs. Once a group has made a final drawing, they can proceed in making a prototype. **learning modality: logical/mathematical**

Monitor Progress L2

Skills Check Have students make a flowchart showing the steps involved in the solution stage of the technology design process.

Answers

Figure 9 Sample answer: Making and playing with a model might demonstrate a constraint that hadn't been thought of before.

Reading Checkpoint Sample answer: A physical characteristic that restricts function; how much money the finished product might cost

Building a Prototype

Teach Key Concepts L2
Using a Working Model

Focus Explain to students that engineers usually build a working model of a design to see if the design meets the needs.

Teach Ask: **What is a prototype?** (*A working model used to test a design*) Make the distinction between an actual model and a virtual model, and emphasize that engineers use both to test their designs. Ask: **For what purposes do engineers build prototypes?** (*Prototypes are used to test the operation of a product, including how well it works, how long it lasts, and how safe it is to use.*) **How did engineers test how long a mouse lasted?** (*They designed a machine that kept the mouse working all day, for the equivalent of years.*)

Apply Ask: **If you were working on a design for a new backpack, which prototype would be best, a virtual model or a full-sized model using the proposed materials?** (*Sample answer: Although various tests could be done on a virtual model, a full-sized model would show whether there are problems with the design. A full-sized model would essentially be just like the final product, and there probably isn't anything better than that.*) **learning modality: verbal**

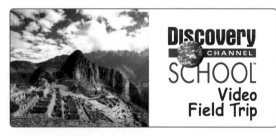

Show the Video Field Trip to let students experience the technology design process. Discussion question: **What are the six steps in the design process?** (*Identifying a need, researching the problem, designing a solution, building a prototype, troubleshooting and redesigning, communicating the solution*)

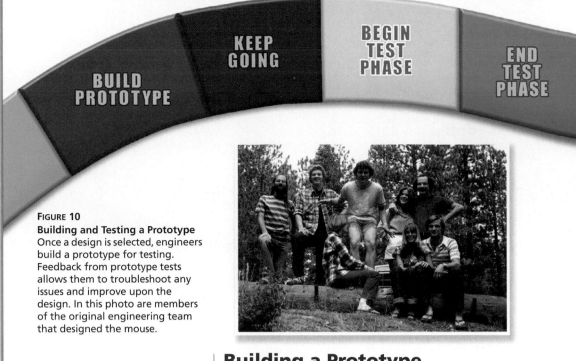

FIGURE 10
Building and Testing a Prototype
Once a design is selected, engineers build a prototype for testing. Feedback from prototype tests allows them to troubleshoot any issues and improve upon the design. In this photo are members of the original engineering team that designed the mouse.

Technology and Engineering

Video Preview
▶ Video Field Trip
Video Assessment

Building a Prototype

After considering constraints and trade-offs, engineers select the design with the most promise. The next phase of the process is to build and test a prototype. A **prototype** is a working model used to test a design. Prototypes are generally full size and made of the materials proposed for the final product. Many prototypes today, however, are completely "virtual," or computer generated.

Prototypes are used to test the operation of a product, including how well it works, how long it lasts, and how safe it is to use. A team might test a prototype by having a small group of people use it and complete a questionnaire. Engineers may also test the prototype in a laboratory to see how it functions. Or they may use computers to test virtual models. The test results help determine how well the product meets the goals and what improvements are needed.

The engineers designed many tests to study the new mouse. For example, they designed a machine that kept the mouse working constantly all day. They found that after the equivalent of three years of constant use, the mouse showed only minor problems in performance.

 Reading Checkpoint What is a virtual prototype?

Troubleshooting and Redesigning

The next stage in the design process is to identify the causes of any problems and to redesign the product to address the problems. The process of analyzing a design problem and finding a way to fix it is called **troubleshooting.**

Prototype tests revealed some problems with the mouse. For example, the mouse was noisy. Through troubleshooting, the engineers identified the rolling steel ball as the cause of the noise. The engineers replaced the steel ball with a rubber ball. This made the mouse quieter and less likely to slip. Engineers also added a ring-shaped cap that users could open without a tool. This redesign made the mouse easy to clean.

✓ Reading Checkpoint What does the process of troubleshooting involve?

Troubleshooting and Redesigning

Teach Key Concepts ⬛L2
Identifying Problems and Redesigning

Focus Explain that most newly designed technology has problems. The next phase in the technology design process is to analyze any problems and redesign the technology.

Teach Ask: **What were some problems with the prototype of the mouse?** *(The mouse was noisy, and the steel ball slipped. The ball also became dirty.)* **What is the process of analyzing problems called?** *(Troubleshooting)* **How did engineers address the problems identified by troubleshooting?** *(They redesigned the mouse, replacing the steel ball with a rubber ball.)*

Apply Divide the class into small groups, and ask students in each group to make a list of any problems they've had with a computer mouse in the past. Have groups also suggest how the mouse might be redesigned to fix those problems. **learning modality: logical/mathematical**

▶ Differentiated Instruction

English Learners/Beginning ⬛L1
Comprehension: Modified Cloze
Distribute a simplified paragraph about the technology design process, but leave some words blank. Model how to fill in the blanks, using a sample sentence on the board. Provide students with the correct answers as choices. **learning modality: verbal**

English Learners/Intermediate ⬛L2
Comprehension: Modified Cloze
Distribute the same paragraph, but include some additional terms as incorrect answer choices. After students complete the paragraph, have them work together to write definitions for the answer choices that were not used. **learning modality: verbal**

Monitor Progress ⬛L2

Oral Presentation Call on students to define the terms *prototype* and *troubleshooting.*

Answers

✓ Reading Checkpoint A computer-generated model used to test a design

✓ Reading Checkpoint Analyzing a design problem and finding a way to fix it

Communicating the Solution

Teach Key Concepts   L2
Explaining the Design

Focus Tell students that the final stage in the technology design process is to communicate information about the technology to consumers.

Teach Ask: **Why did engineers have to communicate to consumers about the computer mouse when it was a new product?** (*Without some explanation, consumers wouldn't know that using a mouse made operating a computer much easier than before. Consumers also had to be taught how to use a mouse when it was a new invention.*)

Apply Divide the class into small groups, and have each group design a magazine ad that would inform consumers about a new product—the computer mouse. **learning modality: verbal**

Patents

Teach Key Concepts   L2
Exclusive Rights to the Invention

Focus Tell students that inventors invest time and money in the invention of a technology, and there is a legal document issued by the government that protects that investment.

Teach Ask: **What is a patent?** (*A legal document issued by the government that gives the inventor exclusive rights to make, use, or sell the invention for a limited time*) Point out that the drawing in Figure 12 is part of the patent application for a computer mouse. Ask: **Why would the inventor include a drawing in the application for a patent?** (*A drawing tries to show exactly what is being patented, so that there is no confusion about what the engineer has invented.*)

Apply Give students this fictional scenario: After years of work, an engineer invents a skateboard that is lighter than any other but also sturdier than any other. She takes it to a convention and shows it to everyone, but she fails to apply for a patent. Ask: **How might the engineer be harmed by not applying for a patent for her invention?** (*Without a patent, she doesn't have exclusive rights to her design. Someone else can make a copy, patent it, and then sell the product. The original engineer receives nothing for her efforts.*)
learning modality: visual

To Do
- Plan a presentation.
- Meet with marketing team.
- Talk to manufacturing group.

FIGURE 11
Communicating the Solution
Engineers must communicate information about their design solution to many groups of people. Presentations about a new technology help bring information to consumers. **Making Judgments** *What kind of information might be most important for consumers to know about a new product?*

Communicating the Solution

What happens after a design has been tested successfully? The team will want to share its accomplishments! The last stage of the technology design process is communicating the solution.

Engineers must communicate to consumers how a product meets their needs. They must also communicate with those involved in bringing the product to consumers. For example, engineers need to explain the design to manufacturers who will produce the product. The engineers must also describe their ideas to marketing people, who will advertise the product. In their presentations, engineers may use slides, models, charts, and graphs to show their ideas.

Through effective communication, information about the mouse reached the public, and the mouse became increasingly popular over the next few years. The mouse solution developed decades ago remains successful today.

Reading Checkpoint   What tools may an engineer use to communicate to others about a design?

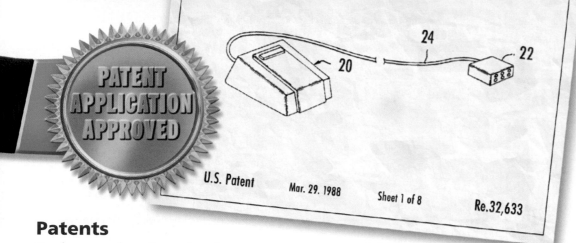

FIGURE 12
Patents
Patent applications often contain diagrams and detailed information on virtually every aspect of a product's design. This illustration is one of many in the mouse patent application.

Patents

You have seen how the engineering process can turn a good idea into a final product people can use. Because new products may bring fame or wealth to an inventor or company, **patents** are usually obtained to protect the inventions. **A patent is a legal document issued by a government that gives the inventor exclusive rights to make, use, or sell the invention for a limited time.** If others want to use the invention, they must obtain the patent owner's permission. After the patent's time runs out, however, anyone can make or sell the invention. Figure 12 shows part of the patent application for the mouse.

 Reading Checkpoint What rights do patents give inventors?

Section 2 Assessment

Target Reading Skill Sequencing Refer to your flowchart about the technology design process as you answer Question 1.

Reviewing Key Concepts

1. **a. Listing** List the stages in the technology design process. Describe each stage in a sentence.
   b. Explaining What are design constraints? Give two examples of constraints that should be considered when designing a cellphone.
   c. Making Judgments A team working on a new bicycle seat design must choose between a comfortable but costly material and a less expensive but uncomfortable material. Which trade-off would you make? Explain.

2. **a. Defining** What is a patent?
   b. Explaining Creativity is a key part of the design process. Explain how patents help reward creativity.
   c. Inferring Why do you think patents remain in effect only for a limited time, rather than forever?

Writing in Science

How-to Paragraph Think about the computer mouse you use most frequently. Suppose your team of engineers has just finished designing this mouse model. Write clear, step-by-step instructions explaining how to use the mouse to move a cursor on a computer screen. You can include a sketch of the mouse to help clarify the instructions.

Chapter 3 P ◆ 105

Lab zone Chapter Project

Keep Students on Track By this time, students should have made sketches of their designs. Review these prototypes, and point out flaws in each design that may make the chair fail to support weight. Encourage students to troubleshoot and redesign and then to begin construction of their chairs.

Writing in Science

Writing Mode Exposition
Scoring Rubric
4 Exceeds criteria; the instructions may be literate and concise, with great clarity in how to proceed from step to step and/or the sketch may be superior
3 Meets all criteria
2 Leaves out a step and/or includes a poor sketch
1 Includes brief and/or inaccurate information

Monitor Progress [L2]

Answers
Figure 11 Sample answer: Consumers need to know what the product does, how it works, and how much it costs.

✓ **Reading Checkpoint** Slides, models, charts, and graphs

✓ **Reading Checkpoint** Exclusive rights to make, use, or sell the invention for a limited time

Assess

Reviewing Key Concepts

1. a. Sample answer: Identify a need: define the problem. Research the problem: gather information. Design a solution: determine ways to solve the problem. Build a prototype: build and test a model. Troubleshoot and redesign: identify problems and redesign to solve them. Communicate the solution: explain the product and how it works.
b. Factors that limit or restrict a design. Examples: size and speaker clarity **c.** Sample answer: I would choose the comfortable but costly design because research shows that riders will not buy an uncomfortable seat.
2. a. A legal document issued by the government that gives the inventor exclusive rights to make, use, or sell the invention for a limited time **b.** By providing a legal way for inventors to gain fame or wealth from their inventions, patents are a way to reward inventors for their creativity. **c.** After a reasonable time, worthwhile inventions should be allowed to benefit everyone by being produced in the most cost-effective and competitive ways.

Reteach [L1]

Have students make their own flowcharts of the technology design process.

Performance Assessment [L2]
Oral Presentation State one of the stages in the technology design process and call on a student to explain what is involved in that stage. Continue through all six stages.

All in One Teaching Resources
- Section Summary: *Technology Design Skills*
- Review and Reinforce: *Technology Design Skills*
- Enrich: *Technology Design Skills*

Design and Build "Egg-ceptional" Packaging

Prepare for Inquiry

Key Concept
The technology design process includes identifying a problem, researching the problem, designing a solution, building a prototype, troubleshooting and redesigning, and communicating.

Skills Objectives
After this lab, students will be able to:
- evaluate the design of packaging made to protect an egg
- troubleshoot the design and redesign packaging that fixes any problems

Prep Time 20 minutes

Time 40 minutes

Advance Planning
Collect the appropriate number of eggs, plastic bags that can be sealed, and scissors. Because a student's first design may not be adequate, each student may need three eggs and three bags. Divide modeling clay into egg-sized pieces, one for each student. Provide access to rolls of tape at a central classroom location. Wide, clear packaging tape works best for constructing cardboard packages. Collect various packaging materials, including several types of fabric, paper, plastic wrap, cardboard, and plastic foam (polystyrene). You could cut cardboard and plastic sections into various-sized pieces. A plastic or paper egg carton could be cut apart into individual egg holders. Filler material might include wood shavings, popped popcorn, and scrap paper. You might consider making available foam plastic packing "popcorn" in a large bag, from which students could grab fistfuls of "popcorn" as needed.

Safety
Physical Safety Tell students that they should be careful with the modeling clay and eggs when dropping these materials, and immediately clean up any breakage of eggs that occurs. Review the safety guidelines in Appendix A.

All in One **Teaching Resources**
- Lab Worksheet: *Design and Build "Egg-ceptional" Packaging*

Design and Build "Egg-ceptional" Packaging

Problem
Can you design and build protective packaging for a breakable object?

Skills Focus
evaluating the design, troubleshooting

Materials
- raw eggs
- plastic bags
- meter stick
- various packaging materials provided by your teacher
- tape
- scissors
- modeling clay

Procedure

PART 1 **Research and Investigate**

1. Mold a piece of modeling clay into the shape of an egg.

2. Hold the clay egg 2 meters above a hard surface. Drop the egg. Examine the egg carefully for damage from the fall. Record your observations in a data table.

3. Reshape the clay egg so it looks like it did in Step 1. Then, choose one of the packaging materials and wrap it around the egg. Repeat Step 2.

4. Repeat Step 3 two more times using different packaging materials each time. Be sure to reshape the egg before each new test.

PART 2 **Design and Build**

5. Based on what you learned in Part 1, design protective packaging for an uncooked egg. Your packaging should
   - prevent the egg from cracking when dropped onto a hard surface from a height of 2 meters
   - use the least amount of packaging material possible
   - be made from materials that are easy to obtain

6. Sketch your design on a sheet of paper and list the materials you will use. You can use materials from Part 1, or other appropriate materials.

7. Obtain your teacher's approval of your design. Then, insert a raw egg in a plastic bag and build your protective packaging around the egg.

PART 3 **Evaluate and Redesign**

8. Your teacher will designate a location where you can drop the egg to test your protective packaging. After the test, unwrap the package and evaluate how well it protected the egg.

9. Based on your results, determine how you might redesign your packaging. Then, make the improvements and test the redesigned packaging with another egg.

Guide Inquiry

Troubleshooting the Experiment
- Set up an area in the classroom for students to carry out the dropping of the modeling clay in Part 1 and the dropping of the egg package in Part 3. At this location, make a line with tape on the wall at a height of 2 meters. Most students will be able to hold a package over their heads at the 2-meter height and let go. Make sure accommodations are planned for students who cannot reach that height.

- Stress that students should handle raw eggs carefully to prevent breakage. Tell students to place each egg in a plastic bag and seal the bag before placing the egg in the designed package.

- Provide a large container for students to dispose of any broken eggs that result from the drop in Part 3. Have students drop the sealed plastic bag with the broken egg into the container.

Analyze and Conclude

1. **Designing a Solution** What did you learn from Part 1 that influenced the design of your protective package? For example, what did you learn about each of the packaging materials you tested?

2. **Evaluating the Design** Did your packaging prevent the egg from breaking? If so, which aspects of your design do you think were the most important in protecting the egg? If not, why not?

3. **Troubleshooting** How did you decide what changes to make in redesigning your packaging? How well did your redesigned packaging work to protect the egg?

4. **Working With Design Constraints** How did factors such as gravity and the fragile nature of the egg affect your design? What limits did the design criteria in Step 5 place on your packaging design?

5. **Evaluating the Impact on Society** Imagine that you work for a company that designs bicycle and skateboard helmets. How would the technology design process you used in this lab apply to the helmet company? What additional factors would you need to consider in designing helmets?

Communicate

You work in the advertising department of a company that specializes in shipping valuable and breakable antiques. Design an ad for your company that highlights your protective packaging designs.

Extend Inquiry

Communicate Designing an ad involves writing the ad copy, creating an informative illustration, and positioning the illustration and text on the page in a way that would catch the eye. A good ad would show with drawings and describe in words more than one type of packaging for more than one type of antique. A typical ad would include mention of the materials used in the packaging, how the packaging prevents breakage and damage to antiques, and the extensive testing done to make sure the packaging does the intended job.

Expected Outcome

Most students will design a package that will protect an egg from breakage, though the final packaging may have to be improved after the first attempt. A typical package may be a cardboard box taped together with some kind of filler inside the box and around the egg.

Analyze and Conclude

1. Sample answer: In testing the various types of packaging material, it became clear that a material had to be quite sturdy to protect an egg from breaking. Plastic wrap, paper, and fabric were not sturdy enough to prevent the modeling clay from being damaged from the fall.

2. Sample answer: The packaging did finally prevent the egg from breaking. The most important aspect of the design was that the outside material had to be sturdy enough not to change its shape when hitting the floor.

3. Sample answer: The decisions used to redesign the packaging followed from identification of how the package was changed in shape or damaged from the fall to the floor. The redesign was an attempt to find solutions to the problems observed.

4. Sample answer: Gravity caused the package with the egg inside to fall with force to the floor, and such a fall would break the egg without some kind of protective covering. Using only common materials and using the least amount of packaging material possible made designing the package difficult.

5. The technology design process would be quite similar to that used here. It would include identifying a problem, researching the problem, designing a solution, building a prototype, troubleshooting and redesigning, and communicating. Perhaps more research would have to be done in designing a helmet. Additional factors that would have to be considered would include appearance of the helmet and final cost to the consumer. In designing a helmet, trade-offs may have to be made in order to ensure the safety of the user. A helmet must protect the user from serious injury, notwithstanding an appearance problem or a high cost.

Objectives

After this lesson, students will be able to

P.3.3.1 Describe how technology is tied to history.

P.3.3.2 Explain how technology affects people in both positive and negative ways.

P.3.3.3 Explain how analyzing risks and benefits can help people make decisions about technology.

Target Reading Skill

Relating Cause and Effect Explain that cause is the reason for what happens. The effect is what happens because of the cause. Relating cause and effect helps students anticipate the ideas for what happens to what happens as a result.

Answers

Sample answers:

Cause Invention of steam-powered looms
Effects Positive effect: greater production
Negative effect: loss of jobs
Cause Pesticide application
Effects Positive effect: protects crops
Negative effect: harmful to plants and animals
Cause Invention of tractors
Effects Positive effect: can plow more land
Negative effect: loss of farm jobs
Cause Invention of computers, electronic equipment, and powerful machinery
Effects Positive effect: workers can do more
Negative effect: quickens pace of life

All in One Teaching Resources

• Transparency P37

Preteach

Build Background Knowledge   L2

Advantages and Disadvantages of Automobiles

Ask: **What are some advantages of Americans' dependence on automobiles for transportation?** (*Sample answer: People can get where they want to go when they want to go there. Autos are comfortable and convenient.*) **What are some disadvantages?** (*Sample answer: Automobiles can be unsafe, and they pollute the air.*)

108 ● P

Section
3 Technology and Society

Reading Preview

Key Concepts

• How is technology tied to history?
• How does technology affect people in both positive and negative ways?
• Why is it important to analyze the risks and benefits of a technology?

Key Term

• risk-benefit analysis

Target Reading Skill

Relating Cause and Effect As you read, identify one positive and one negative effect of each technology discussed in this section. Write the information in a graphic organizer like the one below.

Cause
Invention of air bags

Effects
Positive effect: saves lives

Lab zone | Discover Activity

How Does Technology Affect Your Life?

1. Your teacher will divide the class into groups. Your group should choose a technology product that you rely on or use every day. Think about how the product affects your life.
2. List the advantages of using the product—the ways in which it helps you and improves your life.
3. Now list the disadvantages of the product.

Think It Over
Inferring Do you think that the product you chose has had an overall positive or negative impact on people? Explain.

Your hands fly across the loom. Proudly, you look at the beautiful pattern that begins to take shape in the cloth you are making. You've spent years learning the craft of weaving. Now you are skilled at it, like your father and grandfather before you.

But a factory in town is starting to use a new technology—looms run by steam power. People can operate these machines with little training. An unskilled worker can produce more cloth in a day than you can in weeks. You are about to lose your way of life.

This was the bleak prospect that weavers in England faced in the early 1800s. The new machines threatened their jobs. Some people rebelled against the idea of being replaced by machines. They invaded factories and smashed the machinery.

Hand Loom
It took about **three days** to weave the material for one shirt.

108 ◆ P

Lab zone | Discover Activity

Skills Focus Inferring

Time 10 minutes

Tips Have a volunteer read the definition of *technology* aloud, and review examples of technology.

Expected Outcome Most groups will choose a familiar technology product, such as a bicycle, an automobile, a refrigerator, or a computer. Because these examples are relied on by people every day, their list of advantages will likely be longer than their list of disadvantages.

Think It Over Sample answer: An automobile, for example, has had a positive impact in general, because it provides needed transportation. Its negative impacts include air pollution and traffic deaths.

Technology's Impact on Society

The situation of the skilled weavers is one example of how technology can affect society. The term *society* refers to any group of people who live together in an area, large or small, and have certain things in common, such as a form of government. **In every age of history, technology has had a large impact on society, from the Stone Age thousands of years ago to the Information Age today.** During the Stone Age, for example, people used stones to make tools. Spears, axes, and spades enabled people to hunt animals and grow crops. As the food supply became more stable, people no longer needed to wander in search of food. They began to settle in farming communities and stay in one place.

During the Iron Age, people produced iron, a strong metal. They used iron to make weapons and tools such as chisels and saws. Many machines were also invented during the Iron Age, such as water wheels and grain mills. These inventions enabled farmers to grow more food. As food supplies increased, many people left farm life behind and moved to towns and cities.

There are many other examples from history of the huge impact that technology has had. Today, in the Information Age, cellphones, satellites, and super-fast computers allow people to share information quickly around the world. Societies in distant parts of the world are no longer really isolated from one another. The Information Age has dramatically changed the way that people live, work, and play.

 Reading Checkpoint What is a society?

FIGURE 13
Technology Through History
Before the 1800s, skilled weavers produced cloth on hand-operated looms in their homes. In the early 1800s, factories with steam-powered looms increased the pace of production. Today, even more powerful machines churn out cloth at high speed.

Steam-Powered Loom It took about **one day** to weave the material for one shirt.

Modern Loom It takes **less than a minute** to weave the material for one shirt.

 P ◆ 109

Differentiated Instruction

Less Proficient Readers L1
Answering Questions Select a passage from the text, such as the first paragraph under the heading *Technology's Impact on Society*. Read the passage aloud to students as they follow along in their books. After reading, ask some questions about the passage. If they don't know the answers, challenge them to find the answers in the passage. **learning modality: verbal**

Gifted and Talented L3
Comparing and Contrasting Have students research what technologies contributed to the changes that occurred in human society during the Industrial Revolution. Then, ask them to compare and contrast those changes with the changes that have been occurring in recent years with the advent of the Information Age. **learning modality: verbal**

Impacts of Technology— Good and Bad

Teach Key Concepts L2

Good Effects vs. Bad Effects

Focus Tell students that the same example of technology may have both good effects and bad effects on society.

Teach Bring students together for a round-table discussion about the effects of technology. Ask first for examples of technology and a description of the beneficial effects of each. Write the examples on the board. Then call on volunteers to describe any negative effects of that technology.

Apply: If a student mentions the positive effects of using bicycles for transportation, ask: **Does bicycle transportation have any negative effects?** (*Bicycles can be dangerous, both to the rider and to pedestrians and motorists.*) **learning modality: verbal**

Lab zone Teacher **Demo**

Materials spray can of ant and roach killer

Time 10 minutes

Focus Explain to students that pesticides do the job they are made to do, but they also have harmful effects.

Teach Show students a spray can of ant and roach killer. Ask: **What are the positive effects of this technology?** (*The technology kills insect pests, including ants and roaches.*) Then, read aloud from the "Warning" or "Caution" printed on the can. The user is cautioned against breathing the spray and even allowing it to touch skin or clothing. Ask: **If this insecticide is poison to humans, how do you think it might affect pets and other animals in the environment?** (*Sample answer: It would probably be harmful.*)

Apply Ask: **Is the technology of this insecticide the perfect solution to an insect pest?** (*No, because it has harmful effects to other living things*) Explain that a user of technology always has to take into consideration both its positive and negative effects. **learning modality: verbal**

Plastics

Air Bags

Positive Impact
Plastic is inexpensive and can be made into countless products.

Negative Impact
Discarded plastic products break down slowly and pollute the environment.

Positive Impact
Air bags save lives by protecting passengers during car crashes.

Negative Impact
The force of an inflating air bag can cause severe injuries.

FIGURE 14
The Impact of Technology
Technology does not provide perfect solutions. Air bags and plastics, for example, were designed to improve the quality of life. However, they can also have negative impacts.
Inferring *Why might the negative consequences of a technology remain unrecognized for a while?*

Impacts of Technology— Good and Bad

As you can see, technological advances have done much to move societies forward through the centuries. However, it is important to keep in mind that technology has both good and bad impacts on society. **In addition to positive effects, technology can have negative consequences.** Often, many of the negative consequences are unintentional and are not recognized until long after the technology has been put to use.

Health and Safety From bandages to medicines, technology products that improve people's health and safety are all around you. These products make it possible to live longer and healthier lives. Air bags, for example, have saved thousands of lives. Air bags were designed to protect people in a car crash. During a crash, air bags fill with gases and cushion passengers from the impact of the crash.

Unfortunately, however, air bags also have consequences they were never meant to have. Sometimes air bags have caused injury or even death. Small children, for example, can be severely injured by the explosive force of an inflating air bag. The hot gases that fill an air bag can also cause serious burns.

The Environment Have you ever seen signs on lawns that read "Caution: Pesticide Application—Keep Off Grass"? Pesticides have played a very important role in food production. Because pesticides protect crops from insects, farmers can produce more crops and feed more people. Therefore, food prices can stay low while crop yields stay high.

However, humans and other animals can sometimes be harmed if they eat foods containing pesticides. Pesticides can also be washed by rain into rivers, streams, and water supplies. The pesticides can then affect plants and animals that live in the water, as well as the people who depend on the water supply.

Jobs Technological advances make many jobs easier to perform. They also increase the amount of work that people can accomplish. For example, farmers can plow more land using a tractor than a horse-drawn plow.

However, in some cases, the advance of technology can cause people to lose their jobs. If farmers cannot afford expensive equipment, such as tractors and irrigation systems, their farms may not be as productive as farms that can. Eventually, less productive farms may go out of business and the farmers may lose their jobs. Similarly, factory and office workers may lose their jobs if machines can perform the same work more efficiently. This was the case with the weavers and other crafts people during the 1800s.

Math ▶ Analyzing Data

Working on the Farm

The graph shows the percentage of workers who worked on farms between the years 1860 and 2000. Use the graph to answer the following questions.

1. **Reading Graphs** What factor is plotted on the horizontal axis? What factor is plotted on the vertical axis?

2. **Interpreting Data** Of the years shown on the graph, in which year was the percentage of farm workers highest? In which year was the percentage lowest?

3. **Calculating** By how much did the percentage of farm workers change between 1860 and 2000?

Farm Workers in the United States

4. **Drawing Conclusions** What trend does the graph show?

5. **Inferring** Based on what you know about technological advances, how would you explain the trend shown in the graph?

Math ▶ Analyzing Data

Math Skill Making and interpreting graphs

Focus The line graph shows the decline in the percentage of farm workers among total workers, an example of the impact that technology has had on the American workforce.

Teach Ask: **What is the subject of the graph?** (*Farm workers in the United States*) Tell students that the graph shows how the percentage of farm workers in the total workforce changed over time. Ask: **How has farm technology changed in the last one hundred years?** (*Tractors, combines, and other machinery have improved greatly.*)

Answers

1. Horizontal axis—year, from 1860 to 2000; vertical axis—percentage of total workers that are farm workers

2. Highest—1860; lowest—2000

3. It decreased from about 45 percent to about 2 percent, or a reduction of about 43 percent of the total workforce.

4. The percentage of farm workers in the total workforce of the United States has declined steadily from 1860 to 2000.

5. The progress of technology, including the advance of tractors and other machinery, reduced significantly the need for workers on the farm over the last 150 years.

Monitor Progress _____ L2

Writing Have students describe in a paragraph the good and bad impacts of air bags.

Answer

Figure 14 Sample answer: Negative consequences may not be recognized until the technology has been in use for a period of time. It would be impossible to test a new product for every possible use in the real world.

Focus Tell students that the timeline shows several examples of everyday technology invented over the last two centuries. Point out that the first invention on the timeline was invented in 1817, a time about midway between the American Revolution and the American Civil War. The timeline ends in 1960, the year John F. Kennedy was elected president.

Teach Ask: **What is the first invention on the timeline, and when was it invented?** *(The bicycle, invented in 1817)* Tell students that this technology was invented by a German, and he called his invention the "running machine." Ask: **What important feature is missing on this bicycle that all modern bikes have?** *(Pedals)* **How do you think this example of technology changed people's lives?** *(Sample answer: The bicycle provided an easy and efficient method to move from place to place at a fast speed.)*

Writing in Science

Writing Mode Description

Scoring Rubric

4 Exceeds criteria; includes information about the history of the technology and/or thoughtful insights about the inventor or the period in which the technology was invented

3 Meets all criteria

2 Includes less than full information about the technology, the inventor, and/or the events of that led to the invention

1 Includes only brief and/or inaccurate information about the technology or the inventor

Pace of Life From daily chores to long-distance travel, technological advances enable people to accomplish things much more quickly today. Microwave ovens and frozen foods help you prepare meals in minutes. Planes can take you to the other side of the globe in one day. Computers, electronic equipment, and powerful machinery enable workers to accomplish more tasks in shorter time frames.

Being able to do things quickly, however, may also make people feel stressed or rushed. Life had a much slower pace only a few decades ago. People had fewer choices about where they went, what they did, or the speed at which tasks were accomplished. For example, before plane travel was available, visiting another state may have taken days. But people seldom felt as rushed as they do today, and families spent more time together.

 Reading Checkpoint) **Why is life so fast-paced today?**

Everyday Technology
There are lots of technological devices that you probably take for granted. What would your life be like if these items had not been invented?

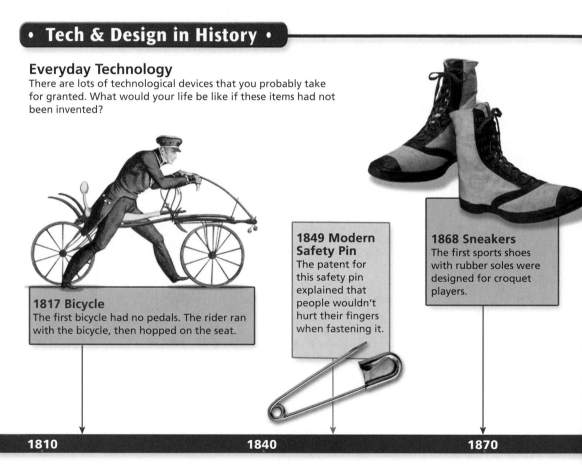

1817 Bicycle
The first bicycle had no pedals. The rider ran with the bicycle, then hopped on the seat.

1849 Modern Safety Pin
The patent for this safety pin explained that people wouldn't hurt their fingers when fastening it.

1868 Sneakers
The first sports shoes with rubber soles were designed for croquet players.

| 1810 | 1840 | 1870 |

Background

History of Science Several inventors are responsible for the development of the modern bicycle. In 1817, German Baron Karl Drais von Sauerbronn invented what he called the "running machine." This bicycle was a wooden device—even the wheels were wood. In the 1700s, a wheeled device had been made in France, but unlike the "running machine" it had no steering. The first bicycle with pedals was invented in about 1840 by Kirkpatrick Macmillan, a Scottish inventor. Rods were connected to the pedals, and these rods supplied the power to turn the back wheel. The rider sat between two equally sized wheels, just as on a modern bike. In 1871, the British engineer James Starley invented the first efficient bicycle, called the Penny Farthing, that became the standard for decades. The Penny Farthing had a very small rear wheel, a very large front wheel, a tubular frame, and rubber tires.

Analyzing Risks and Benefits

If technology can create problems, how then can people decide whether or not to use a new technology? And how do governments determine whether a new technology should be regulated, or limited by laws?

In deciding whether to use a particular technology—or how to use it—people must analyze its possible risks and benefits. The process of **risk-benefit analysis** involves evaluating the possible problems, or risks, of a technology compared to the expected advantages, or benefits. This analysis requires logical thinking and common sense. Different people may make different decisions about whether—and how—a technology should be used.

Writing in Science

Research and Write Choose one invention described in the timeline and find out more about it. Write a short biography of the inventor and discuss the events that led up to the invention.

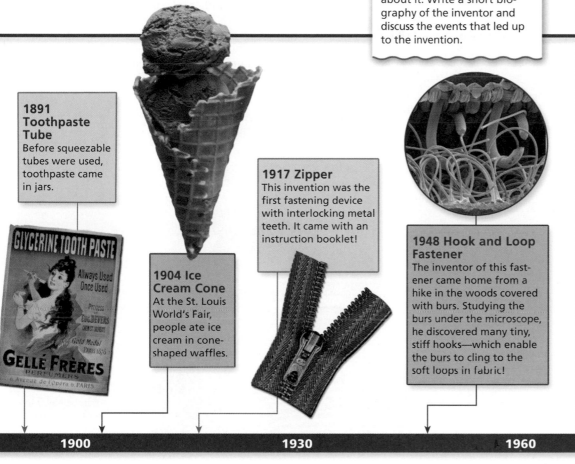

1891 Toothpaste Tube Before squeezable tubes were used, toothpaste came in jars.

1904 Ice Cream Cone At the St. Louis World's Fair, people ate ice cream in cone-shaped waffles.

1917 Zipper This invention was the first fastening device with interlocking metal teeth. It came with an instruction booklet!

1948 Hook and Loop Fastener The inventor of this fastener came home from a hike in the woods covered with burs. Studying the burs under the microscope, he discovered many tiny, stiff hooks—which enable the burs to cling to the soft loops in fabric!

1900   1930   1960

Analyzing Risks and Benefits

Teach Key Concepts L2
Weighing Advantages and Disadvantages

Focus Tell students that people have to decide whether and how to use technology by analyzing the risks and benefits of that use.

Teach Ask: **What is a risk-benefit analysis?** *(A process that involves evaluating possible problems, or risks, of a technology compared to the expected advantages, or benefits)* Explain that before a risk-benefit analysis can be made, both the risks and the benefits of a technology have to be clearly identified.

Apply Ask: **When a person rides a bicycle without wearing a helmet, what trade-off is that person making?** *(The person is trading the safety the helmet provides for the freedom and convenience of riding without a helmet.)* **Do you think that trade-off is wise?** *(Some students may think it is, while others will argue it is unwise.)* Tell students that people make similar trade-offs about technology every day. **learning modality: verbal**

Differentiated Instruction

Less Proficient Readers L1
Comprehension: Key Concept On the board, rewrite the boldface sentence about analyzing risks and benefits into two sentences: "In deciding whether to use a particular technology, people must analyze its possible risks and benefits"; and "In deciding how to use a particular technology, people must analyze its possible risks and benefits." Then, review the meanings of *analyze, risk,* and *benefit.* Finally, introduce the key term *risk-benefit analysis* and relate that term to the key concept. **learning modality: verbal**

Monitor Progress L2

Oral Presentation Ask students to explain in their own words what a risk-benefit analysis is.

Answer

✓ **Reading Checkpoint** Technological advances enable people to accomplish things much more quickly today, sometimes causing people to feel stressed or rushed.

Focus Tell students that the figure shows both the benefits and the risks of using headphones.

Teach After students have read the caption and annotations, ask: **What are the benefits and the risks of using headphones to listen to music?** *(Students should cite the benefits and risks listed in the figure.)* Discuss whether the risks outweigh the benefits or the benefits outweigh the risks.

Apply Ask: **Have you ever been told that listening to music through headphones can damage your ears if the volume is too high?** *(Most students will have heard such warnings.)* **Do you still listen to music through headphones at high volumes?** *(Most will answer that they do.)* Point out that they probably have never done a risk-benefit analysis of headphone use. The companies that make these products likely have done such analyses. Ask: **How would a risk-benefit analysis by a medical doctor probably be different than one by an electrical engineer?** *(The medical doctor would probably emphasize the risks, while the electrical engineer might emphasize the benefits.)* Emphasize that different people may make different decisions about how a technology should be used. **learning modality: visual**

Go Online
SciLINKS **NSTA**

For: Links on technology and society
Visit: www.SciLinks.org
Web Code: scn-1633

Download a worksheet that will guide students' review of Internet resources on technology and society.

Identifying the Risks and Benefits Look at Figure 15 to see how risk-benefit analysis can help you make a personal decision, such as whether or not to use headphones. Risk-benefit analysis also helps governments establish regulations about new technology products. For example, suppose a company has developed a new bicycle helmet made of a lightweight material. The helmet provides less protection than older, heavier helmets, but it is much more comfortable and stylish.

In determining whether the new helmet is acceptable safety gear, a government agency first identifies both its risks and its benefits. The main risk of the new helmet is the greater possibility of injury than with heavier helmets. But because some riders find heavier helmets uncomfortable and unattractive, they may avoid wearing helmets at all. Since the new helmet is more comfortable and looks better, more people may wear it. The benefit of the new helmet, then, is that more people would have some form of head protection, rather than no protection at all.

Values and Trade-Offs Often, in evaluating a technology's risks and benefits, individuals and societies must consider human values. A value is something that a person or society regards as important, such as health, honesty, convenience, and personal freedom.

FIGURE 15
The Risks and Benefits of Using Headphones
Should you use headphones? Evaluating the risks and benefits can help you decide.
Problem Solving *What decision would you make and why?*

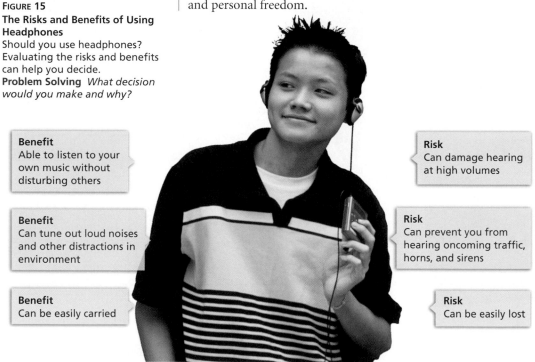

Benefit
Able to listen to your own music without disturbing others

Benefit
Can tune out loud noises and other distractions in environment

Benefit
Can be easily carried

Risk
Can damage hearing at high volumes

Risk
Can prevent you from hearing oncoming traffic, horns, and sirens

Risk
Can be easily lost

Difficulties can arise when different values conflict—when one value favors a technology while another value cautions against it. In the case of the new helmets, the conflicting values could be safety versus people's freedom of choice. When values conflict, a decision involves trade-offs. As you learned in Section 2, a trade-off consists of exchanging one benefit for another. For example, by choosing the lightweight helmet, people trade safety for style.

Using Technology Wisely Technology will continue to play a large role in the lives of most people. That is why it is important to remember that technology does not provide perfect solutions to the problems it helps solve. Also keep in mind that technology cannot solve every problem. For example, suppose your friend dreams of being a pop star but cannot sing. Unfortunately, even the most high-tech recording equipment might not help your friend achieve that dream. By keeping these cautions in mind, you will be able to approach decisions about technology wisely.

 Reading Checkpoint What is meant by a value?

For: Links on technology and society
Visit: www.SciLinks.org
Web Code: scn-1633

Section 3 Assessment

Target Reading Skill Relating Cause and Effect Refer to your graphic organizer about the effects of technology to help you answer Question 2 below.

Reviewing Key Concepts

1. a. **Reviewing** Give one example of how technological advances affected the society in which they were introduced.
   b. **Making Judgments** Do you think that technology has had a greater impact on society in the past or today? Explain.

2. a. **Explaining** Explain this statement: Technology does not provide perfect solutions to the problems it helps solve.
   b. **Applying Concepts** Suppose a robot that cooks meals in minutes has been invented. What positive impacts might it have?
   c. **Relating Cause and Effect** What negative impacts might the robot have over time on jobs, the pace of life, and other things?

3. a. **Defining** What is a risk-benefit analysis?
   b. **Problem Solving** What risks and benefits should be considered when deciding whether or not to buy an insect repellent?
   c. **Making Judgments** Do you think that government agencies should perform risk-benefit analyses on all insect repellents? Explain your reasoning.

Writing in Science

Summary Suppose you are a curator of a history museum. You are organizing an exhibit featuring inventions that have had dramatic impacts on society. Choose one invention that changed people's lives after it was invented. Write a summary about the invention to be posted at the exhibit.

Chapter 3 P ◆ 115

Lab zone Chapter Project

Keep Students on Track By this time, students should have completed construction of their chairs. Examine each chair, and ask what tests have been carried out to check the strength of the chairs. Tell students that they should begin planning the presentation of their chairs to the class. They will want to describe the design, relate any problems encountered, and demonstrate the final product.

Writing in Science

Writing Mode Description
Scoring Rubric
4 Exceeds criteria; includes a superior description of the invention and/or shows great insight about how the invention changed people's lives
3 Meets all criteria
2 Includes only one of two criteria
1 Includes only brief and/or inaccurate information

Technology and Society

The Internet

Key Concept
Technology has both good and bad impacts on society.

Build Background Knowledge
Accessing the Internet

Explain that over half of American homes now have a home computer. Point out that buying a computer or paying a monthly fee to an Internet service provider (ISP) is still too expensive for many American families. Ask: **How might having access to the Internet affect a student's future?** *(Sample answer: A student who has access to the Internet may be able to do better in school than a student who doesn't, and thus may have a brighter future.)*

Introduce the Debate
Ask: **What benefits has the Internet had on society?** *(Sample answer: People can become informed about a topic quickly and efficiently. E-mail helps people and businesses communicate.)* **What negative impacts has the Internet had on society?** *(Sample answer: The Internet is full of both good information and bad information, and it is hard to tell the difference. Some people have access to the Internet, whiles others do not; this disparity creates unfairness in society.)*

Facilitate the Debate

- Have students read the feature and answer the Weigh the Impact questions individually as a homework assignment. Allow a day for research about the reliability of Internet sources. On the second day, divide the class into small groups for discussion. Have students consider these questions: What good impacts has the Internet had on society? What negative impacts has the Internet had on society?

- Divide the class into two groups. Arbitrarily assign one group to argue that the benefits of the Internet outweigh any negative impacts it may have. Assign the other group to argue that the negative impacts outweigh the benefits, at least so far.

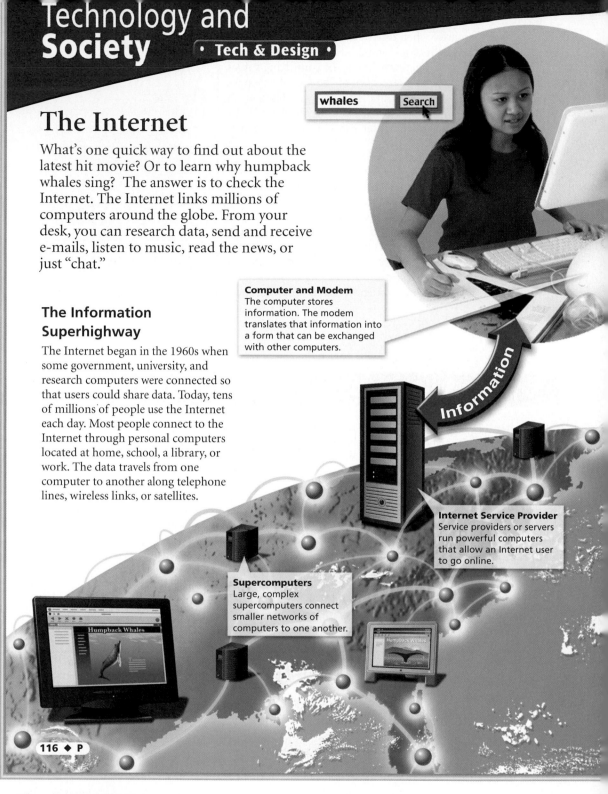

The Internet

What's one quick way to find out about the latest hit movie? Or to learn why humpback whales sing? The answer is to check the Internet. The Internet links millions of computers around the globe. From your desk, you can research data, send and receive e-mails, listen to music, read the news, or just "chat."

The Information Superhighway

The Internet began in the 1960s when some government, university, and research computers were connected so that users could share data. Today, tens of millions of people use the Internet each day. Most people connect to the Internet through personal computers located at home, school, a library, or work. The data travels from one computer to another along telephone lines, wireless links, or satellites.

Computer and Modem
The computer stores information. The modem translates that information into a form that can be exchanged with other computers.

Internet Service Provider
Service providers or servers run powerful computers that allow an Internet user to go online.

Supercomputers
Large, complex supercomputers connect smaller networks of computers to one another.

116 ◆ P

Background

History of Science In 1969, a network of computers was established called ARPANET (Advanced Research Projects Agency network). Part of the motivation for putting the network together was to connect all of the relatively few powerful research computers in the United States. The first data were exchanged between computers at Stanford University and UCLA. The first e-mail—a simple message from one person to another through the network—was sent in 1971. Computer engineer Ray Tomlinson, who invented e-mail, chose the @ symbol to indicate which user was "at" a certain computer. In 1983, ARPANET expanded to become the Internet, an international computer network. Computer scientist Vinton Cerf was instrumental in that transformation.

Too Much Information?

The Internet contains huge volumes of data that can be stored, accessed, and transmitted within minutes. This quick transfer of information has many benefits.

The Internet is fast, but people must consider the drawbacks. Not all the information posted on the Internet is accurate or appropriate. In addition, viruses can be transmitted via the Internet and damage the computers that receive them. Another drawback is that Internet users must own their own computer or have access to one. There is also a service fee to access the Internet.

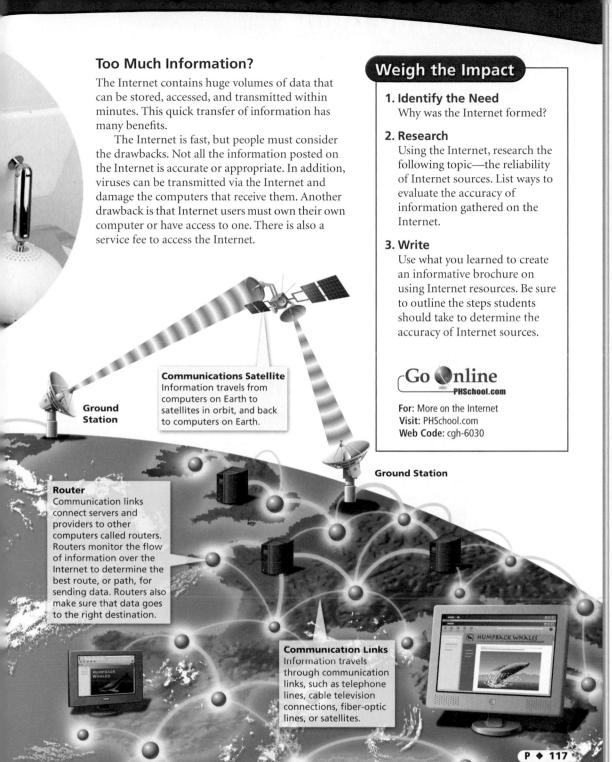

Communications Satellite
Information travels from computers on Earth to satellites in orbit, and back to computers on Earth.

Ground Station

Ground Station

Router
Communication links connect servers and providers to other computers called routers. Routers monitor the flow of information over the Internet to determine the best route, or path, for sending data. Routers also make sure that data goes to the right destination.

Communication Links
Information travels through communication links, such as telephone lines, cable television connections, fiber-optic lines, or satellites.

P ◆ 117

Weigh the Impact

1. Identify the Need
Why was the Internet formed?

2. Research
Using the Internet, research the following topic—the reliability of Internet sources. List ways to evaluate the accuracy of information gathered on the Internet.

3. Write
Use what you learned to create an informative brochure on using Internet resources. Be sure to outline the steps students should take to determine the accuracy of Internet sources.

Go Online
PHSchool.com

For: More on the Internet
Visit: PHSchool.com
Web Code: cgh-6030

Weigh the Impact

1. The Internet was formed to connect government, university, and research computers so that computer users could share data.

2. Sample answer: There are three main considerations when evaluating the reliability of an Internet source. First, does the web site have a bias? The user has to evaluate whether the person or organization that created the web site wanted to impart a message or perspective to the user. In evaluating bias, the user should think about why the web site was created and what organization created it. Second, is the supplier of the information on the web site qualified to write about the topic? Qualified sources of information include museums, schools and universities, and government agencies, as well as established sources such as a well-known encyclopedia. Third, does the web site have original material or documents—primary sources—or is the information interpretations by a writer? Original material is best because the user can make his or her own interpretations rather than relying on someone else's interpretation.

3. Students' brochures should contain a series of steps students can take to determine the accuracy of information on a web site. In addition to the three main considerations in determining the reliability of a web site, as mentioned in the answer to question 2, students also might mention other indications of a web site's accuracy. These may include whether the web site has a little or a lot of information and whether there is advertising on the web site. Students might also suggest that when researching a topic, it is best to confirm information found on one web site with the same information from another web site.

Go Online
PHSchool.com

For: More on the Internet
Visit: PHSchool.com
Web Code: cgh-6030

Students can research this issue online.

Extend

Encourage students to find out where people who have no home computer can go to get access to the Internet. Students can check at the local library. Have students find out whether there are other public places where people can access the Internet for a small fee.

Chapter 3 **Study Guide**

Help Students Read

Building Vocabulary

Words in Context Help students learn the meaning of new words or phrases by examining context. Tell students to look for familiar words or phrases that surround a new term—these are clues to the new term's meaning. Have students reread the third paragraph under the heading *What Is Technology?* Ask: **Which two words in the same sentence as *technology* help you to remember its meaning?** (*The words* change *and* solve.)

Word/Part Analysis Have students look up the prefix *proto-* in a dictionary. They should find that this word part means "first." Then, have students write a definition of *prototype* using the definition they learned of *proto-*. Prototype, means "first type" or "first form."

Connecting Concepts

Concept Maps Help students develop one way to show how the information in this chapter is related. Technology can be classified into six major areas. Each area includes numerous examples. Each example of technology may have obsolete, current, emerging, and coexisting examples of technology. Each of those examples has good and bad impacts on society.

Tell students that this concept map will be organized in hierarchical order and to begin at the top with the title *Technology* and the six major areas underneath that. An example of each falls below the major area, and then classifications fall below the examples.

Prompt students by using connecting words or phrases, such as "includes" or "can be classified as." The phrases should form a sentence between or among a set of concepts.

Interactive Textbook
- Complete student edition
- Section and chapter self-assessments
- Assessment reports for teachers

---

① Understanding Technology

Key Concepts
- The goal of technology is to improve the way people live.
- Science is the study of the natural world to understand how it functions. Technology changes, or modifies, the natural world to meet human needs or solve problems.
- Technology progresses as people's knowledge increases and as new needs can be satisfied.
- A technological system includes a goal, inputs, processes, outputs, and, in some cases, feedback.

Key Terms
technology
obsolete
system
goal
input
process
output
feedback

118 ◆ P

② Technology Design Skills

Key Concepts
- When engineers identify a need, they clearly define the problem they are trying to solve.
- When researching a problem, engineers gather information that will help them in their tasks.
- The solution stage involves thinking about different ways to solve the problem, and then choosing the best one.
- Prototypes are used to test the operation of a product.
- After testing a prototype, engineers identify the causes of any problems and redesign the product to address the problems.
- The last stage of the technology design process is communicating the solution.
- A patent is a legal document that gives the inventor exclusive rights to make, use, or sell the invention for a limited time.

Key Terms
engineer
brainstorming
constraint
trade-off
prototype
troubleshooting
patent

③ Technology and Society

Key Concepts
- Technology has always had a large impact on society, from the Stone Age thousands of years ago to the Information Age today.
- In addition to positive effects, technology can have negative consequences.
- In deciding whether to use a particular technology—or how to use it—people must analyze its possible risks and benefits.

Key Term
risk-benefit analysis

Answer Accept logical presentations by students.

All in One Teaching Resources
- Key Terms Review: *Technology and Engineering*
- Transparency P38

Review and Assessment

Go Online
PHSchool.com
For: Self-Assessment
Visit: PHSchool.com
Web Code: cga-6030

Organizing Information

Comparing and Contrasting Copy the Venn diagram comparing science and technology onto a separate sheet of paper. Then complete it and add a title. (For more on Comparing and Contrasting, see the Skills Handbook.)

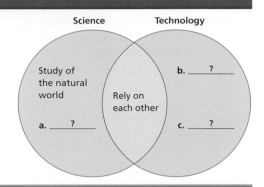

Science   Technology

Study of the natural world

Rely on each other

a. _____?_____

b. _____?_____

c. _____?_____

Reviewing Key Terms

Choose the letter of the best answer.

1. An obsolete technology is one that is
   a. currently used.
   b. high tech.
   c. broken.
   d. no longer being used.

2. The sequence of actions that a technological system undergoes is called the
   a. input.   b. feedback.
   c. process.   d. output.

3. Any factor that limits or restricts the design of a technology product is a
   a. prototype.   b. patent.
   c. trade-off.   d. constraint.

4. The process of identifying the causes of any problems in a design and finding ways to fix them is called
   a. troubleshooting.
   b. prototyping.
   c. patenting.
   d. communicating.

5. The process of evaluating the possible problems of a technology compared to its expected advantages is called
   a. feedback.
   b. risk-benefit analysis.
   c. brainstorming.
   d. prototyping.

If the statement is true, write _true_. If it is false, change the underlined word or words to make the statement true.

6. <u>Science</u> is how people change the natural world around them to meet their needs.

7. All <u>systems</u> are made of parts that work together.

8. An <u>input</u> is something put into a system.

9. A <u>trade-off</u> is an exchange in which one benefit is given up in order to obtain another.

10. The government issues a <u>prototype</u> to protect a person's invention.

Writing in Science

News Report Choose a modern day technology product, such as airplanes, with which you are familiar. Imagine that you are a news reporter covering the product's first introduction to the public. Write a 30-second informative report to be broadcast on the evening news.

Discovery CHANNEL SCHOOL
Technology and Engineering
Video Preview
Video Field Trip
▶ Video Assessment

Chapter 3 P ◆ 119

Go Online
PHSchool.com
For: Self-Assessment
Visit: PHSchool.com
Web Code: cga-6030

Students can take a practice test online that is automatically scored.

All in One Teaching Resources
- Transparency P39
- Chapter Test
- Performance Assessment Teacher Notes
- Performance Assessment Student Worksheet
- Performance Assessment Scoring Rubric

💿 **ExamView® Computer Test Bank CD-ROM**

Review and Assessment

Organizing Information
a. To understand how it functions
b. To change it to meet human needs
c. To change it to solve problems

Reviewing Key Terms
1. d **2.** c **3.** d **4.** a **5.** b
6. Technology
7. true
8. true
9. true
10. patent

Writing in Science

Writing Mode Description
Scoring Rubric
4 Exceeds criteria; includes an excellent description of a complicated technology and/or is well written in a way that captures the reader's interest
3 Meets criteria
2 Does not describe a technology well and/or is less than a 30-second report
1 Includes only brief and/or inaccurate information

Discovery CHANNEL SCHOOL Video Assessment

Technology and Engineering

Show the Video Assessment to review chapter content and as a prompt for the writing assignment. Discussion questions: **How did the design process help the Wright brothers perfect their aircraft?** *(They identified the need of motorized flight. Wilbur researched the problem by reading everything he could about flight. Wilbur designed a solution called wing warp. He built a full-scale glider as a prototype. The brothers spent three years troubleshooting and redesigning their glider.)* **How did they achieve the final step of the design process—communicating their achievement?** *(After their successful flight, they informed the press. Later, they demonstrated their aircraft for the U.S. government.)*

Checking Concepts

11. Technology's overall goal is to improve the way people live.

12. Sample answer: Obsolete technology—manual typewriters; emerging technology—writing with computers and voice-recognition software

13. Sample answer: They might read articles, attend conferences, perform experiments, and discuss the problem with others, including potential customers.

14. Sample answer: The prototype can be used to test the effectiveness of a design.

15. Sample answer: Yes. One example is that when my great-grandparents were children, their families didn't have telephones. So, they communicated only with neighbors and with others at community and social events. When they were older, however, they communicated with others all over the world using telephones and even electronic mail.

16. Sample answer: Cellphone. It allows me to talk with others at nearly any time. Because I carry my cellular phone almost everywhere, however, I sometimes feel as if I have no time and place to think or to read quietly.

17. Sample answer: Risk-benefit analysis can help you decide whether or not to buy and use a new technology by comparing the possible risks and advantages of using it.

Thinking Critically

18. Sample answer: The meteorologist might use satellite images to predict, detect, and track hurricanes and to warn residents in places that might be affected by them. When scientists discover how to make satellite images clearer, satellite engineers can apply the methods to improve satellite technology.

19. Input—step on the gas pedal; process—gas makes the engine run; output—car moves forward; feedback—how fast the car moves forward

20. Sample answer: I would research ways in which the keyboard could be made of more durable materials and redesigned to improve appearance without increasing hand strain.

Checking Concepts

11. What is the overall goal of technology?

12. Give an example of an obsolete technology and an emerging technology.

13. What steps might engineers take to research a design problem fully?

14. Why is building a prototype an important part of the technology design process?

15. Do you think that technology affected the lives of people living in your great-grandparents' generation? Explain.

16. List one example of technology that has increased the pace of your life. What positive and negative impact has this technology had?

17. Why is risk-benefit analysis important in deciding whether to use a new technology?

Thinking Critically

18. Relating Cause and Effect How might a meteorologist who tracks hurricanes depend on satellite technology? How might satellite engineers depend on the work of scientists?

19. Classifying For the system shown below, identify the input, process, and output.

Car moves forward   Driver steps on gas pedal   Gas makes engine run

20. Problem Solving Your team is designing a new computer keyboard. From prototype tests, you learn that the keyboard successfully reduces hand strain, but that it breaks easily. Users also complained about the keyboard's appearance. How would you proceed?

21. Predicting What "Age" do you think people will be living in 100 years from now? What types of technological products will be most common then?

22. Making Judgments How do you think consumers can best obtain information about the risks and benefits of a technology before they purchase it?

Applying Skills

Use the table to answer Questions 23–26.

This table shows the types of trains in use in the United States in 1900 and 1960.

Number of Trains in Use in the United States, 1900 and 1960		
Type	**1900**	**1960**
Steam trains	37,463	374
Electric trains	200	498
Diesel trains	0	30,240

23. Interpreting Data What kinds of trains existed in the United States in 1900? In 1960?

24. Calculating How did the number of steam trains change between 1900 and 1960? How did the number of electric and diesel trains change?

25. Inferring Which type of train met people's needs best in 1960? What is your evidence?

26. Drawing Conclusions Based on this table, what can you conclude about the progress of train technology between 1900 and 1960?

Lab zone Chapter **Project**

Performance Assessment Before testing your chair, explain to your classmates why you designed your chair the way you did. How did you join the pieces of cardboard together? How did you address the design constraints? When you test your model, examine how sturdy your chair is while supporting 20 kilograms of books. How could you improve your chair's design?

Lab zone Chapter **Project**

Performance Assessment Talk with each student or group before the presentation. Offer encouragement, and make suggestions about how to present the chair in an interesting and informative way. Assess the presentations on the basis of how well the chair is constructed and how well the group or student communicates the good qualities of the chair's design.

In assessing their chairs, students should reflect on the design process used, the materials utilized, the final design of the chair, and how well the chair held the weight of the books. Students should assess their chairs compared with the chairs of others in the class and suggest ways in which they could have improved their designs.

Standardized Test Prep

Choose the letter of the best answer.

1. A jacket made of a new, lightweight material has just been designed. Which of the following prototypes could be used to test how comfortable the jacket is to wear?

   A a computer model of the jacket
   B a miniature version of the jacket
   C a full-sized version of the jacket, made of cotton
   D a full-sized version of the jacket, made of the new material

2. Engineers have designed a car with a new engine and body design. Which of the following trade-offs would have a negative impact on public safety?

   F choosing lower-cost materials over good results in crash tests
   G choosing the appearance of the car seats over their comfort
   H choosing to install a more powerful music system over a better air conditioning system
   J choosing a more powerful engine over better gas mileage

3. A new robotic vacuum cleaner that was developed this year is an example of

   A an obsolete technology.
   B an emerging technology.
   C a construction technology.
   D a communication technology.

Use the graph below to answer Questions 4–5. The graph shows predicted worldwide sales of digital versatile disc (DVD) recorders.

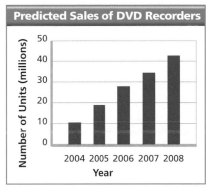

Predicted Sales of DVD Recorders

4. What are predicted sales for the year 2006?

   F 100,000   **G** 1,000,000
   H 280,000   **J** 2,800,000

5. What prediction can you make about the sale of DVD recorders after 2008?

   A No DVD recorders will be sold in 2009.
   B People will buy DVD recorders forever.
   C People will continue to buy DVD recorders until a new technology better fulfills their needs.
   D The number of DVD recorders sold will be unaffected by any emerging technology.

Constructed Response

6. Suppose a newly designed robot automatically scans products at checkout lines in supermarkets. The robot can perform no other function. The cost to install a robot at a cash register is less than the cost of hiring a cashier. Describe some of the positive and negative impacts that this new technology might have on society.

21. Students' answers may be creative. Sample answer: It will be called the Teleport Age. Typical U.S. homes will have shower-sized teleports that will send and receive people electronically anywhere on Earth and nearby planets in seconds.

22. Sample answer: Consumers can research through books, articles, and the Internet and by consulting experts and government agencies that may have information about the technology.

Applying Skills

23. 1900—steam trains and electric trains; 1960—steam trains, electric trains, diesel trains

24. The number of steam trains decreased from 37,463 to 374. The number of electric trains increased from 200 to 498. The number of diesel trains increased from 0 to 30,240.

25. Diesel trains met their needs best, since 30,240 diesel trains were in use compared with 498 electric trains and 364 steam trains.

26. Technologies that affected steam trains progressed little or not at all. Technologies that affected electric trains may have progressed slightly. Technologies that affected diesel trains progressed greatly.

Standardized Test Prep

1. D   **2.** F   **3.** B   **4.** J   **5.** C

6. Sample answer: Positive impacts will include lower cost of operation for the supermarket, fewer errors in the checkout process, and faster checkout for consumers. Negative impacts will include loss of jobs at the supermarket and a more impersonal experience for the consumer.

Interdisciplinary Exploration

Edison—Genius of Invention

This interdisciplinary feature presents the central theme of the American Thomas Edison as a genius of invention by connecting four different disciplines: science, language arts, mathematics, and social studies. The four explorations are designed to capture students' interest and help them see how the content they are studying in science relates to other school subjects and to real-world events. Share with others for a team-teaching experience.

All in One Teaching Resources

- Interdisciplinary Exploration: *Science*
- Interdisciplinary Exploration: *Language Arts*
- Interdisciplinary Exploration: *Mathematics*
- Interdisciplinary Exploration: *Social Studies*

Build Background Knowledge
Technology Powered by Electricity

Help students recall what they have previously learned about electric charges and electric currents. Ask: **What causes a current to flow through an electric circuit?** *(Voltage)* **What are examples of voltage sources?** *(Batteries and generators)* **How do series and parallel circuits differ?** *(In a series circuit, there is only one path for the charges to follow. In a parallel circuit, there are several paths.)* **What is resistance?** *(Resistance is something that slows down the flow of charge.)*

Introduce the Exploration

Ask: **Have you ever been without electricity? What was it like?** *(Sample answer: The electricity went out in a storm and stayed out for hours. It was scary without electric lights.)* **Have you ever had to make do using only candles or oil lamps? How is electricity better?** *(Sample answer: During electric outages, candles and oil lamps have provided some light. Electric lights are much brighter. They also seem safer, because they provide light without a flame.)* Then, tell students a little about Thomas Edison, including that he received little school education and was mostly home schooled.

Edison— Genius of Invention

What inventor gave us
- sound recording?
- motion pictures?
- electric lighting?

In 1881, the electric light was a novelty. City streets and some homes were lit with gas. Most homes used oil lamps or candles. Thomas Edison was still developing his system of indoor electric lighting.

Electric lights brought with them a system of power distribution, which made other uses of electricity possible. Imagine living without any electrical appliances, and you'll understand the changes in everyday life that Edison started.

Thomas Edison (1847–1931) had almost no schooling. Yet his mind bubbled with ideas. At the time of his death, Edison held 1,093 patents. A patent is a government license protecting an inventor's right to make and sell a product. One of Edison's most important ideas was never patented. He created the first laboratory for industrial research.

The First Light Bulb
This is a model of Edison's first successful lamp. The light bulb is made of a carbon filament inside a glass bulb. Electricity flowing through the filament makes the filament white hot, so that it glows. Below, a drawing of the light bulb appears in a Menlo Park notebook.

Thomas Edison at 14
Edison worked as a telegrapher for about ten years.

122 ◆ P

The Wizard of Menlo Park

Before 1900, most inventors worked alone. Edison, in contrast, depended on a strong team of research co-workers to carry out his ideas. Edison had an unusual ability to inspire those who worked for him. Some of his original team stayed with him for years. A very hard worker himself, Edison demanded that everyone on his team also work long hours.

By 1876, Edison had enough money to set up an "invention factory." He chose the small town of Menlo Park, New Jersey. His Menlo Park laboratory became the world's first industrial research laboratory.

Edison's team often made improvements on other people's inventions. The light bulb is an example. Other scientists had invented electric lamps, but their light bulbs burned rapidly. The problem was to find a material for the filament that would not overheat or burn out quickly.

The Menlo Park team spent months testing hundreds of materials. First, they rolled each material into a long, thin strand. Then, they carbonized it, which meant baking it until it turned to charcoal. Finally, they tested it in a vacuum, or in the absence of air. Most materials failed in only a few minutes or a few hours. The breakthrough came in 1879. The first successful filament was a length of ordinary cotton thread, carefully carbonized. The newspapers carried the headlines "Success in a Cotton Thread" and "It Makes a Light, Without Gas or Flame."

Edison's Lab
Edison set up his research laboratory in Menlo Park.

Science Activity

Work together as a team to invent a new electrical device.

- What could a new electrical device help you do? How could it make your life easier?
- Brainstorm for possible products that would help you in some way. Write down all possible ideas.
- Evaluate each solution and agree on the best one.
- Plan your design and make a labeled drawing. List the supplies you will need. Note any new skills you should learn.
- Write down the steps you will use to build your device.

Science

Explore Science Concepts

Discuss Ask: **Why do you think many inventors work alone?** *(Sample answer: An inventor is often a creative person who might not accomplish anything for a while and then suddenly have an inspiration that works out.)* Point out that Edison worked long hours with a loyal team of employees. **Why do you think people worked so hard for Edison?** *(Sample answer: People worked hard because Edison set an example by working hard himself.)*

Use Visuals Have students look at the photo and diagram of an early light bulb, and ask a student to read the caption aloud. Ask: **What is a light bulb's filament?** *(A long, thin strand of material or wire)* **What causes the light produced by a light bulb?** *(Electricity flowing through the filament makes the filament white hot, producing light.)* Explain that most material from living things is made of molecules that contain carbon. Baking a carbon material can turn it into a kind of charcoal, a process called carbonization. Ask: **What was Edison's first successful filament?** *(A length of ordinary cotton thread, carefully carbonized)*

Science Activity

Focus Ask: **What are some electrical devices that you think don't work very well?** *(Sample answer: A toaster too often burns the bread. The alarm of an electric alarm clock sometimes doesn't go off on time.)* Ask students to suggest ways in which these devices might be improved.

Teach Preview the activity with students, and then divide the class into teams. Give teams 10–15 minutes to brainstorm a list of possible products, and then briefly review the list with each team, suggesting which ideas might be productive. Encourage each team to choose one idea and proceed on to the design phase.

Expected Outcome Students on each team should specifically describe how a new electrical device could make life easier. A design for a new device should be detailed, with a labeled drawing that shows the different parts and the electrical circuitry. Each team should have a list of supplies they would need, as well as a procedure that could be used to build the device.

Background

History After having scarlet fever as a child, Edison began to lose his hearing. Eventually he was completely deaf in one ear and had only slight hearing in the other. Edison felt this was a benefit because he could not hear what he called "foolish small talk" and had more time to think. Despite ear surgeries, Edison's hearing continued to decline.

Possibly because of his hearing loss,

Edison did poorly in school. One of Edison's teachers was very strict and punished students for asking questions. Because Edison liked to ask questions, he was punished. The teacher declared Edison was too confused to be able to learn. Edison's mother met with the teacher and became very angry. She then decided to teach Edison at home.

Explore Language Arts Concepts

Use Maps Some students may not know where Manhattan is. Use a large map of the United States to show the location of New York state and New York City. Use a road atlas to show the location of Manhattan. Show the route of Broadway through lower Manhattan, where Edison's first generating station supplied power.

Oral Presentation Ask a volunteer to read the Times article. Point out that this period was before the advent of the automobile. Ask: **What kind of artificial light does the writer compare the electric lamps to?** (*Gas burners*) **How did the writer describe the quality of the light from the electric lamps?** (*The writer wrote that the "light was soft, mellow, and grateful to the eye."*) **What does the writer mean by the phrase "without a particle of flicker"?** (*The writer means that the light was steady and not flickering like a flame flickers.*)

Language Arts Activity

Focus Show students a junk-mail letter that attempts to persuade the reader to buy a product or pay for a service. Ask: **What are some strategies such letters use to persuade the reader to try the product or service?** (*They describe in glowing detail how the product or service will improve the reader's life.*)

Teach Before students tackle the writing activity, ask: **What advantages could Edison relate about electric light bulbs that might persuade readers of his time?** (*Sample answer: The warm, stead glow of an electric light; the convenience and safety of light bulbs versus gas lamps*) Point out that people are often suspicious of new technologies. Ask students to imagine the fears people might have had about having electricity in their homes.

Writing Mode Persuasion
Scoring Rubric
4 Exceeds criteria; provides accurate details about the Edison's light bulbs and power system in an imaginative and persuasive context
3 Meets criteria
2 Meets some criteria; is only somewhat descriptive and/or persuasive
1 Includes few details about the electric lights and/or fails in writing persuasively

Lighting Manhattan

Edison recognized the value of publicity. Besides being a productive inventor, he knew how to promote himself. He made glowing predictions about his new electric system. Electricity would soon be so cheap, he said, that "only the rich would be able to afford candles."

When he built his first neighborhood generating station, Edison made a shrewd choice of location. The Pearl Street power station brought light and power to about 2.6 square kilometers of downtown Manhattan. It supplied businesses and factories, as well as private homes. The circuits could light 400 light bulbs. Some of those lights were in the offices of J. P. Morgan, the leading banker and financier of the time. Other lights were located in the offices of *The New York Times*. Here's what the *Times* reporter wrote on September 5, 1882.

New York City
This photo shows Broadway in the 1880s.

SEPTEMBER 5, 1882—Yesterday for the first time The Times Building was illuminated by electricity. Mr. Edison had at last perfected his incandescent light, had put his machinery in order, and had started up his engines, and last evening his company lighted up about one-third of the lower City district in which The Times Building stands.

It was not until about seven o'clock, when it began to grow dark, that the electric light really made itself known and showed how bright and steady it is. It was a light that a man could sit down under and write for hours without the consciousness of having any artificial light about him. There was a very slight amount of heat from each lamp, but not nearly as much as from a gas-burner—one-fifteenth as much as from gas, the inventor says. The light was soft, mellow, and grateful to the eye, and it seemed almost like writing by daylight to have a light without a particle of flicker and with scarcely any heat to make the head ache. The decision was unanimously in favor of the Edison electric lamp as against gas.

——Excerpted with permission from *The New York Times*.

Language Arts Activity

The reporter who wrote the newspaper story observed details carefully and used them to write about an event—the first lights in his office. Look back at the story. Now write about the event as Edison would have told it to convince people to buy light bulbs and install electrical power systems. You could make an advertisement. Inform your readers about the product and persuade them to buy it.

Background

History Edison's mother loved to read, and he adopted her love of reading. Before he was 10 years old, his mother gave him a basic science book. He began performing the experiments he found in the book. Soon he was spending his pocket money on chemical supplies to use in more experiments. By the time he was 12, he got a job selling newspapers and candy to passengers on the train in order to buy books and supplies for a chemistry laboratory in the basement.

Solving Practical Problems

As he grew older, Edison worried that American students were not learning mathematics well enough. To motivate students, he suggested using problems that related to real-life situations. In 1925, when he was 78, he proposed these problems below as recorded in his notebooks. Note that light bulbs were called lamps. Tungsten is a metal used in light bulbs.

Edison Lamp
This advertisement promotes reading by Edison's Mazda lamp.

Problem 1

American power plants now serve 9,500,000 homes. The estimated number of homes in the United States is 21,000,000. What percentage receives electric power?

Problem 2

It needs about 280,000,000 tungsten lamps [bulbs] each year to supply the market today. And yet the first lamp factory in the world—the Edison Lamp Works. . .—was not started until 1880, and I was told it would never pay. The output for our first year was about 25,000 globes [bulbs]. How many times that figure would be required for the present market?

Problem 3

A household using 21 lamps requires about 7 new lamps each year. What percentage is this?

Problem 4

If these lamps had been bought at the retail prices of the first year of the lamp factory, they would have cost $1.25 each. How much would the family save by the decreased prices of today?

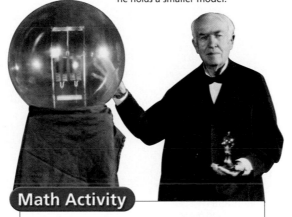

Inventor Thomas Edison
Edison stands next to his original light bulb invention. In his hand, he holds a smaller model.

Math Activity

Solve the four math problems that Edison wrote. To solve Problem 4, use 1902 prices. That year, incandescent light bulbs (or lamps) cost $.30 each.

P ◆ 125

Background

Facts and Figures The incandescent light bulb is not the only type of lighting available. Electric-discharge lamps were developed in the early 1900s. These lamps produce light by applying a voltage to two electrodes at either end of a tube filled with a small amount of gas, such as mercury or sodium. Lights filled with mercury give off a bright, whitish, blue-green light. These lights found use as street lighting in the early part of the twentieth century in the United States. Lights filled with sodium vapor give off a yellow-orange glow. They are used to light streets, highways, and tunnels all over the world. Fluorescent lighting is another type of electric-discharge lamp. Fluorescent lights are used as interior lighting in factories, schools, and office buildings.

Explore Mathematics Concepts

Show Examples If possible, bring to class some very old math textbooks. Have students examine the pages to see how rarely real-world problems were featured in such texts. Ask: **Do you think real-life problems motivate students to learn? Justify your answer.** (*Sample answer: Real-life problems would motivate students by showing them that learning math skills will help in everyday activities.*) Invite students to think of other ways math textbooks could motivate students to learn. Then ask: **What do you think Edison would think of today's math books?** (*Sample answer: He would think they are much more colorful and lively than the old books. There are now more questions that relate to real life.*)

Extend Invite students to make a display of math questions that relate to real-life problems. Challenge students to write problems that they think would motivate others to learn math.

Review Help students recall their understanding of how to calculate percentages. Explain that to find a percentage of a portion of a whole, divide the portion by the whole. The answer is a decimal to the hundredths. For example, suppose there are 14 boys in a class of 30. To calculate the percentage of boys in the class, divide 14 by 30. The result is 0.47. Multiply by 100 to determine the percentage, or 47%.

Math Activity

Focus Tell students that part of marketing a new product is determining how large the market is and what people would pay for the product.

Teach Point out that Problem 2 has extraneous information—the year 1882—that has no bearing on the math problem. Explain that part of problem solving is learning what data you need and don't need to determine an answer. Point out that for Problem 4 students should calculate how much a family would save per lamp.

Answers
1. 45%
2. 11,200
3. 33%
4. $0.95 per lamp

Explore Social Studies Concepts

Discuss Explain that it is a common misconception that Thomas Edison invented the electric light. Point out that Edison did not invent the first electric light; rather, he invented the first practical incandescent light bulb. Ask: **What did Edison develop to distribute electricity to homes and businesses?** (*A central power system*) **Where does the electricity come from that powers the electric devices in your home?** (*Sample answer: From the power plant on the outskirts of town*)

Social Studies Activity

Focus Tell students that electric lights are so bright that they can be seen from satellites orbiting Earth. A satellite image can show population distribution in a country by comparing how bright various areas are at night.

Teach Provide students with a large wall map of the United States, or provide several smaller maps from atlases or encyclopedias to be used by small groups of students. Explain that students should compare the satellite image to the map of the United States and find where lighted areas on the image correlate with large cities on the map. Demonstrate how to do this with New York City or Los Angeles.

Expected Outcome Students' answers may vary because it is difficult to judge where state lines are on the satellite image. Students are likely to note that, with the exception of coastal California and a few scattered cities, the eastern half of the country is more brightly lit and thus more populated than the western half.

According to the U.S. Census Bureau, the population of the United States on April 1, 2000, was 281,421,906. According to the 2000 census, the top five cities were: New York City, 8 million; Los Angeles, 3.7 million; Chicago, 2.9 million; Houston, 2 million; and Philadelphia, 1.3 million. These are populations for cities proper; students may find rankings of U.S. metropolitan areas.

Daily Life Transformed

Edison's inventions in the late 1800s helped spark a technological and social revolution. Some of these inventions forever transformed the way people live, play, and work.

Edison's light bulb made indoor lighting practical. Along with the light bulb, he developed the idea of a central power system to distribute electricity to homes and businesses. That system included generators, underground cables, junction boxes, and meters. Other inventors improved on Edison's ideas for lights and electricity.

Other Edison inventions influenced ways that people entertain themselves. Edison created the phonograph, a rotating disk that could record and play back sounds. About that same time, Edison invented the first movie camera, a device that could store pictures. These inventions spurred the development of the recording and film industries.

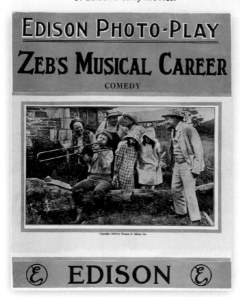

Edison Movie
This poster advertises one of Edison's early movies.

EDISON PHOTO-PLAY
ZEB'S MUSICAL CAREER
COMEDY

EDISON

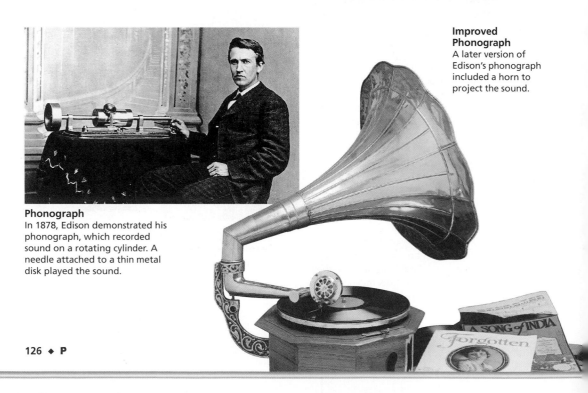

Phonograph
In 1878, Edison demonstrated his phonograph, which recorded sound on a rotating cylinder. A needle attached to a thin metal disk played the sound.

Improved Phonograph
A later version of Edison's phonograph included a horn to project the sound.

A SONG of INDIA
Forgotten

126 ◆ P

Background

Facts and Figures That street lights are visible from space is evidence of the great amount of light they give off. Light pollution is a problem faced by amateur and professional astronomers. The amount of illumination from street lamps, buildings, billboards, and other light sources pointing toward the sky masks stars that should be visible. Light pollution is caused by poorly designed or improperly installed light fixtures. It is estimated that in the United States, $1.5 billion per year in electricity bills is wasted on light going upward into the sky.

Because of light pollution, only a few hundred stars of the more than 320,000 stars that should be visible over North America can be seen in the night sky from most cities and towns in the United States.

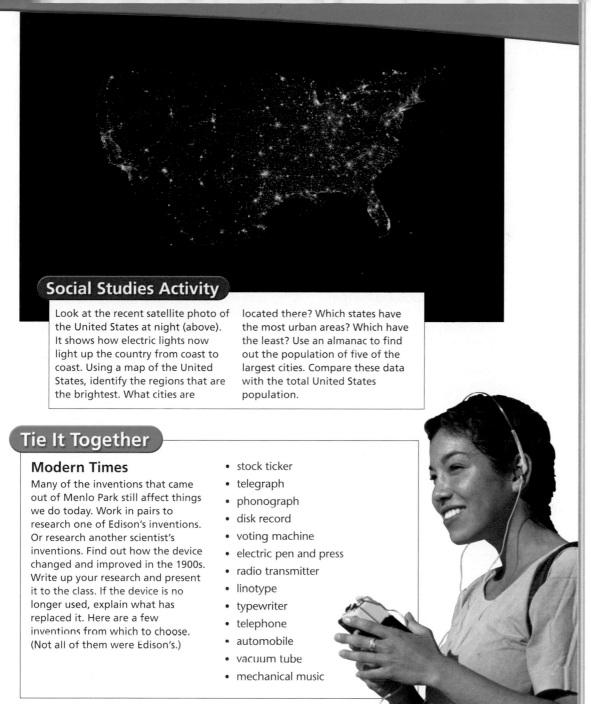

Social Studies Activity

Look at the recent satellite photo of the United States at night (above). It shows how electric lights now light up the country from coast to coast. Using a map of the United States, identify the regions that are the brightest. What cities are located there? Which states have the most urban areas? Which have the least? Use an almanac to find out the population of five of the largest cities. Compare these data with the total United States population.

Tie It Together

Modern Times

Many of the inventions that came out of Menlo Park still affect things we do today. Work in pairs to research one of Edison's inventions. Or research another scientist's inventions. Find out how the device changed and improved in the 1900s. Write up your research and present it to the class. If the device is no longer used, explain what has replaced it. Here are a few inventions from which to choose. (Not all of them were Edison's.)

- stock ticker
- telegraph
- phonograph
- disk record
- voting machine
- electric pen and press
- radio transmitter
- linotype
- typewriter
- telephone
- automobile
- vacuum tube
- mechanical music

Cassette Player
Is this device related to Edison's invention?

P ◆ 127

Modern Times

Time 3 days (2 days for research; 1 day for presentations)

Tips Encourage students to choose any invention from Edison's time that interests them. Display a sheet in the classroom where students can record the invention they will research to ensure that different groups research different inventions.

• Encourage students to make photocopies or flag the pages of books that show illustrations of the inventor, early versions of the invention, or other interesting graphics. Tell students to research enough material to be able to give a five-minute presentation.

• In the research stage, suggest that students visit a local historical museum or center of science and technology to see some of these inventions firsthand.

Other Resources Many excellent books have been published about inventors and inventions. Encyclopedias, both print and online, are also good sources of information. In addition, using the term *inventions* in an Internet search engine will yield a number of informative web sites. Your school media specialist can help you plan this activity and work with students to help them develop their information literacy skills as they locate resources, conduct research, and prepare their presentations.

Extend Students may wish to combine their research findings to make a classroom display or hall display for the school.

• Some students may want to research the lives of other inventors who lived during Edison's time period. Encourage these students to present their findings as biographies.

• Suggest that students find out about present-day inventors by researching one of the organizations that help inventors. Students may also be able to find information on web sites or in magazines published by these organizations. Have these students present their findings to the class.

Think Like a Scientist

The Skills Handbook is designed as a reference for students to use whenever they need to review inquiry, reading, or math skills. You can use the activities in this part of the Skills Handbook to teach or reinforce inquiry skills.

Observing

Focus Remind students that an observation is what they can see, hear, smell, taste, or feel.

Teach Invite students to make observations of the classroom. List these observations on the board. Challenge students to identify the senses they used to make each observation. Then, ask: **Which senses will you use to make observations from the photograph on this page?** (Sight is the only sense that can be used to make observations from the photograph.)

Activity

Some observations that students might make include that the boy is skateboarding, wearing a white helmet, and flying in the air. Make sure that students' observations are confined to only things that they can actually see in the photograph.

Inferring

Focus Choose one or two of the classroom observations listed on the board, and challenge students to interpret them. Guide students by asking why something appears as it does.

Teach Encourage students to describe their thought processes in making their inferences. Point out where they used their knowledge and experience to interpret the observations. Then invite students to suggest other possible interpretations for the observations. Ask: **How can you find out whether an inference is correct?** (By further investigation)

Activity

One possible inference is that the boy just skated off a ramp at a skate park. Invite students to share their experiences that helped them make the inference.

Predicting

Focus Discuss the weather forecast for the next day. Point out that this prediction is an inference about what will happen in the

Think Like a Scientist

Although you may not know it, you think like a scientist every day. Whenever you ask a question and explore possible answers, you use many of the same skills that scientists do. Some of these skills are described on this page.

Observing

When you use one or more of your five senses to gather information about the world, you are **observing.** Hearing a dog bark, counting twelve green seeds, and smelling smoke are all observations. To increase the power of their senses, scientists sometimes use microscopes, telescopes, or other instruments that help them make more detailed observations.

An observation must be an accurate report of what your senses detect. It is important to keep careful records of your observations in science class by writing or drawing in a notebook. The information collected through observations is called evidence, or data.

Inferring

When you interpret an observation, you are **inferring,** or making an inference. For example, if you hear your dog barking, you may infer that someone is at your front door. To make this inference, you combine the evidence—the barking dog—and your experience or knowledge—you know that your dog barks when strangers approach—to reach a logical conclusion.

Notice that an inference is not a fact; it is only one of many possible interpretations for an observation. For example, your dog may be barking because it wants to go for a walk. An inference may turn out to be incorrect even if it is based on accurate observations and logical reasoning. The only way to find out if an inference is correct is to investigate further.

Predicting

When you listen to the weather forecast, you hear many predictions about the next day's weather—what the temperature will be, whether it will rain, and how windy it will be. Weather forecasters use observations and knowledge of weather patterns to predict the weather. The skill of **predicting** involves making an inference about a future event based on current evidence or past experience.

Because a prediction is an inference, it may prove to be false. In science class, you can test some of your predictions by doing experiments. For example, suppose you predict that larger paper airplanes can fly farther than smaller airplanes. How could you test your prediction?

Activity

Use the photograph to answer the questions below.

Observing Look closely at the photograph. List at least three observations.

Inferring Use your observations to make an inference about what has happened. What experience or knowledge did you use to make the inference?

Predicting Predict what will happen next. On what evidence or experience do you base your prediction?

future based on observations and experience.

Teach Help students differentiate between a prediction and an inference. You might organize the similarities and differences in a Venn diagram on the board. Both are interpretations of observations using experience and knowledge, and both can be incorrect. Inferences describe current or past events. Predictions describe future events.

Activity

Students might predict that the boy will land and skate to the other side. Others might predict that the boy will fall. Students should also describe the evidence or experience on which they based their predictions.

Classifying

Could you imagine searching for a book in the library if the books were shelved in no particular order? Your trip to the library would be an all-day event! Luckily, librarians group together books on similar topics or by the same author. Grouping together items that are alike in some way is called **classifying.** You can classify items in many ways: by size, by shape, by use, and by other important characteristics.

Like librarians, scientists use the skill of classifying to organize information and objects. When things are sorted into groups, the relationships among them become easier to understand.

Activity

Classify the objects in the photograph into two groups based on any characteristic you choose. Then use another characteristic to classify the objects into three groups.

Activity

This student is using a model to demonstrate what causes day and night on Earth. What do the flashlight and the tennis ball in the model represent?

Making Models

Have you ever drawn a picture to help someone understand what you were saying? Such a drawing is one type of model. A model is a picture, diagram, computer image, or other representation of a complex object or process. **Making models** helps people understand things that they cannot observe directly.

Scientists often use models to represent things that are either very large or very small, such as the planets in the solar system, or the parts of a cell. Such models are physical models—drawings or three-dimensional structures that look like the real thing. Other models are mental models—mathematical equations or words that describe how something works.

Communicating

Whenever you talk on the phone, write a letter, or listen to your teacher at school, you are communicating. **Communicating** is the process of sharing ideas and information with other people. Communicating effectively requires many skills, including writing, reading, speaking, listening, and making models.

Scientists communicate to share results, information, and opinions. Scientists often communicate about their work in journals, over the telephone, in letters, and on the Internet.

They also attend scientific meetings where they share their ideas with one another in person.

Activity

On a sheet of paper, write out clear, detailed directions for tying your shoe. Then exchange directions with a partner. Follow your partner's directions exactly. How successful were you at tying your shoe? How could your partner have communicated more clearly?

Classifying

Focus Encourage students to think of common things that are classified.

Teach Ask: **What things at home are classified?** (*Clothing might be classified in order to place it in the appropriate dresser drawer; glasses, plates, and silverware are grouped in different parts of the kitchen; screws, nuts, bolts, washers, and nails might be separated into small containers.*) **What are some things that scientists classify?** (*Scientists classify many things they study, including organisms, geological features and processes, and kinds of machines.*)

Activity

Some characteristics students might use include color, pattern of color, use of balls, and size. Students' criteria for classification should clearly divide the balls into two, and then three, distinct groups.

Making Models

Focus Ask: **What are some models you have used to study science?** (*Students might have used human anatomical models, solar system models, maps, or stream tables.*) **How have these models helped you?** (*Models can help you learn about things that are difficult to study because they are very large, very small, or highly complex.*)

Teach Be sure students understand that a model does not have to be three-dimensional. For example, a map is a model, as is a mathematical equation. Have students look at the photograph of the student modeling the causes of day and night on Earth. Ask: **What quality of each item makes this a good model?** (*The flashlight gives off light, and the ball is round and can be rotated by the student.*)

Activity

The flashlight represents the sun and the ball represents Earth.

Communicating

Focus Have students identify the methods of communication they have used today.

Teach Ask: **How is the way you communicate with a friend similar to and different from the way scientists communicate about their work to other scientists?** (*Both may communicate using various methods, but scientists must be very detailed and precise, whereas communication between friends may be less detailed and precise.*) Encourage students to communicate like a scientist as they carry out the activity.

Activity

Students' answers will vary but should identify a step-by-step process for tying a shoe. Help students identify communication errors such as leaving out a step, putting steps in the wrong order, or disregarding the person's handedness.

Making Measurements

Students can refer to this part of the Skills Handbook whenever they need to review how to make measurements with SI units. You can use the activities here to teach or reinforce SI units.

Measuring in SI

Focus Review SI units with students. Begin by providing metric rulers, graduated cylinders, balances, and Celsius thermometers. Use these tools to reinforce that the meter is the unit of length, the liter is the unit of volume, the gram is the unit of mass, and the degree Celsius is the unit of temperature.

Teach Ask: **If you want to measure the length and the width of the classroom, which SI unit would you use?** *(Meter)* **Which unit would you use to measure the amount of mass in your textbook?** *(Gram)* **Which would you use to measure how much water a drinking glass holds?** *(Liter)* **When would you use the Celsius scale?** *(To measure the temperature of something)* Then use the measuring equipment to review SI prefixes. For example, ask: **What are the smallest units on the metric ruler?** *(Millimeters)* **How many millimeters are there in one centimeter?** *(10 millimeters)* **How many in 10 centimeters?** *(100 millimeters)* **How many centimeters are there in one meter?** *(100 centimeters)* **What does 1,000 meters equal?** *(One kilometer)*

Activity

Length The length of the shell is 7.8 centimeters, or 78 millimeters. If students need more practice measuring length, have them use meter sticks and metric rulers to measure various objects in the classroom.

Activity

Liquid Volume The volume of water in the graduated cylinder is 62 milliliters. If students need more practice, have them use a graduated cylinder to measure different volumes of water.

Making Measurements

When scientists make observations, it is not sufficient to say that something is "big" or "heavy." Instead, scientists use instruments to measure just how big or heavy an object is. By measuring, scientists can express their observations more precisely and communicate more information about what they observe.

Measuring in SI

The standard system of measurement used by scientists around the world is known as the International System of Units, which is abbreviated as SI (in French, **Système International d'Unités**). SI units are easy to use because they are based on multiples of 10. Each unit is ten times larger than the next smallest unit and one tenth the size of the next largest unit. The table lists the prefixes used to name the most common SI units.

Common SI Prefixes		
Prefix	Symbol	Meaning
kilo-	k	1,000
hecto-	h	100
deka-	da	10
deci-	d	0.1 (one tenth)
centi-	c	0.01 (one hundredth)
milli-	m	0.001 (one thousandth)

Length To measure length, or the distance between two points, the unit of measure is the **meter (m)**. The distance from the floor to a doorknob is approximately one meter. Long distances, such as the distance between two cities, are measured in kilometers (km). Small lengths are measured in centimeters (cm) or millimeters (mm). Scientists use metric rulers and meter sticks to measure length.

Common Conversions	
1 km	= 1,000 m
1 m	= 100 cm
1 m	= 1,000 mm
1 cm	= 10 mm

Liquid Volume To measure the volume of a liquid, or the amount of space it takes up, you will use a unit of measure known as the **liter (L)**. One liter is the approximate volume of a medium-size carton of milk. Smaller volumes are measured in milliliters (mL). Scientists use graduated cylinders to measure liquid volume.

Activity

The graduated cylinder in the picture is marked in milliliter divisions. Notice that the water in the cylinder has a curved surface. This curved surface is called the *meniscus*. To measure the volume, you must read the level at the lowest point of the meniscus. What is the volume of water in this graduated cylinder?

Common Conversion
1 L = 1,000 mL

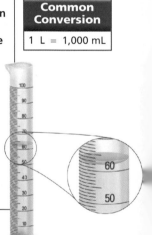

Activity

The larger lines on the metric ruler in the picture show centimeter divisions, while the smaller, unnumbered lines show millimeter divisions. How many centimeters long is the shell? How many millimeters long is it?

Mass To measure mass, or the amount of matter in an object, you will use a unit of measure known as the **gram (g).** One gram is approximately the mass of a paper clip. Larger masses are measured in kilograms (kg). Scientists use a balance to find the mass of an object.

Common Conversion

1 kg = 1,000 g

Activity

The mass of the potato in the picture is measured in kilograms. What is the mass of the potato? Suppose a recipe for potato salad called for one kilogram of potatoes. About how many potatoes would you need?

0.25 KG

Temperature To measure the temperature of a substance, you will use the **Celsius scale.** Temperature is measured in degrees Celsius (°C) using a Celsius thermometer. Water freezes at 0°C and boils at 100°C.

Time The unit scientists use to measure time is the **second (s).**

Activity

What is the temperature of the liquid in degrees Celsius?

Converting SI Units

To use the SI system, you must know how to convert between units. Converting from one unit to another involves the skill of **calculating,** or using mathematical operations. Converting between SI units is similar to converting between dollars and dimes because both systems are based on multiples of ten.

Suppose you want to convert a length of 80 centimeters to meters. Follow these steps to convert between units.

1. Begin by writing down the measurement you want to convert—in this example, 80 centimeters.

2. Write a conversion factor that represents the relationship between the two units you are converting. In this example, the relationship is 1 meter = 100 centimeters. Write this conversion factor as a fraction, making sure to place the units you are converting from (centimeters, in this example) in the denominator.

3. Multiply the measurement you want to convert by the fraction. When you do this, the units in the first measurement will cancel out with the units in the denominator. Your answer will be in the units you are converting to (meters, in this example).

Example

80 centimeters = ■ meters

$$80 \text{ centimeters} \times \frac{1 \text{ meter}}{100 \text{ centimeters}} = \frac{80 \text{ meters}}{100}$$

$$= 0.8 \text{ meters}$$

Activity

Convert between the following units.
1. 600 millimeters = ■ meters
2. 0.35 liters = ■ milliliters
3. 1,050 grams = ■ kilograms

Skills Handbook ◆ 131

Activity

Mass The mass of the potato is 0.25 kilograms. You would need 4 potatoes to make one kilogram. If students need more practice, give them various objects, such as coins, paper clips, and books, to measure mass.

Activity

Temperature The temperature of the liquid is 35°C. Students who need more practice can measure the temperatures of various water samples.

Converting SI Units

Focus Review the steps for converting SI units, and work through the example with students.

Teach Ask: **How many millimeters are in 80 centimeters?** (*With the relationship 10 millimeters = 1 centimeter, students should follow the steps to calculate that 80 centimeters is equal to 800 millimeters.*) Have students do the conversion problems in the activity.

Activity

1. *600 millimeters = 0.6 meters*
2. *0.35 liters = 350 milliliters*
3. *1,050 grams = 1.05 kilograms*
If students need more practice converting SI units, have them make up conversion problems to trade with partners.

Conducting a Scientific Investigation

Students can refer to this part of the Skills Handbook whenever they need to review the steps of a scientific investigation. You can use the activities here to teach or reinforce these steps.

Posing Questions

Focus Ask: **What do you do when you want to learn about something?** *(Answers might include asking questions about it or looking for information in books or on the Internet.)* Explain that scientists go through the same process to learn about something.

Teach Tell students that the questions scientists ask may have no answers or many different answers. To answer their questions, scientists often conduct experiments. Ask: **Why is a scientific question important to a scientific investigation?** *(It helps the scientist decide if an experiment is necessary; the answer might already be known. It also helps focus the idea so that the scientist can form a hypothesis.)* **What is the scientific question in the activity on the next page?** *(Is a ball's bounce affected by the height from which it is dropped?)*

Developing a Hypothesis

Focus Emphasize that a hypothesis is one possible explanation for a set of observations. It is *not* a guess. It is often based on an inference.

Teach Ask: **On what information do scientists base their hypotheses?** *(Their observations and previous knowledge or experience)* Point out that a hypothesis does not always turn out to be correct. Ask: **When a hypothesis turns out to be incorrect, do you think the scientist wasted his or her time? Explain.** *(No. The scientist learned from the investigation and will develop another hypothesis that could prove to be correct.)*

Designing an Experiment

Focus Have a volunteer read the Experimental Procedure in the box. Invite students to identify the manipulated variable *(amount of salt)*, the variables kept constant *(amount and temperature of water, location of containers)*, the control *(Container 3)*, and the responding variable *(time required for the water to freeze)*.

Conducting a Scientific Investigation

In some ways, scientists are like detectives, piecing together clues to learn about a process or event. One way that scientists gather clues is by carrying out experiments. An experiment tests an idea in a careful, orderly manner. Although experiments do not all follow the same steps in the same order, many follow a pattern similar to the one described here.

Posing Questions

Experiments begin by asking a scientific question. A scientific question is one that can be answered by gathering evidence. For example, the question "Which freezes faster—fresh water or salt water?" is a scientific question because you can carry out an investigation and gather information to answer the question.

Developing a Hypothesis

The next step is to form a hypothesis. A **hypothesis** is a possible explanation for a set of observations or answer to a scientific question. In science, a hypothesis must be something that can be tested. A hypothesis can be worded as an *If . . . then . . .* statement. For example, a hypothesis might be *"If I add salt to fresh water, then the water will take longer to freeze."* A hypothesis worded this way serves as a rough outline of the experiment you should perform.

132 ◆ P

Teach Ask: **How might the experiment be affected if Container 1 had only 100 milliliters of water?** *(It wouldn't be an accurate comparison with the containers that have more water.)* Also make sure that students understand the importance of the control. Then, ask: **What operational definition is used in this experiment?** *("Frozen" means the time at which a wooden stick can no longer move in a container.)*

Designing an Experiment

Next you need to plan a way to test your hypothesis. Your plan should be written out as a step-by-step procedure and should describe the observations or measurements you will make.

Two important steps involved in designing an experiment are controlling variables and forming operational definitions.

Controlling Variables In a well-designed experiment, you need to keep all variables the same except for one. A **variable** is any factor that can change in an experiment. The factor that you change is called the manipulated variable. In this experiment, the **manipulated variable** is the amount of salt added to the water. Other factors, such as the amount of water or the starting temperature, are kept constant.

The factor that changes as a result of the manipulated variable is called the **responding variable.** The responding variable is what you measure or observe to obtain your results. In this experiment, the responding variable is how long the water takes to freeze.

An experiment in which all factors except one are kept constant is called a **controlled experiment.** Most controlled experiments include a test called the control. In this experiment, Container 3 is the control. Because no salt is added to Container 3, you can compare the results from the other containers to it. Any difference in results must be due to the addition of salt alone.

Forming Operational Definitions Another important aspect of a well-designed experiment is having clear operational definitions. An **operational definition** is a statement that describes how a particular variable is to be measured or how a term is to be defined. For example, in this experiment, how will you determine if the water has frozen? You might decide to insert a stick in each container at the start of the experiment. Your operational definition of "frozen" would be the time at which the stick can no longer move.

Experimental Procedure
1. Fill 3 containers with 300 millileters of cold tap water.
2. Add 10 grams of salt to Container 1; stir. Add 20 grams of salt to Container 2; stir. Add no salt to Container 3.
3. Place the 3 containers in a freezer.
4. Check the containers every 15 minutes. Record your observations.

Interpreting Data

The observations and measurements you make in an experiment are called **data.** At the end of an experiment, you need to analyze the data to look for any patterns or trends. Patterns often become clear if you organize your data in a data table or graph. Then think through what the data reveal. Do they support your hypothesis? Do they point out a flaw in your experiment? Do you need to collect more data?

Drawing Conclusions

A **conclusion** is a statement that sums up what you have learned from an experiment. When you draw a conclusion, you need to decide whether the data you collected support your hypothesis or not. You may need to repeat an experiment several times before you can draw any conclusions from it. Conclusions often lead you to pose new questions and plan new experiments to answer them.

Activity

Is a ball's bounce affected by the height from which it is dropped? Using the steps just described, plan a controlled experiment to investigate this problem.

Skills Handbook ◆ 133

Interpreting Data

Focus Ask: **What kind of data would you collect from the experiment with freezing salt water?** *(Time and state of the water)*

Teach Ask: **What if you forgot to record some data during an investigation?** *(You wouldn't be able to draw valid conclusions because some data are missing.)* Then, ask: **Why are data tables and graphs a good way to organize data?** *(They make it easier to record data accurately, as well as compare and analyze data.)* **What kind of data table and graph might you use for this experiment?** *(A table would have columns for each container with a row for each time interval in which the state of water is recorded. A bar graph would show the time elapsed until water froze for each container.)*

Drawing Conclusions

Focus Help students understand that a conclusion is not necessarily the end of a scientific investigation. A conclusion about one experiment may lead right into another experiment.

Teach Point out that in scientific investigations, a conclusion is a summary and explanation of the results of an experiment. For the Experimental Procedure described on this page, tell students to suppose that they obtained the following results: Container 1 froze in 45 minutes, Container 2 in 80 minutes, and Container 3 in 25 minutes. Ask: **What conclusions can you draw from this experiment?** *(Students might conclude that water takes longer to freeze as more salt is added to it. The hypothesis is supported, and the question of which freezes faster is answered—fresh water.)*

Activity

You might wish to have students work in pairs to plan the controlled experiment. Students should develop a hypothesis, such as, "If I increase the height from which a ball is dropped, then the height of its bounce will increase." They can test the hypothesis by dropping a ball from varying heights (the manipulated variable). All trials should be done with the same kind of ball and on the same surface (constants). For each trial, they should measure the height of the bounce (responding variable). After students have designed the experiment, provide rubber balls, and invite them to carry out the experiment so they can collect and interpret data and draw conclusions.

Technology Design Skills

Students can refer to this part of the Skills Handbook whenever they need to review the process of designing new technologies. You can use the activities here to teach or reinforce the steps in this process.

Identify a Need

Focus Solicit from students any situations in which they have thought that a tool, machine, or other object would be really helpful to them or others. Explain that this is the first step in the design of new products.

Teach Point out that identifying specific needs is very important to the design process. Ask: **If it was not specified that the toy boat be wind-powered, how might that affect the design?** (*The boat would likely be designed without sails.*)

Research the Problem

Focus Explain that research focuses the problem so that the design is more specific.

Teach Ask: **What might happen if you didn't research the problem before designing the solution?** (*Answers include developing a design that has already been found to fail, using materials that aren't the best, or designing a solution that already exists.*) **What would you research before designing your wind-powered toy boat?** (*Students might research designs and materials.*)

Design a Solution

Focus Emphasize the importance of a design team. Ask: **Why are brainstorming sessions important in product design?** (*A group will propose more new ideas than one person.*)

Teach Divide the class into teams to design the wind-powered toy boat. Instruct them to brainstorm design ideas. Then, ask: **Why do you think engineers evaluate constraints after brainstorming?** (*Evaluating constraints while brainstorming often stops the flow of new ideas.*) **What design constraints do you have for your wind-powered toy boat?** (*Materials must be lightweight, sturdy, and teacher-approved. The boat must be 10 centimeters or less in length and must float across a dishpan in 10 seconds or less.*)

Technology Design Skills

Engineers are people who use scientific and technological knowledge to solve practical problems and design new technologies. To design new products, engineers usually follow the process described here, even though they may not follow these steps in the exact order. As you read the steps, think about how you might apply them in technology labs.

Identify a Need

Before engineers begin designing a new product, they must first identify the need they are trying to meet. For example, suppose you are a member of a design team in a company that manufactures toys. Your team has identified a need: a toy boat that is powered by wind. The new toy needs to be inexpensive and easy to assemble.

Research the Problem

Engineers need to research the problem to gather information that will help them with their new design. This research may include finding articles in books, magazines, or on the Internet. It may also include talking to other designers who have developed similar technologies or solved similar problems. Engineers almost always perform experiments related to the product they want to design.

For your wind-powered toy boat, you could look at toys that are similar to the one you want to design. You might also do research on the Internet. You will probably want to test some materials to see how well they float and other materials to see whether they can function as sails.

Design a Solution

Research gives engineers information that lets them begin designing the product. When engineers design new products, they usually work in groups.

Generating Ideas Often design groups hold brainstorming meetings in which any group member can contribute ideas. Brainstorming is a creative process in which one group member's suggestions often spark ideas in other group members. Together, the creativity of different group members leads to proposed solutions.

Evaluating Constraints Chances are good that during brainstorming, a design group will come up with several possible designs. The group must then evaluate each proposal.

As part of their evaluation, engineers consider constraints, which are factors that place limitations or restrictions on a product design. Physical characteristics, such as the properties of the materials used to make products, are typical constraints. The materials in your proposed toy boat, for example, can't be too heavy, or the boat won't float. The sails need to be made of materials that are lightweight enough not to weigh down the boat. But they also need to be sturdy enough that the sails won't collapse in breezes.

Money and time are other typical constraints. If the materials in a product cost a lot, or if the product takes a long time to manufacture, the design may be impractical.

Making Trade-offs Design teams usually need to make trade-offs, in which they give up one benefit of a proposed design in order to obtain another. In designing your toy boat, you may have to make trade-offs when choosing materials. For example, suppose one material is lightweight but not fully waterproof. An alternative material is sturdy and more waterproof, but also heavier. You may decide to give up the benefit of low weight in order to obtain the benefits of sturdiness and waterproofing.

Build and Evaluate a Prototype

Once the team has chosen a design plan, the engineers build a prototype of the product. A prototype is a working version of the chosen design, made of the materials that have been proposed for the product. Engineers construct a prototype so that it can be tested and evaluated. They evaluate the product to see whether it works well, is easy to operate, is safe to use, and holds up to repeated use.

Think of your wind-powered boat. What would the prototype be like? Of what materials would it be made? How would you test it?

Troubleshoot and Redesign

Few prototypes work perfectly, which is why they need to be tested. Once a design team has tested a prototype, the members analyze the results and identify any problems. The team then tries to troubleshoot, or correct the problems. The design of the prototype is changed or adjusted to address any problems. For example, if your prototype toy boat leaks or wobbles, the boat should be redesigned to eliminate those problems.

Communicate the Solution

Once a team has decided on a final design, the team needs to communicate the design to people who will manufacture and use the product. Teams often use a variety of methods, including sketches and word descriptions, to communicate the design of their product.

Activity

Now it's your turn. Design and build a toy boat that is powered by wind. Follow the steps in the technology design process.

Your boat must
- be made of materials approved by your teacher
- be no longer than 10 cm
- float the length of a rectangular dishpan in 10 seconds or less, powered by a breeze from an electric fan
- be built following the safety guidelines in Appendix A

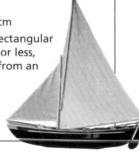

Skills Handbook ♦ 135

Build and Evaluate a Prototype

Focus Explain that building a prototype enables engineers to test design ideas.

Teach Relate building and testing a prototype to conducting an experiment. Explain that engineers set up controlled experiments to test the prototype. Ask: **Why do you think engineers set up controlled experiments?** *(From the data, they can determine which component of the design is working and which is failing.)* **How would you test your prototype of the wind-powered boat?** *(Students might float it across the dishpan using the breeze from an electric fan.)*

Troubleshoot and Redesign

Focus Make sure students know what it means to troubleshoot. If necessary, give an example. One example is a stapler that isn't working. In that case, you would check to see if it is out of staples or if the staples are jammed. Then you would fix the problem and try stapling again. If it still didn't work, you might check the position of staples and try again.

Teach Explain that engineers often are not surprised if the prototype doesn't work. Ask: **Why isn't it a failure if the prototype doesn't work?** *(Engineers learn from the problems and make changes to address the problems. This process makes the design better.)* Emphasize that prototypes are completely tested before the product is made in the factory.

Communicate the Solution

Focus Inquire whether students have ever read the instruction manual that comes with a new toy or electronic device.

Teach Emphasize the importance of good communication in the design process. Ask: **What might happen if engineers did not communicate their design ideas clearly?** *(The product might not be manufactured correctly or used properly.)*

Activity

The design possibilities are endless. Students might use small plastic containers, wood, foil, or plastic drinking cups for the boat. Mast materials may include toothpicks, straws, or small wooden dowels. Sails might be made of paper or fabric. The boats may be any shape, but must be no longer than 10 centimeters. The boats must also float across the dishpan in 10 seconds or less.

As student groups follow the steps in the design process, have them record their sources, brainstorming ideas, and prototype design in a logbook. Also give them time to troubleshoot and redesign their boats. When students turn in their boats, they should include assembly directions with a diagram, as well as instructions for use.

Creating Data Tables and Graphs

Students can refer to this part of the Skills Handbook whenever they need to review the skills required to create data tables and graphs. You can use the activities provided here to teach or reinforce these skills.

Data Tables

Focus Emphasize the importance of organizing data. Ask: **What might happen if you didn't use a data table for an experiment?** *(Possible answers include that data might not be collected or they might be forgotten.)*

Teach Have students create a data table to show how much time they spend on different activities during one week. Suggest that students first list the main activities they do every week. Then they should determine the amount of time they spend on each activity each day. Remind students to give the data table a title. A sample data table is shown below.

Bar Graphs

Focus Have students compare and contrast the data table and the bar graph on this page. Ask: **Why would you make a bar graph if the data are already organized in a table?** *(The bar graph organizes the data in a visual way that makes them easier to interpret.)*

Teach Students can use the data from the data table they created to make a bar graph that shows the amount of time they spend on different activities during a week. The vertical axis should be divided into units of time, such as hours. Remind students to label both axes and give their graph a title. A sample bar graph is shown below.

Creating Data Tables and Graphs

How can you make sense of the data in a science experiment? The first step is to organize the data to help you understand them. Data tables and graphs are helpful tools for organizing data.

Data Tables

You have gathered your materials and set up your experiment. But before you start, you need to plan a way to record what happens during the experiment. By creating a data table, you can record your observations and measurements in an orderly way.

Suppose, for example, that a scientist conducted an experiment to find out how many Calories people of different body masses burn while doing various activities. The data table shows the results.

Notice in this data table that the manipulated variable (body mass) is the heading of one column. The responding variable (for

Calories Burned in 30 Minutes			
Body Mass	Experiment 1: Bicycling	Experiment 2: Playing Basketball	Experiment 3: Watching Television
30 kg	60 Calories	120 Calories	21 Calories
40 kg	77 Calories	164 Calories	27 Calories
50 kg	95 Calories	206 Calories	33 Calories
60 kg	114 Calories	248 Calories	38 Calories

Experiment 1, the number of Calories burned while bicycling) is the heading of the next column. Additional columns were added for related experiments.

Bar Graphs

To compare how many Calories a person burns doing various activities, you could create a bar graph. A bar graph is used to display data in a number of separate, or distinct, categories. In this example, bicycling, playing basketball, and watching television are the three categories.

To create a bar graph, follow these steps.

1. On graph paper, draw a horizontal, or *x*-, axis and a vertical, or *y*-, axis.
2. Write the names of the categories to be graphed along the horizontal axis. Include an overall label for the axis as well.
3. Label the vertical axis with the name of the responding variable. Include units of measurement. Then create a scale along the axis by marking off equally spaced numbers that cover the range of the data collected.

4. For each category, draw a solid bar using the scale on the vertical axis to determine the height. Make all the bars the same width.
5. Add a title that describes the graph.

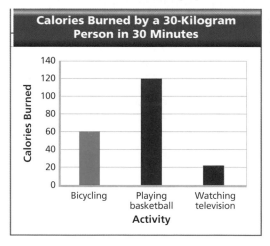

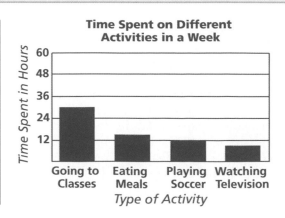

Time Spent on Different Activities in a Week				
	Going to Classes	Eating Meals	Playing Soccer	Watching Television
Monday	6	2	2	0.5
Tuesday	6	1.5	1.5	1.5
Wednesday	6	2	1	2
Thursday	6	2	2	1.5
Friday	6	2	2	0.5
Saturday	0	2.5	2.5	1
Sunday	0	3	1	2

Line Graphs

To see whether a relationship exists between body mass and the number of Calories burned while bicycling, you could create a line graph. A line graph is used to display data that show how one variable (the responding variable) changes in response to another variable (the manipulated variable). You can use a line graph when your manipulated variable is **continuous,** that is, when there are other points between the ones that you tested. In this example, body mass is a continuous variable because there are other body masses between 30 and 40 kilograms (for example, 31 kilograms). Time is another example of a continuous variable.

Line graphs are powerful tools because they allow you to estimate values for conditions that you did not test in the experiment. For example, you can use the line graph to estimate that a 35-kilogram person would burn 68 Calories while bicycling.

To create a line graph, follow these steps.

1. On graph paper, draw a horizontal, or x-, axis and a vertical, or y-, axis.

2. Label the horizontal axis with the name of the manipulated variable. Label the vertical axis with the name of the responding variable. Include units of measurement.

3. Create a scale on each axis by marking off equally spaced numbers that cover the range of the data collected.

4. Plot a point on the graph for each piece of data. In the line graph above, the dotted lines show how to plot the first data point (30 kilograms and 60 Calories). Follow an imaginary vertical line extending up from the horizontal axis at the 30-kilogram mark. Then follow an imaginary horizontal line extending across from the vertical axis at the 60-Calorie mark. Plot the point where the two lines intersect.

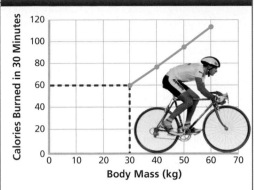

Effect of Body Mass on Calories Burned While Bicycling

5. Connect the plotted points with a solid line. (In some cases, it may be more appropriate to draw a line that shows the general trend of the plotted points. In those cases, some of the points may fall above or below the line. Also, not all graphs are linear. It may be more appropriate to draw a curve to connect the points.)

6. Add a title that identifies the variables or relationship in the graph.

Activity

Create line graphs to display the data from Experiment 2 and Experiment 3 in the data table.

Activity

You read in the newspaper that a total of 4 centimeters of rain fell in your area in June, 2.5 centimeters fell in July, and 1.5 centimeters fell in August. What type of graph would you use to display these data? Use graph paper to create the graph.

Skills Handbook ◆ 137

Line Graphs

Focus Ask: **Would a bar graph show the relationship between body mass and the number of calories burned in 30 minutes?** (*No. Bar graphs can only show data in distinct categories.*) Explain that line graphs are used to show how one variable changes in response to another variable.

Teach Walk students through the steps involved in creating a line graph using the example illustrated on the page. For example, ask: **What is the label on the horizontal axis? On the vertical axis?** (*Body Mass (kg); Calories Burned in 30 Minutes*) **What scale is used on each axis?** (*10 kg on the x-axis and 20 calories on the y-axis*) **What does the second data point represent?** (*77 calories burned for a body mass of 40 kg*) **What trend or pattern does the graph show?** (*The number of calories burned in 30 minutes of cycling increases with body mass.*)

Activity

Students should make a different graph for each experiment. Each graph should have a different x-axis scale that is appropriate for the data. See sample graphs below.

Activity

Students should conclude that a bar graph would be best for displaying the data. A sample bar graph for these data is shown below.

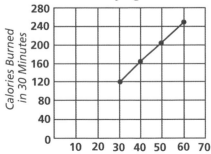

Effect of Body Mass on Calories Burned While Playing Basketball

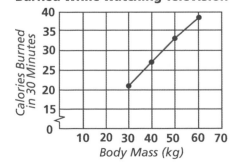

Effect of Body Mass on Calories Burned While Watching Television

P ● 137

Circle Graphs

Focus Emphasize that a circle graph must include 100 percent of the categories for the topic being graphed. For example, ask: **Could the data in the bar graph titled "Calories Burned by a 30-kilogram Person in Various Activities"** (on the previous page) be shown in a circle graph? Why or why not? (*No. It does not include all the possible ways a 30-kilogram person can burn calories.*)

Teach Walk students through the steps for making a circle graph. If necessary, help them with the compass and the protractor. Use the protractor to illustrate that a circle has 360 degrees. Make sure students understand the mathematical calculations involved in making a circle graph.

You might have students work in pairs to complete the activity. Students' circle graphs should look like the graph below.

Ways Students Get to School

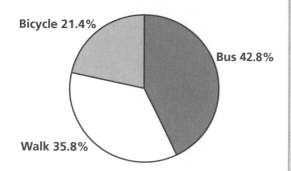

Bicycle 21.4%

Bus 42.8%

Walk 35.8%

Circle Graphs

Like bar graphs, circle graphs can be used to display data in a number of separate categories. Unlike bar graphs, however, circle graphs can only be used when you have data for *all* the categories that make up a given topic. A circle graph is sometimes called a pie chart. The pie represents the entire topic, while the slices represent the individual categories. The size of a slice indicates what percentage of the whole a particular category makes up.

The data table below shows the results of a survey in which 24 teenagers were asked to identify their favorite sport. The data were then used to create the circle graph at the right.

Favorite Sports	
Sport	Students
Soccer	8
Basketball	6
Bicycling	6
Swimming	4

To create a circle graph, follow these steps.

1. Use a compass to draw a circle. Mark the center with a point. Then draw a line from the center point to the top of the circle.

2. Determine the size of each "slice" by setting up a proportion where x equals the number of degrees in a slice. (*Note:* A circle contains 360 degrees.) For example, to find the number of degrees in the "soccer" slice, set up the following proportion:

$$\frac{\text{Students who prefer soccer}}{\text{Total number of students}} = \frac{x}{\text{Total number of degrees in a circle}}$$

$$\frac{8}{24} = \frac{x}{360}$$

Cross-multiply and solve for x.

$$24x = 8 \times 360$$
$$x = 120$$

The "soccer" slice should contain 120 degrees.

Sports That Teens Prefer

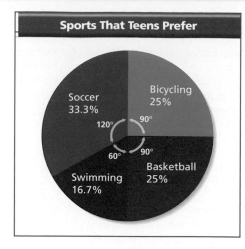

Soccer 33.3%

Bicycling 25%

120°

90°

60°

90°

Swimming 16.7%

Basketball 25%

3. Use a protractor to measure the angle of the first slice, using the line you drew to the top of the circle as the 0° line. Draw a line from the center of the circle to the edge for the angle you measured.

4. Continue around the circle by measuring the size of each slice with the protractor. Start measuring from the edge of the previous slice so the wedges do not overlap. When you are done, the entire circle should be filled in.

5. Determine the percentage of the whole circle that each slice represents. To do this, divide the number of degrees in a slice by the total number of degrees in a circle (360), and multiply by 100%. For the "soccer" slice, you can find the percentage as follows:

$$\frac{120}{360} \times 100\% = 33.3\%$$

6. Use a different color for each slice. Label each slice with the category and with the percentage of the whole it represents.

7. Add a title to the circle graph.

In a class of 28 students, 12 students take the bus to school, 10 students walk, and 6 students ride their bicycles. Create a circle graph to display these data.

Math Review

Math is a key tool in the study of science. Scientists use math to organize, analyze, and present data. This appendix will help you review some basic math skills.

Mean, Median, and Mode

When scientists analyze data, they may use the terms *mean*, *median*, and *mode*. The **mean** is the average, or the sum of the data divided by the number of data items. The **median** is the middle number in a set of ordered data. The **mode** is the number that appears most often in a set of data.

Example

A scientist counted the number of distinct songs sung by seven different male birds and collected the data shown below.

Male Bird Songs							
Bird	A	B	C	D	E	F	G
Number of Songs	36	29	40	35	28	36	27

To determine the mean number of songs, add the total number of songs and divide by the number of data items—in this case, the number of male birds.

$$\text{Mean} = \frac{231}{7} = 33 \text{ songs}$$

To find the median number of songs, arrange the data in numerical order and find the number in the middle of the series.

27 28 29 35 36 36 40

The number in the middle is 35, so the median number of songs is 35.

The mode is the value that appears most frequently. In the data, 36 appears twice, while each other item appears only once. Therefore, 36 songs is the mode.

Practice

Find out how many minutes it takes each student in your class to get to school. Then find the mean, median, and mode for the data.

Area

The **area** of a surface is the number of square units that cover it. The front cover of your textbook has an area of about 600 cm^2.

Area of a Rectangle and a Square To find the area of a rectangle, multiply its length times its width. The formula for the area of a rectangle is

$$A = \ell \times w, \text{ or } A = \ell w$$

Since all four sides of a square have the same length, the area of a square is the length of one side multiplied by itself, or squared.

$$A = s \times s, \text{ or } A = s^2$$

Example

A scientist is studying the plants in a field that measures 75 m × 45 m. What is the area of the field?

$$A = \ell \times w$$
$$A = 75 \text{ m} \times 45 \text{ m}$$
$$A = 3{,}375 \text{ m}^2$$

Area of a Circle The formula for the area of a circle is

$$A = \pi \times r \times r, \text{ or } A = \pi r^2$$

The length of the radius is represented by r, and the value of π is approximately $\frac{22}{7}$.

Math Review

Students can refer to this part of the Skills Handbook whenever they need to review some basic math skills. You can use the activities provided here to teach or reinforce these skills.

Mean, Median, and Mode

Focus Remind students that data from an experiment might consist of hundreds or thousands of numbers. Unless analyzed, the numbers likely will not be helpful.

Teach Work through the process of determining mean, median, and mode using the example in the book. Make sure students realize that these three numbers do not always equal each other. Point out that taken together, these three numbers give more information about the data than just one of the numbers alone.

Practice

Answers will vary based on class data. The mean should equal the total number of minutes divided by the number of students. The median should equal the number in the middle after arranging the data in numerical order. The mode should equal the number of minutes that is given most frequently.

Area

Focus Ask: **Who knows what area is?** (*Area is equal to the number of squares needed to cover a certain shape or object.*) On the board, write the formulas for the area of a rectangle and a circle.

Teach Give students various objects of different shapes. Have them measure each object and determine its area based on the measurements. Point out that the units of the answer are squared because they are multiplied together. If students are interested, you might also explain that π is equal to the ratio of the circumference of a circle to its diameter. For circles of all sizes, π is approximately equal to the number 3.14, or $\frac{22}{7}$.

Practice

The area of the circle is equal to 21 m × 21 m × $\frac{22}{7}$, or 1,386 m^2.

Circumference

Focus Draw a circle on the board. Then trace the outline with your finger and explain that this is the circumference of the circle, or the distance around it.

Teach Show students that the radius is equal to the distance from the center of the circle to any point on it. Point out that the diameter of a circle is equal to two times the radius. Give students paper circles of various sizes, and have them calculate the circumference of each.

Practice

The circumference is equal to 2×28 m $\times \frac{22}{7}$, or 176 m.

Volume

Focus Fill a beaker with 100 milliliters of water. Ask: **What is the volume of water?** *(100 milliliters)* Explain that volume is the amount of space that something takes up. Then point out that one milliliter is equal to one cubic centimeter (cm^3).

Teach Write on the board the formulas for calculating the volumes of a rectangle and a cylinder. Point out that volume is equal to the area of an object multiplied by its height. Then measure the beaker to show students the relationship between liquid volume (100 milliliters) and the number of cubic units it contains (100 cubic centimeters).

Practice

The volume of the cylinder is equal to $\frac{22}{7} \times 7$ m $\times 7$ m $\times 5$ m, or 770 m^3.

Fractions

Focus Draw a circle on the board, and divide it into eight equal sections. Shade in one of the sections, and explain that one out of eight, or one eighth, of the sections is shaded. Also use the circle to show that four eighths is the same as one half.

Teach Write the fraction $\frac{3}{4}$ on the board. Ask: **What is the numerator?** *(Three)* **What is the denominator?** *(Four)* Emphasize that when adding and subtracting fractions, the denominators of the two fractions must be the same. If necessary, review how to find the least common denominator. Remind students that when multiplying and dividing, the denominators do not have to be the same.

Example

Find the area of a circle with a radius of 14 cm.

$$A = \pi r^2$$
$$A = 14 \times 14 \times \frac{22}{7}$$
$$A = 616 \text{ cm}^2$$

Practice

Find the area of a circle that has a radius of 21 m.

Circumference

The distance around a circle is called the circumference. The formula for finding the circumference of a circle is

$$C = 2 \times \pi \times r, \text{ or } C = 2\pi r$$

Example

The radius of a circle is 35 cm. What is its circumference?

$$C = 2\pi r$$
$$C = 2 \times 35 \times \frac{22}{7}$$
$$C = 220 \text{ cm}$$

Practice

What is the circumference of a circle with a radius of 28 m?

Volume

The volume of an object is the number of cubic units it contains. The volume of a wastebasket, for example, might be about 26,000 cm^3.

Volume of a Rectangular Object To find the volume of a rectangular object, multiply the object's length times its width times its height.

$$V = \ell \times w \times h, \text{ or } V = \ell w h$$

Example

Find the volume of a box with length 24 cm, width 12 cm, and height 9 cm.

$$V = \ell w h$$
$$V = 24 \text{ cm} \times 12 \text{ cm} \times 9 \text{ cm}$$
$$V = 2{,}592 \text{ cm}^3$$

Volume of a Cylinder To find the volume of a cylinder, multiply the area of its base times its height. Since the base of a cylinder is a circle, the formula for its area is $A = \pi r^2$. Therefore, the formula for the volume of a cylinder is

$$V = (\pi r^2)h$$

Example

Find the volume of a coffee can with radius 5 cm and height 14 cm.

$$V = (\pi r^2)h$$
$$V = \frac{22}{7} \times 5 \text{ cm} \times 5 \text{ cm} \times 14 \text{ cm}$$
$$V = 1{,}100 \text{ cm}^3$$

Practice

What is the volume of a cylinder with height 5 m and base radius of 7 m?

Fractions

A **fraction** is a way to express a part of a whole. For example, a baseball team has nine players. The three outfielders make up three parts of the nine-part team. This can be expressed as $\frac{3}{9}$ of the team. In the fraction $\frac{3}{9}$, 3 is the numerator and 9 is the denominator.

Adding and Subtracting Fractions To add or subtract two or more fractions that have a common denominator, first add or subtract the numerators. Then write the sum or difference over the common denominator.

Example

$$\frac{2}{7} + \frac{3}{7} = \frac{2 + 3}{7} = \frac{5}{7}$$

Practice

$$\frac{3}{7} \div \frac{4}{5} = \frac{3}{7} \times \frac{5}{4} = \frac{15}{28}$$

To find the sum or difference of fractions with different denominators, first find the least common multiple of the denominators. This is known as the least common denominator. Then convert each fraction to equivalent fractions with the least common denominator. Add or subtract the numerators. Then write the sum or difference over the common denominator.

Example

$$\frac{5}{6} - \frac{3}{4} = \frac{10}{12} - \frac{9}{12} = \frac{10-9}{12} = \frac{1}{12}$$

Multiplying Fractions To multiply two fractions, first multiply the two numerators to find the product's numerator. Then multiply the two denominators to find the product's denominator.

Example

$$\frac{5}{6} \times \frac{2}{3} = \frac{5 \times 2}{6 \times 3} = \frac{10}{18} = \frac{5}{9}$$

Dividing Fractions Dividing by a fraction is the same as multiplying by its reciprocal. Reciprocals are numbers whose numerators and denominators have been switched. To divide one fraction by another, first invert the fraction you are dividing by—in other words, turn it upside down. Then multiply the two fractions.

Example

$$\frac{2}{5} \div \frac{7}{8} = \frac{2}{5} \times \frac{8}{7} = \frac{2 \times 8}{5 \times 7} = \frac{16}{35}$$

Practice

Solve the following: $\frac{3}{7} \div \frac{4}{5}$.

Decimals

Fractions whose denominators are 10, 100, or some other power of 10 are often expressed as decimals. For example, the fraction $\frac{9}{10}$ can be expressed as the decimal 0.9, and the fraction $\frac{7}{100}$ can be written as 0.07.

Adding and Subtracting With Decimals
To add or subtract decimals, line up the decimal points before you carry out the operation.

Example

```
   27.4          278.635
 + 6.19        − 191.4
 ──────        ────────
  33.59          87.235
```

Multiplying With Decimals When you multiply two numbers with decimals, the number of decimal places in the product is equal to the total number of decimal places in each number being multiplied.

Example

```
   46.2   (one decimal place)
 × 2.37   (two decimal places)
 ───────
 109.494  (three decimal places)
```

Dividing With Decimals To divide a decimal by a whole number, put the decimal point in the quotient above the decimal point in the dividend.

Example

$$15.5 \div 5$$

```
      3.1
  5)15.5
```

To divide a decimal by a decimal, you need to rewrite the divisor as a whole number. Do this by multiplying both the divisor and dividend by the same multiple of 10.

Example

$$1.68 \div 4.2 = 16.8 \div 42$$

```
     0.4
 42)16.8
```

Practice

Multiply 6.21 by 8.5.

Converting Fractions to Decimals To convert a fraction to a decimal, divide the numerator by the denominator.

Example

$$\frac{5}{8} = \begin{array}{r} 0.625 \\ 8)5 \end{array}$$

Skills Handbook ◆ 141

Decimals

Focus Write the number *129.835* on the board. Ask: **What number is in the ones position?** *(9)* **The tenths position?** *(8)* **The hundredths position?** *(3)* Make sure students know that 0.8 is equal to $\frac{8}{10}$ and 0.03 is equal to $\frac{3}{100}$.

Teach Use the examples in the book to review addition, subtraction, multiplication, and division with decimals. Make up a worksheet of similar problems to give students additional practice. Also show students how a fraction is converted to a decimal by dividing the numerator by the denominator. For example, $\frac{1}{2}$ is equal to 0.5.

Practice

$6.21 \times 8.5 = 52.785$

Ratio and Proportion

Focus Differentiate a ratio from a fraction. Remind students that a fraction tells how many parts of the whole. In contrast, a ratio compares two different numbers. For example, $\frac{12}{22}$, or $\frac{6}{11}$, of a class are girls. But the ratio of boys to girls in the class is 10 to 12, or $\frac{5}{6}$.

Teach Use the example in the book to explain how to use a proportion to find an unknown quantity. Provide students with additional practice problems, if needed.

Practice

$6 \times 49 = 7x$
$294 = 7x$
$294 \div 7 = x$
$x = 42$

Percentage

Focus On the board, write $50\% = \frac{50}{100}$. Explain that a percentage is a ratio that compares a number to 100.

Teach Point out that when calculating percentages, you are usually using numbers other than 100. In this case, you set up a proportion. Go over the example in the book. Emphasize that the number representing the total goes on the bottom of the ratio, as does the 100%.

Practice

Students should set up the proportion
$\frac{24 \text{ beans}}{80 \text{ beans}} = \frac{x\%}{100\%}$
$24 \times 100 = 80x$

$2400 = 80x$

$2400 \div 80 = 30\%$

Precision and Significant Digits

Focus Measure the length of a paper clip using two different rulers. Use one ruler that is less precise than the other. Compare the two measurements. Ask: **Which measurement is more precise?** (*The ruler with the smallest units will give the more precise measurement.*)

Teach Give students the opportunity to take measurements of an object using tools with different precision. Encourage students to add and subtract their measurements, making sure that they round the answers to reflect the precision of the instruments. Go over the example for significant digits. Check

Ratio and Proportion

A **ratio** compares two numbers by division. For example, suppose a scientist counts 800 wolves and 1,200 moose on an island. The ratio of wolves to moose can be written as a fraction, $\frac{800}{1,200}$, which can be reduced to $\frac{2}{3}$. The same ratio can also be expressed as 2 to 3 or 2 : 3.

A **proportion** is a mathematical sentence saying that two ratios are equivalent. For example, a proportion could state that $\frac{800 \text{ wolves}}{1,200 \text{ moose}} = \frac{2 \text{ wolves}}{3 \text{ moose}}$. You can sometimes set up a proportion to determine or estimate an unknown quantity. For example, suppose a scientist counts 25 beetles in an area of 10 square meters. The scientist wants to estimate the number of beetles in 100 square meters.

Example

1. Express the relationship between beetles and area as a ratio: $\frac{25}{10}$, simplified to $\frac{5}{2}$.
2. Set up a proportion, with x representing the number of beetles. The proportion can be stated as $\frac{5}{2} = \frac{x}{100}$.
3. Begin by cross-multiplying. In other words, multiply each fraction's numerator by the other fraction's denominator.

$$5 \times 100 = 2 \times x, \text{ or } 500 = 2x$$

4. To find the value of x, divide both sides by 2. The result is 250, or 250 beetles in 100 square meters.

Practice

Find the value of x in the following proportion: $\frac{6}{7} = \frac{x}{49}$.

Percentage

A **percentage** is a ratio that compares a number to 100. For example, there are 37 granite rocks in a collection that consists of 100 rocks. The ratio $\frac{37}{100}$ can be written as 37%. Granite rocks make up 37% of the rock collection.

You can calculate percentages of numbers other than 100 by setting up a proportion.

Example

Rain falls on 9 days out of 30 in June. What percentage of the days in June were rainy?

$$\frac{9 \text{ days}}{30 \text{ days}} = \frac{d\%}{100\%}$$

To find the value of d, begin by cross-multiplying, as for any proportion:

$$9 \times 100 = 30 \times d \qquad d = \frac{900}{30} \qquad d = 30$$

Practice

There are 80 beans in a jar, and 24 of those beans are red. What percentage of the beans are red?

Precision and Significant Figures

The **precision** of a measurement depends on the instrument you use to take the measurement. For example, suppose you measure a box with a ruler. If the smallest unit on the ruler is millimeters, then the most precise measurement you can make will be in millimeters.

The sum or difference of measurements can only be as precise as the least precise measurement being added or subtracted. Round your answer so that it has the same number of digits after the decimal as the least precise measurement. Round up if the last digit is 5 or more, and round down if the last digit is 4 or less.

Example

Subtract a temperature of 5.2°C from the temperature 75.47°C.

$$75.46 - 5.2 = 70.26$$

5.2 has the fewest digits after the decimal, so it is the least precise measurement. Since the last digit of the answer is 6, round up to 3. The most precise difference between the measurements is 70.3°C.

for understanding by asking: **How many significant digits are in the number 324,000?** (*Three*) **In the number 5,901?** (*Four*) **In the number 0.706?** (*Three*) If students need additional practice, create a worksheet with problems in multiplying and dividing numbers with various significant digits.

Practice

$26.4 \text{ m} + 8.37 \text{ m} = 34.77 \text{ m}$
This answer should be rounded to 34.8 m because the least precise measurement has only one digit after the decimal. This number is rounded up to 8 because the last digit is more than 5.

Practice

$306 \text{ L} \div 2.5 \text{ L} = 122.4 \text{ L}$
Because 2.5 has only two significant digits, the answer is rounded to 120 L.

Practice

Add 26.4 m to 8.37 m. Round your answer according to the precision of the measurements.

Significant figures are the number of nonzero digits in a measurement. Zeroes between nonzero digits are also significant. For example, the measurements 12,500 L, 0.125 cm, and 2.05 kg all have three significant figures. When you multiply and divide measurements, the one with the fewest significant figures determines the number of significant figures in your answer.

Example

Multiply 110 g by 5.75 g.

110 × 5.75 = 632.5

Because 110 has only two significant figures, round the answer to 630 g.

Practice

Divide 306 L by 2.5 L.

Scientific Notation

A **factor** is a number that divides into another number with no remainder. In the example, the number 3 is used as a factor four times.

Example

3 × 3 × 3 × 3 = 81

An **exponent** tells how many times a number is used as a factor. For example, $3 \times 3 \times 3 \times 3$ can be written as 3^4. The exponent ^{4} indicates that the number 3 is used as a factor four times. Another way of expressing this is to say that 81 is equal to 3 to the fourth power.

Scientific notation uses exponents and powers of ten to write very large or very small numbers in shorter form. When you write a number in scientific notation, you write the number as two factors. The first factor is any number between 1 and 10. The second factor is a power of 10, such as 10^3 or 10^6.

Example

The average distance between the planet Mercury and the sun is 58,000,000 km. To write the first factor in scientific notation, insert a decimal point in the original number so that you have a number between 1 and 10. In the case of 58,000,000, the number is 5.8.

To determine the power of 10, count the number of places that the decimal point moved. In this case, it moved 7 places.

58,000,000 km = 5.8 × 10^7 km

Practice

Express 6,590,000 in scientific notation.

Probability

Probability is the chance that an event will occur. Probability can be expressed as a ratio, a fraction, or a percentage. For example, when you flip a coin, the probability that the coin will land heads up is 1 in 2, or $\frac{1}{2}$, or 50 percent.

The probability that an event will happen can be expressed in the following formula.

$$P(\text{event}) = \frac{\text{Number of times the event can occur}}{\text{Total number of possible events}}$$

Example

A paper bag contains 25 blue marbles, 5 green marbles, 5 orange marbles, and 15 yellow marbles. If you close your eyes and pick a marble from the bag, what is the probability that it will be yellow?

$$P(\text{yellow marbles}) = \frac{15 \text{ yellow marbles}}{50 \text{ marbles total}}$$

$$P = \frac{15}{50}, \text{ or } \frac{3}{10}, \text{ or } 30\%$$

Practice

Each side of a cube has a letter on it. Two sides have A, three sides have B, and one side has C. If you roll the cube, what is the probability that A will land on top?

Scientific Notation

Focus Write a very large number on the board, such as 100 million, using all the zeros. Then, write the number using scientific notation. Ask: **Why do you think scientists prefer to write very large numbers using scientific notation?** (*Possible answers include that it is easier to do calculations, convert units, and make comparisons with other numbers.*)

Teach Go over the examples, and ask: **In the second example, which numbers are the factors?** (*5.8 and 10^7*) **Which number is the exponent?** (*7*) Explain that very small numbers have a negative exponent because the decimal point is moved to the right to produce the first factor. For example, 0.00000628 is equal to 6.28×10^{-6}.

Practice

$6,590,000 = 6.59 \times 10^6$

Probability

Focus Show students a coin and ask: **What is the chance that I will get tails when I flip the coin?** (*Some students might know that there is a 1 in 2, or 50 percent, chance of getting tails.*)

Teach Set up a bag of marbles like the one in the example. Allow students to practice determining the probabilities of picking marbles of different colors. Then, encourage them to actually pick marbles and compare their actual results with those results predicted by probability.

Practice

$P(A) = 2$ sides with $\frac{A}{6}$ sides total

$P = \frac{2}{6}$, or $\frac{1}{3}$, or 33%

Reading Skills

Students can refer to this part of the Skills Handbook whenever they need to review a reading skill. You can use the activities provided here to teach or reinforce these skills.

Introduction: Learning From Science Textbooks

Reading in a content area presents challenges different from those encountered when reading fiction. Science texts often have more new vocabulary and more unfamiliar concepts that place greater emphasis on inferential reasoning. Students who can apply reading skills and information-organizing strategies will be more successful in reading and understanding a science textbook.

Activity

Turn with students to the first page of any section. Walk through the Reading Preview with students, showing them the Key Concepts that provide a guiding set of questions that students can answer from the text. Next, point out the Key Terms list, which highlights the science vocabulary. Last, have students find the Target Reading Skill emphasized with the sample graphic organizer. Make the connection for students to the additional help found in this Skills Handbook.

All in One Teaching Resources

• Reading Skills Handbook

Building Vocabulary

Focus Explain to students that knowing the definitions of key concept words can help them understand what they read.

Teach List on the board various strategies to learn the definitions of new terms. Also solicit from students strategies that work for them. Other strategies include drawing a picture for the term, acting it out, or using it in conversation. Challenge students to choose a new strategy to learn the Key Terms in your next section.

Using Prior Knowledge

Focus Explain to students that using prior knowledge helps connect what they already know to what they are about to read.

Teach Point out that students should consider carefully what they remember. Their prior knowledge might not be accurate because memories have faded or

---

Target Reading Skills

Your textbook is an important source of science information. As you read your science textbook, you will find that the book has been written to assist you in understanding the science concepts.

Introduction: Learning From Science Textbooks

As you study science in school, you will learn science concepts in a variety of ways. Sometimes you will do interesting activities and experiments to explore science ideas. To fully understand what you observe in experiments and activities, you will need to read your science textbook. To help you read, some of the important ideas are highlighted so that you can easily recognize what they are. In addition, a target reading skill in each section will help you understand what you read.

By using the target reading skills, you will become a strategic reader—that is, one who can easily apply the appropriate reading skills. As you learn science, you will build knowledge that will help you understand even more of what you read. This knowledge will help you learn about all the topics presented in this textbook.

And—guess what?—these reading skills can be useful whenever you are reading. Reading to learn is important for your entire life. You have an opportunity to begin that process now.

The target reading skills that will make you a strategic reader are described below.

Building Vocabulary

To understand the science concepts taught in this textbook, you need to remember the meanings of the Key Terms. One strategy consists of writing the definitions of these terms in your own words. You can also practice using the terms in sentences and make lists of words or phrases you associate with each term.

Using Prior Knowledge

Your prior knowledge is what you already know before you begin to read about a topic. Building on what you already know gives you a head start on learning new information. Before you begin a new assignment, think about what you know. You might page through your reading assignment, looking at the headings and the visuals to spark your memory. You can list what you know in the graphic organizer provided in the section opener. Then, as you read, consider questions like the ones below to connect what you learn to what you already know.

• How does what you learn relate to what you know?
• How did something you already know help you learn something new?
• Did your original ideas agree with what you have just learned? If not, how would you revise your original ideas?

Asking Questions

Asking yourself questions is an excellent way to focus on and remember new information in your textbook. You can learn how to ask good questions.

One way is to turn the text headings into questions. Then your questions can guide you to identify and remember the important information as you read. Look at these examples:

Heading: Using Seismographic Data
Question: How are seismographic data used?
Heading: Kinds of Faults
Question: What are the kinds of faults?

---

their perspective was different. Encourage students to ask questions to resolve discrepancies between their prior knowledge and what they have learned

Asking Questions

Focus Demonstrate to students how to change a text heading into a question to help them anticipate the concepts, facts, and events they will read about.

Teach Encourage students to use this reading skill for the next section they read. Instruct them to turn the text headings into questions. Also challenge students to write at least four *what, how, why, who, when,* or *where* questions. Then, have students evaluate the skill. Ask: **Did asking questions about the text help you focus on the reading and remember what you read?** (*Answers will vary, but encourage honesty.*) If this reading skill didn't help, challenge them to assess why not.

You do not have to limit your questions to the text headings. Ask questions about anything that you need to clarify or that will help you understand the content. *What* and *how* are probably the most common question words, but you may also ask *why*, *who*, *when*, or *where* questions. Here is an example:

Properties of Waves

Question	Answer
What is amplitude?	Amplitude is . . .

Previewing Visuals

Visuals are photographs, graphs, tables, diagrams, and illustrations. Visuals, such as this diagram of a normal fault, contain important information. Look at visuals and their captions before you read. This will help you prepare for what you will be reading about.

Often you will be asked what you want to learn about a visual. For example, after you look at the normal fault diagram, you might ask: What is the movement along a normal fault? Questions about visuals give you a purpose for reading—to answer your questions. Previewing visuals also helps you see what you already know.

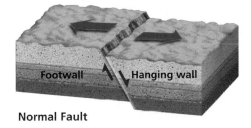

Footwall   **Hanging wall**

Normal Fault

Outlining

An outline shows the relationship between main ideas and supporting ideas. An outline has a formal structure. You write the main ideas, called topics, next to Roman numerals. The supporting ideas, sometimes called subtopics, are written under the main ideas and labeled A, B, C, and so on. An outline looks like this:

Technology and Society

I. Technology through history

II. The impact of technology on society

   A.

   B.

When you have completed an outline like this, you can see at a glance the structure of the section. You can use this outline as a study tool.

Identifying Main Ideas

When you are reading, it is important to try to understand the ideas and concepts that are in a passage. As you read science material, you will recognize that each paragraph has a lot of information and detail. Good readers try to identify the most important—or biggest—idea in every paragraph or section. That's the main idea. The other information in the paragraph supports or further explains the main idea.

Sometimes main ideas are stated directly. In this book, some main ideas are identified for you as key concepts. These are printed in boldface type. However, you must identify other main ideas yourself. In order to do this, you must identify all the ideas within a paragraph or section. Then ask yourself which idea is big enough to include all the other ideas.

Previewing Visuals

Focus Explain to students that looking at the visuals before reading will help them activate prior knowledge and predict what they are about to read.

Teach Assign a section for students to preview the visuals. First, instruct them to write a sentence describing what the section will be about. Then, encourage them to write one or two questions for each visual to give purpose to their reading. Also have them list any prior knowledge about the subject.

Outlining

Focus Explain that using an outline format helps organize information by main topic, subtopic, and details.

Teach Choose a section in the book, and demonstrate how to make an outline for it. Make sure students understand the structure of the outline by asking: **Is this a topic or a subtopic? Where does this information go in the outline? Would I write this heading next to a Roman numeral or a capital letter?** *(Answers depend on the section being outlined.)* Also show them how to indent and add details to the outline using numerals and lowercase letters.

Identifying Main Ideas

Focus Explain that identifying main ideas and details helps sort the facts from the information into groups. Each group can have a main topic, subtopics, and details.

Teach Tell students that paragraphs are often written so that the main idea is in the first or second sentence, or in the last sentence. Assign students a page in the book. Instruct them to write the main idea for each paragraph on that page. If students have difficulty finding the main idea, suggest that they list all of the ideas given in the paragraph, and then choose the idea that is big enough to include all the others.

Comparing and Contrasting

Focus Explain that comparing and contrasting information shows how concepts, facts, and events are similar or different. The results of the comparison can have importance.

Teach Point out that Venn diagrams work best when comparing two things. To compare more than two things, students should use a compare/contrast table. Have students make a Venn diagram or compare/contrast table using two or more different sports or other activities, such as playing musical instruments. Emphasize that students should select characteristics that highlight the similarities and differences in the activities.

Sequencing

Focus Tell students that organizing information from beginning to end will help them understand a step-by-step process.

Teach Encourage students to create a flowchart to show the things they did this morning to get ready for school. Remind students that a flowchart should show the correct order in which events occur. *(A typical flowchart might include: got up ➤ took a shower ➤ got dressed ➤ ate breakfast ➤ brushed teeth ➤ gathered books and homework ➤ put on jacket.)* Then explain that a cycle diagram shows a sequence of events that is continuous. Challenge students to create a cycle diagram that shows how the weather changes with the seasons where they live. *(Most cycle diagrams will include four steps, one for each season.)*

Comparing and Contrasting

When you compare and contrast, you examine the similarities and differences between things. You can compare and contrast in a Venn diagram or in a table. Your completed diagram or table shows you how the items are alike and how they are different.

Venn Diagram A Venn diagram consists of two overlapping circles. In the space where the circles overlap, you write the characteristics that the two items have in common. In one of the circles outside the area of overlap, you write the differing features or characteristics of one of the items. In the other circle outside the area of overlap, you write the differing characteristics of the other item.

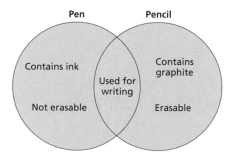

Table In a compare/contrast table, you list the items to be compared across the top of the table. Then list the characteristics or features to be compared in the left column. Complete the table by filling in information about each characteristic or feature.

	Loop One	Loop Two
Side of heart		
Blood flows to		
Blood returns from		

Sequencing

A sequence is the order in which a series of events occurs. Recognizing and remembering the sequence of events is important to understanding many processes in science. Sometimes the text uses words like *first, next, during,* and *after* to signal a sequence. A flowchart or a cycle diagram can help you visualize a sequence.

Flowchart To make a flowchart, write a brief description of each step or event in a box. Place the boxes in order, with the first event at the top of the page. Then draw an arrow to connect each step or event to the next.

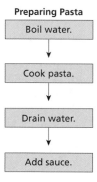

Cycle Diagram A cycle diagram shows a sequence that is continuous, or cyclical. A continuous sequence does not have an end because when the final event is over, the first event begins again. To create a cycle diagram, write the starting event in a box placed at the top of a page in the center. Then, moving in a clockwise direction around an imaginary circle, write each event in a box in its proper sequence. Draw arrows that connect each event to the one that occurs next, forming a continuous circle.

Identifying Supporting Evidence

A hypothesis is a possible explanation for observations made by scientists or an answer to a scientific question. A hypothesis is tested over and over again. The tests may produce evidence that supports the hypothesis. When enough supporting evidence is collected, a hypothesis may become a theory.

Identifying the supporting evidence for a hypothesis or theory can help you understand the hypothesis or theory. Evidence consists of facts—information whose accuracy can be confirmed by testing or observation.

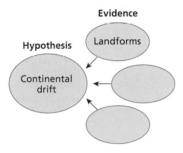

Relating Cause and Effect

Identifying causes and effects helps you understand relationships among events. A cause makes something happen. An effect is what happens. When you recognize that one event causes another, you are relating cause and effect. Words like *cause, because, effect, affect,* and *result* often signal a cause or an effect.

Sometimes an effect can have more than one cause, or a cause can produce several effects. For example, car exhaust and smoke from industrial plants are two causes of air pollution. Some effects of air pollution include breathing difficulties for some people, death of plants along some highways, and damage to some building surfaces.

Science involves many cause-and-effect relationships. Seeing and understanding these relationships helps you understand science processes.

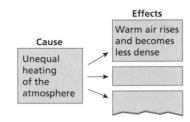

Concept Mapping

Concept maps are useful tools for organizing information on any topic. A concept map begins with a main idea or core concept and shows how the idea can be subdivided into related subconcepts or smaller ideas. In this way, relationships between concepts become clearer and easier to understand.

You construct a concept map by placing concepts (usually nouns) in ovals and connecting them with linking words. The biggest concept or idea is placed in an oval at the top of the map. Related concepts are arranged in ovals below the big idea. The linking words are often verbs and verb phrases and are written on the lines that connect the ovals.

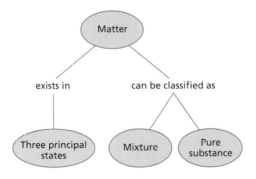

Identifying Supporting Evidence

Focus Explain to students that identifying the supporting evidence will help them to understand the relationship between the facts and the hypothesis.

Teach Remind students that a hypothesis is neither right nor wrong, but it is either supported or not supported by the evidence from testing or observation. If evidence is found that does not support a hypothesis, the hypothesis can be changed to accommodate the new evidence, or it can be dropped.

Relating Cause and Effect

Focus Explain to students that cause is the reason for what happens. The effect is what happens in response to the cause. Relating cause and effect helps students relate the reason for what happens to what happens as a result.

Teach Emphasize that not all events that occur together have a cause-and-effect relationship. For example, tell students that you went to the grocery store and your car stalled. Ask: **Is there a cause-and-effect relationship in this situation? Explain.** *(No. Going to the grocery store could not cause a car to stall. There must be another cause to make the car stall.)*

Concept Mapping

Focus Elicit from students how a map shows the relationship of one geographic area to another. Connect this idea to how a concept map shows the relationship between terms and concepts.

Teach Challenge students to make a concept map with at least three levels of concepts to organize information about types of transportation. All students should start with the phrase *Types of transportation* at the top of the concept map. After that point, their concepts may vary. *(For example, some students might place* private transportation *and* public transportation *at the next level, while other students might choose* human-powered *and* gas-powered.) Make sure students connect the concepts with linking words.

- Complete student edition
- Video and audio
- Simulations and activities
- Section and chapter activities

Appendix A Laboratory Safety

Laboratory Safety

Laboratory safety is an essential element of a successful science class. Students need to understand exactly what is safe and unsafe behavior and what the rationale is behind each safety rule.

All in One Teaching Resources

- Laboratory Safety Teacher Notes
- Laboratory Safety Rules
- Laboratory Safety Symbols
- Laboratory Safety Contract

General Precautions

- Post safety rules in the classroom, and review them regularly with students before beginning every science activity.
- Familiarize yourself with the safety procedures for each activity before introducing it to your students.
- For open-ended activities like Chapter Projects, have students submit their procedures or design plans in writing and check them for safety considerations.
- Always act as an exemplary role model by displaying safe behavior.
- Know how to use safety equipment, such as fire extinguishers and fire blankets, and always have it accessible.
- Have students practice leaving the classroom quickly and orderly to prepare them for emergencies.
- Explain to students how to use the intercom or other available means of communication to get help during an emergency.
- Never leave students unattended while they are engaged in science activities.
- Provide enough space for students to safely carry out science activities.
- Instruct students to report all accidents and injuries to you immediately.

Safety Symbols

These symbols warn of possible dangers in the laboratory and remind you to work carefully.

 Safety Goggles Wear safety goggles to protect your eyes in any activity involving chemicals, flames or heating, or glassware.

 Lab Apron Wear a laboratory apron to protect your skin and clothing from damage.

 Breakage Handle breakable materials, such as glassware, with care. Do not touch broken glassware.

 Heat-Resistant Gloves Use an oven mitt or other hand protection when handling hot materials such as hot plates or hot glassware.

 Plastic Gloves Wear disposable plastic gloves when working with harmful chemicals and organisms. Keep your hands away from your face, and dispose of the gloves according to your teacher's instructions.

 Heating Use a clamp or tongs to pick up hot glassware. Do not touch hot objects with your bare hands.

 Flames Before you work with flames, tie back loose hair and clothing. Follow instructions from your teacher about lighting and extinguishing flames.

 No Flames When using flammable materials, make sure there are no flames, sparks, or other exposed heat sources present.

 Corrosive Chemical Avoid getting acid or other corrosive chemicals on your skin or clothing or in your eyes. Do not inhale the vapors. Wash your hands after the activity.

 Poison Do not let any poisonous chemical come into contact with your skin, and do not inhale its vapors. Wash your hands when you are finished with the activity.

 Fumes Work in a ventilated area when harmful vapors may be involved. Avoid inhaling vapors directly. Only test an odor when directed to do so by your teacher, and use a wafting motion to direct the vapor toward your nose.

 Sharp Object Scissors, scalpels, knives, needles, pins, and tacks can cut your skin. Always direct a sharp edge or point away from yourself and others.

 Animal Safety Treat live or preserved animals or animal parts with care to avoid harming the animals or yourself. Wash your hands when you are finished with the activity.

 Plant Safety Handle plants only as directed by your teacher. If you are allergic to certain plants, tell your teacher; do not do an activity involving those plants. Avoid touching harmful plants such as poison ivy. Wash your hands when you are finished with the activity.

 Electric Shock To avoid electric shock, never use electrical equipment around water, or when the equipment is wet or your hands are wet. Be sure cords are untangled and cannot trip anyone. Unplug equipment not in use.

 Physical Safety When an experiment involves physical activity, avoid injuring yourself or others. Alert your teacher if there is any reason you should not participate.

 Disposal Dispose of chemicals and other laboratory materials safely. Follow the instructions from your teacher.

 Hand Washing Wash your hands thoroughly when finished with the activity. Use antibacterial soap and warm water. Rinse well.

 General Safety Awareness When this symbol appears, follow the instructions provided. When you are asked to develop your own procedure in a lab, have your teacher approve your plan before you go further.

End-of-Experiment Rules

- Always have students use warm water and soap for washing their hands.

Heating and Fire Safety

- No flammable substances should be in use around hot plates, light bulbs, or open flames.
- Test tubes should be heated only in water baths.

- Students should be permitted to strike matches to light candles or burners *only* with strict supervision. When possible, you should light the flames, especially when working with younger students.
- Be sure to have proper ventilation when fumes are produced during a procedure.
- All electrical equipment used in the lab should have GFI switches.

Science Safety Rules

General Precautions
Follow all instructions. Never perform activities without the approval and supervision of your teacher. Do not engage in horseplay. Never eat or drink in the laboratory. Keep work areas clean and uncluttered.

Dress Code
Wear safety goggles whenever you work with chemicals, glassware, heat sources such as burners, or any substance that might get into your eyes. If you wear contact lenses, notify your teacher.

Wear a lab apron or coat whenever you work with corrosive chemicals or substances that can stain. Tie back long hair. Remove or tie back any article of clothing or jewelry that can hang down and touch chemicals, flames, or equipment. Roll up long sleeves. Never wear open shoes or sandals.

First Aid
Report all accidents, injuries, or fires to your teacher, no matter how minor. Be aware of the location of the first-aid kit, emergency equipment such as the fire extinguisher and fire blanket, and the nearest telephone. Know whom to contact in an emergency.

Heating and Fire Safety
Keep all combustible materials away from flames. When heating a substance in a test tube, make sure that the mouth of the tube is not pointed at you or anyone else. Never heat a liquid in a closed container. Use an oven mitt to pick up a container that has been heated.

Using Chemicals Safely
Never put your face near the mouth of a container that holds chemicals. Never touch, taste, or smell a chemical unless your teacher tells you to.

Use only those chemicals needed in the activity. Keep all containers closed when chemicals are not being used. Pour all chemicals over the sink or a container, not over your work surface. Dispose of excess chemicals as instructed by your teacher.

Be extra careful when working with acids or bases. When mixing an acid and water, always pour the water into the container first and then add the acid to the water. Never pour water into an acid. Wash chemical spills and splashes immediately with plenty of water.

Using Glassware Safely
If glassware is broken or chipped, notify your teacher immediately. Never handle broken or chipped glass with your bare hands.

Never force glass tubing or thermometers into a rubber stopper or rubber tubing. Have your teacher insert the glass tubing or thermometer if required for an activity.

Using Sharp Instruments
Handle sharp instruments with extreme care. Never cut material toward you; cut away from you.

Animal and Plant Safety
Never perform experiments that cause pain, discomfort, or harm to animals. Only handle animals if absolutely necessary. If you know that you are allergic to certain plants, molds, or animals, tell your teacher before doing an activity in which these are used. Wash your hands thoroughly after any activity involving animals, animal parts, plants, plant parts, or soil.

During field work, wear long pants, long sleeves, socks, and closed shoes. Avoid poisonous plants and fungi as well as plants with thorns.

End-of-Experiment Rules
Unplug all electrical equipment. Clean up your work area. Dispose of waste materials as instructed by your teacher. Wash your hands after every experiment.

Handling Organisms Safely
- In an activity where students are directed to taste something, be sure to store the material in clean, *nonscience* containers. Distribute the material to students in *new* plastic or paper dispensables, which should be discarded after the tasting. Tasting or eating should never be done in a lab classroom.
- When growing bacterial cultures, use only disposable petri dishes. After streaking, the dishes should be sealed and not opened again by students. After the lab, students should return the unopened dishes to you.
- Two methods are recommended for the safe disposal of bacterial cultures. *First method:* Autoclave the petri dishes and discard without opening. *Second method:* If no autoclave is available, carefully open the dishes (never have a student do this) and pour full-strength bleach into the dishes and let stand for a day. Then pour the bleach from the petri dishes down a drain, and flush the drain with lots of water. Tape the petri dishes back together, and place in a sealed plastic bag. Wrap the plastic bag with a brown paper bag or newspaper, and tape securely. Throw the sealed package in the trash. Thoroughly disinfect the work area with bleach.
- To grow mold, use a new, sealable plastic bag that is two to three times larger than the material to be placed inside. Seal the bag and tape it shut. After the bag is sealed, students should not open it. To dispose of the bag and mold culture, make a small cut near an edge of the bag, and cook in a microwave oven on high setting for at least one minute. Discard the bag according to local ordinance, usually in the trash.
- Students should wear disposable nitrile, latex, or food-handling gloves when handling live animals or nonliving specimens.

Using Glassware Safely
- Use plastic containers, graduated cylinders, and beakers whenever possible. If using glass, students should wear safety goggles.
- Use only nonmercury thermometers with anti-roll protectors.

Using Chemicals Safely
- When students use both chemicals and microscopes in one activity, microscopes should be in a separate part of the room from the chemicals so that when students remove their goggles to use the microscopes, their eyes are not at risk.

The microscope is an essential tool in the study of life science. It allows you to see things that are too small to be seen with the unaided eye.

You will probably use a compound microscope like the one you see here. The compound microscope has more than one lens that magnifies the object you view.

Typically, a compound microscope has one lens in the eyepiece, the part you look through. The eyepiece lens usually magnifies 10 ×. Any object you view through this lens would appear 10 times larger than it is.

The compound microscope may contain one or two other lenses called objective lenses. If there are two objective lenses, they are called the low-power and high-power objective lenses. The low-power objective lens usually magnifies 10 ×. The high-power objective lens usually magnifies 40 ×.

To calculate the total magnification with which you are viewing an object, multiply the magnification of the eyepiece lens by the magnification of the objective lens you are using. For example, the eyepiece's magnification of 10 × multiplied by the low-power objective's magnification of 10 × equals a total magnification of 100 ×.

Use the photo of the compound microscope to become familiar with the parts of the microscope and their functions.

The Parts of a Compound Microscope

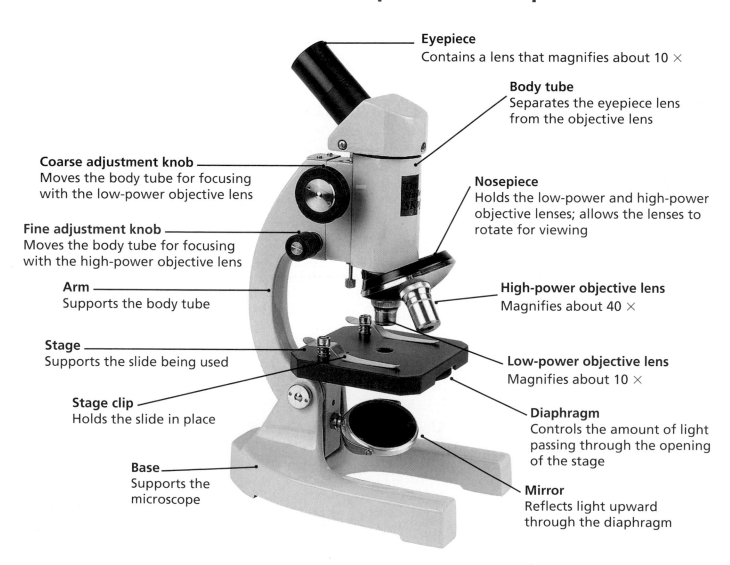

Eyepiece
Contains a lens that magnifies about 10 ×

Body tube
Separates the eyepiece lens from the objective lens

Coarse adjustment knob
Moves the body tube for focusing with the low-power objective lens

Nosepiece
Holds the low-power and high-power objective lenses; allows the lenses to rotate for viewing

Fine adjustment knob
Moves the body tube for focusing with the high-power objective lens

Arm
Supports the body tube

High-power objective lens
Magnifies about 40 ×

Stage
Supports the slide being used

Low-power objective lens
Magnifies about 10 ×

Stage clip
Holds the slide in place

Diaphragm
Controls the amount of light passing through the opening of the stage

Base
Supports the microscope

Mirror
Reflects light upward through the diaphragm

Using the Microscope

Use the following procedures when you are working with a microscope.

1. To carry the microscope, grasp the microscope's arm with one hand. Place your other hand under the base.
2. Place the microscope on a table with the arm toward you.
3. Turn the coarse adjustment knob to raise the body tube.
4. Revolve the nosepiece until the low-power objective lens clicks into place.
5. Adjust the diaphragm. While looking through the eyepiece, also adjust the mirror until you see a bright white circle of light. **CAUTION:** *Never use direct sunlight as a light source.*
6. Place a slide on the stage. Center the specimen over the opening on the stage. Use the stage clips to hold the slide in place. **CAUTION:** *Glass slides are fragile.*
7. Look at the stage from the side. Carefully turn the coarse adjustment knob to lower the body tube until the low-power objective almost touches the slide.
8. Looking through the eyepiece, very slowly turn the coarse adjustment knob until the specimen comes into focus.
9. To switch to the high-power objective lens, look at the microscope from the side. Carefully revolve the nosepiece until the high-power objective lens clicks into place. Make sure the lens does not hit the slide.
10. Looking through the eyepiece, turn the fine adjustment knob until the specimen comes into focus.

Making a Wet-Mount Slide

Use the following procedures to make a wet-mount slide of a specimen.

1. Obtain a clean microscope slide and a coverslip. **CAUTION:** *Glass slides and coverslips are fragile.*
2. Place the specimen on the slide. The specimen must be thin enough for light to pass through it.
3. Using a plastic dropper, place a drop of water on the specimen.
4. Gently place one edge of the coverslip against the slide so that it touches the edge of the water drop at a 45° angle. Slowly lower the coverslip over the specimen. If air bubbles are trapped beneath the coverslip, tap the coverslip gently with the eraser end of a pencil.
5. Remove any excess water at the edge of the coverslip with a paper towel.

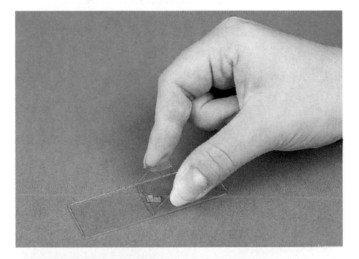

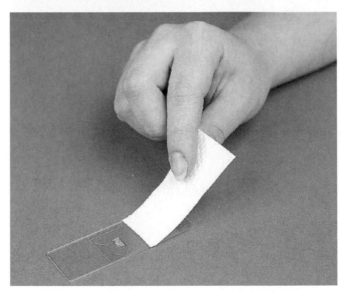

The laboratory balance is an important tool in scientific investigations. You can use a balance to determine the masses of materials that you study or experiment with in the laboratory.

Different kinds of balances are used in the laboratory. One kind of balance is the triple-beam balance. The balance that you may use in your science class is probably similar to the balance illustrated in this Appendix. To use the balance properly, you should learn the name, location, and function of each part of the balance you are using. What kind of balance do you have in your science class?

The Triple-Beam Balance

The triple-beam balance is a single-pan balance with three beams calibrated in grams. The back, or 100-gram, beam is divided into ten units of 10 grams each. The middle, or 500-gram, beam is divided into five units of 100 grams each. The front, or 10-gram, beam is divided into ten major units of 1 gram each. Each of these units is further divided into units of 0.1 gram. What is the largest mass you could find with a triple-beam balance?

The following procedure can be used to find the mass of an object with a triple-beam balance:

1. Place the object on the pan.

2. Move the rider on the middle beam notch by notch until the horizontal pointer drops below zero. Move the rider back one notch.

3. Move the rider on the back beam notch by notch until the pointer again drops below zero. Move the rider back one notch.

4. Slowly slide the rider along the front beam until the pointer stops at the zero point.

5. The mass of the object is equal to the sum of the readings on the three beams.

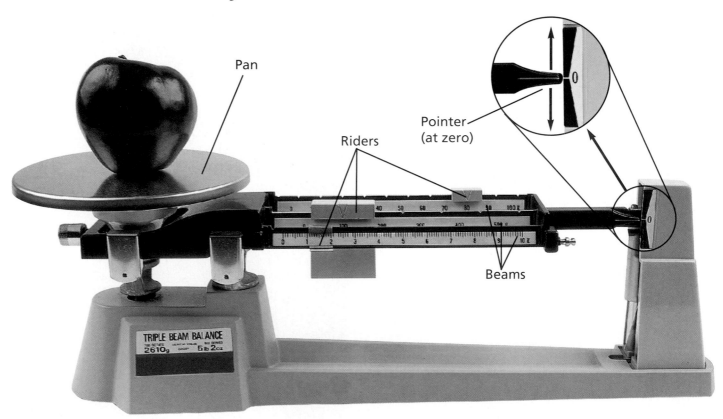

Triple-Beam Balance

A

accuracy How close a measurement is to the true or accepted value. (p. 62)
exactitud Cuán cerca está una medida del valor verdadero o aceptado.

B

brainstorming A process in which group members freely suggest any creative solutions that come to mind. (p. 100)
lluvia de ideas Proceso mediante el cual los miembros de un grupo sugieren libremente cualquier solución creativa que se les ocurre.

C

classifying The process of grouping together items that are alike in some way. (p. 10)
clasificar Proceso de agrupar objetos con algún tipo de semejanza.

communicating The process of sharing ideas with others through writing and speaking. (p. 21)
comunicar Proceso de compartir ideas con otras personas a través de la escritura o el lenguage hablado.

constraint Any factor that limits or restricts a design. (p. 100)
restricción Cualquier factor que limita o restringe un diseño.

controlled experiment An experiment in which only one variable is manipulated at a time. (p. 17)
experimento controlado Experimento en el cual sólo una variable es manipulada a la vez.

D

coordinate A pair of numbers used to determine the position of a point on a graph. (p. 70)
coordenada Par de números que se usa para determinar la posición de un punto en una gráfica.

data Facts, figures, and other evidence gathered through observations. (p. 18)
dato Hechos, cifras u otra evidencia reunida por medio de las observaciones.

data point A point on a graph showing the location of a piece of data. (p. 71)
punto de dato Punto en una gráfica que muestra la ubicación de parte de los datos.

density A measure of how much mass is contained in a given volume. (p. 52)
densidad Medida de cuánta masa contiene un determinado volumen.

E

engineer A person who is trained to use both technological and scientific knowledge to solve practical problems. (p. 98)
ingeniero Persona capacitada para usar conocimientos tecnológicos y científicos para resolver problemas prácticos.

estimate An approximation of a number based on reasonable assumptions. (p. 61)
estimación Aproximación de un número basado en conjeturas razonables.

F

feedback The information a technological system uses to monitor the input, process, and output so that the system can adjust itself to meet the goal. (p. 95)
retroalimentación Información que usa un sistema tecnológico para comprobar la entrada, proceso y salida para autoajustarse con el fin de conseguir un objetivo.

G

goal The overall purpose of a technological system. (p. 95)
objetivo El propósito general de un sistema tecnológico.

graph A picture of information from a data table; shows the relationship between variables. (p. 69)
gráfica Ilustración con información de una de tabla datos; muestra la relación entre las variables.

H

horizontal axis (or *x*-axis) A line that runs left to right along the bottom of a graph, on which the manipulated variable (or independent variable) is labeled. (p. 70)
eje horizontal (o eje *x*) Recta que va de izquierda a derecha en la base de una gráfica, en la cual se rotula la variable manipulada (o variable independiente).

hypothesis A possible explanation for a set of observations or answer to a scientific question; must be testable. (p. 15)
hipótesis Explicación posible a un conjunto de observaciones o respuesta a una pregunta científica; debe ser verificable.

I

inferring The process of making an inference, an interpretation based on observations and prior knowledge. (p. 8)
inferir Proceso de realizar una inferencia; interpretación basada en observaciones y en el conocimiento previo.

input Something that is put into a technological system in order to achieve a goal. (p. 95)
entrada Algo que se agrega a un sistema tecnológico para conseguir un propósito.

L

linear graph A line graph in which the data points yield a straight line. (p. 71)
gráfica lineal Gráfica en la cual los puntos de los datos forman una línea recta.

line of best fit A smooth line that reflects the general pattern in a graph. (p. 71)
recta de mayor aproximación Recta que refleja el patrón general en una gráfica.

M

making models The process of creating representations of complex objects or processes. (p. 11)
hacer modelos Proceso de crear representaciones de objetos o procesos complejos.

manipulated variable The one factor that a scientist changes during an experiment; also called independent variable. (p. 16)
variable manipulada Único factor que un científico cambia durante un experimento; también llamada variable independiente.

mass A measure of the amount of matter an object contains. (p. 48)
masa Medida de la cantidad de materia que contiene un objeto.

mean The numerical average of the numbers in a list. (p. 66)
media Promedio numérico de los números en una lista.

median The middle number in a list of numbers. (p. 66)
mediana Número en la mitad, en una lista de números.

meniscus The curved upper surface of a liquid in a column of liquid. (p. 50)
menisco Superficie superior curvada de un líquido en una columna de líquido.

metric system A system of measurement based on the number 10. (p. 45)
sistema métrico Sistema de medida basado en el número 10.

mode The number that appears most often in a list of numbers. (p. 67)
moda Número que aparece más a menudo en una lista de números.

nonlinear graph A line graph in which the data points do not fall along a straight line. (p. 74)
gráfica no lineal Gráfica lineal en la que los puntos de datos no forman una línea recta.

observing The process of using one or more of your senses to gather information. (p. 7)
observar Proceso de usar uno o más de tus sentidos para reunir información.

obsolete No longer in use. (p. 92)
obsoleto Que ya no está en uso.

operational definition A statement that describes how to measure a particular variable or how to define a particular term. (p. 17)
definición operativa Enunciado que describe cómo medir una variable determinada o cómo definir un término determinado.

origin The point where the x-axis and y-axis cross on a graph. (p. 70)
origen Punto en donde el eje x y el eje y se cruzan en una gráfica.

output The result or product from the operation of a technological system. (p. 95)
salida Resultado o producto de la operación de un sistema tecnológico.

patent A legal document issued by a government that gives an inventor exclusive rights to make, use, or sell an invention for a limited time. (p. 105)
patente Documento legal emitido por el gobierno que otorga a un inventor los derechos exclusivos de hacer, usar o vender un invento por un tiempo limitado.

percent error A calculation used to determine how accurate, or close to the true value, an experimental value really is. (p. 65)
error porcentual Cálculo usado para determinar cuán exacto, o cercano al valor verdadero, es realmente un valor.

precision How close a group of measurements are to each other. (p. 62)
precisión Cuán cerca se encuentran un grupo de medidas entre ellas.

predicting The process of forecasting what will happen in the future based on past experience or evidence. (p. 9)
predecir Proceso de pronosticar lo que va a suceder en el futuro, basado en la experiencia pasada o en evidencia.

process A sequence of actions that a technological system undergoes to produce an output. (p. 95)
proceso Secuencia de acciones que experimenta un sistema tecnológico para producir un resultado.

prototype A working model used to test a design. (p. 102)
prototipo Modelo funcional usado para probar un diseño.

qualitative observation An observation that deals with characteristics that cannot be expressed in numbers. (p. 7)
observación cualitativa Observación que se centra en las características que no se pueden expresar con números.

quantitative observation An observation that deals with a number or amount. (p. 7)
observación cuantitativa Observación que se centra en un número o cantidad.

R

responding variable The factor that changes as a result of changes to the manipulated, or independent, variable in an experiment; also called dependent variable. (p. 16)
variable de respuesta Factor que cambia como resultado del cambio de la variable manipulada, o independiente, en un experimento; también llamada variable dependiente.

risk-benefit analysis The process of evaluating the possible problems of a technology compared to the expected advantages. (p. 113)
análisis de riesgo y beneficios Proceso por el cual se evalúan los posibles problemas de una tecnología y se compara con las ventajas deseadas.

S

science A way of learning about the natural world through observations and logical reasoning; leads to a body of knowledge. (p. 12)
ciencia Estudio del mundo natural a través de observaciones y del razonamiento lógico; conduce a un conjunto de conocimientos.

scientific inquiry The ongoing process of discovery in science; the diverse ways in which scientists study the natural world and propose explanations based on evidence they gather. (p. 13)
investigación científica Proceso continuo de descubrimiento en la ciencia; diversidad de métodos con los que los científicos estudian el mundo natural y proponen explicaciones del mismo basadas en la evidencia que reúnen.

scientific law A statement that describes what scientists expect to happen every time under a particular set of conditions. (p. 22)
ley científica Enunciado que describe lo que los científicos esperan que suceda cada vez que se da una serie de condiciones determinadas.

scientific literacy The knowledge and understanding of scientific terms and principles required for evaluating information, making personal decisions, and taking part in public affairs. (p. 28)
alfabetismo científico Conocimiento y comprensión de los términos y principios científicos necesarios para evaluar información, tomar decisiones personales y participar en actividades públicas.

scientific theory A well-tested explanation for a wide range of observations or experimental results. (p. 21)
teoría científica Explicación comprobada de una gran variedad de observaciones o resultados de experimentos.

SI (*Système International d'Unités*) International System of Units; a version of the metric system used by scientists all over the world. (p. 45)
SI (*Système International d'Unités*) Sistema Internacional de Unidades; versión del sistema métrico usado por científicos de todo el mundo.

significant figures All the digits in a measurement that have been measured exactly, plus one digit whose value has been estimated. (p. 63)
cifras significativas Todos los dígitos en una medida que se han medido con exactitud, más un dígito cuyo valor se ha estimado.

The length "2.25 m" has three significant figures, while the width "3 m" has one. Therefore, my answer can only have one significant figure.

skepticism An attitude of doubt. (p. 12)
escepticismo Actitud de duda.

slope The steepness of a graph line; the ratio of the vertical change (the rise) to the horizontal change (the run). (p. 73)
pendiente Inclinación de una gráfica lineal; la razón del cambio vertical (el ascenso) al cambio horizontal (el avance).

system A group of related parts that work together. (p. 95)
sistema Grupo de partes relacionadas que funcionan en conjunto.

technology How people modify the world around them to meet their needs or to solve practical problems. (p. 89)
tecnología Cómo la gente modifica el mundo que la rodea para satisfacer sus necesidades o para solucionar problemas prácticos.

trade-off An exchange in which one benefit is given up in order to obtain another. (p. 101)
intercambio Cambio entre dos o más partes en el cual se renuncia a un beneficio para obtener otro.

troubleshooting The process of analyzing a design problem and finding a way to fix it. (p. 103)
solución de problemas Proceso por el cual se analiza un problema de diseño y se halla una forma de solucionarlo.

variable A factor that can change in an experiment. (p. 16)
variable Factor que puede cambiar en un experimento.

vertical axis (or *y*-axis) A line that runs up and down along the side of a graph, on which the responding variable (or dependent variable) is labeled. (p. 70)
eje vertical (o eje *y*) Recta que va de arriba a abajo en el lado vertical de una gráfica, en la cual se rotula la variable respuesta (o variable dependiente).

volume The amount of space an object takes up. (p. 50)
volumen Cantidad de espacio que ocupa un objeto.

weight A measure of the force of gravity acting on an object. (p. 49)
peso Medida de la fuerza de gravedad que actúa sobre un objeto.

Index

Teacher's Edition entries appear in **blue type**. The page on which a term is defined is indicated in **boldface** type.

A

absolute zero 54
accident in lab, handling 81
accuracy *62*
Activities for students who need additional help, Teacher's Edition pages
adding measurements, significant figures in 63
Address Misconceptions, See Misconceptions
advertised claims, evaluating 26
air bags, impact of 110
Analyzing Data, See Math Skills
artist, science and 37
area 61, **139**
astronauts *33*
attitudes, scientific 12
average, ways to calculate 66–67.
See also **mean, median, mode**
axes of line graph 70

B

balance
triple-beam 49, 152
biofuels 34
biological and chemical technology 90
body temperature, human 54
botanists *34*
brainstorming *100*
branches of science 31
Build Inquiry Activities, See Science Skills
Building Vocabulary, See Vocabulary

C

calculating, skill of 131
careers
in science 30–35
science in nonscience 36–37
Celsius scale 54, **131**
centimeter (cm) 47, 48
Charlemagne 47
chef, science and *36, 37*
chemistry 31
chemists *31,* 34

classifying *10*
skill of **129**
clocks 53
coexisting technologies 93
common conversions. *See* **conversion tables**
communicating *21*
in scientific inquiry 21
skill of **129**
technology design solution 104
communication technology 90
compound microscope 150–151
computer mouse *86F,* 97–105
technology design process and 97–105
computer scientists 33
computers, Internet and 116–117
conclusions, drawing 19–20, 133
Connecting Concepts, See Reading Skills
constraints 100
evaluating 100–101
construction technology 90
Content Refresher
Careers in Science
Using Science in the Workplace 4H
Graphs in Science
Types of Graphs 42G
Mathematics and Science
Significant Figures 42G
Measurements—A Common Language
A Common Measurement System 42G
Safety in the Laboratory
Safety First 42H
Scientific Inquiry
A Process of Inquiry 4G
Technology and Society
Everyday Technology 86F
Technology Design Skills
Mouse Function 86F
Thinking Like a Scientist
Skills and Attitudes 4G
Understanding Technology
A Common Technological System 86F
Why Study Science?
Science in Everyday Life 4H
controlled experiment *17,* **133**
conversion factor 54–55
conversion tables
for length *46*

for mass *48*
for temperature *54*
for time *53*
for volume *50*
coordinate **70**
creativity 12
in technology design process 100
crystallographers 31
cubic centimeter 50
cubic meter 51
curiosity 12
current technologies 92

D

data 18, **133**
collecting and interpreting 18
Internet and access to 116–117
organizing 18
data point 71
data table 18
Demonstration, See Teacher's Demo
density *52*–53
calculating 52
of common substances *53*
units of 52
dependent variable. *See* **responding variable**
designing experiment 16–17
design skills. *See* **technology design skills**
Developing Vocabulary, See Vocabulary
Differentiated Learning, See
dividing measurements, significant figures in 64

E

Earth
exploring beyond 32
resources of, learning wise use of 27
Earth and space science 31
Edison, Thomas 122–126
electric lights, invention of *122–125,* 126
emergency in lab, handling *81*
emerging technologies 93
endoscopes 91
energy, developing new sources of 34
energy and power technology 90
engineer 98

Index

Index

Acknowledgments

Acknowledgment for page 6: Excerpt from *My Life with the Chimpanzees, Revised Edition* by Jane Goodall. Copyright © 1988, 1996 by Byron Preiss Visual Publications, Inc. Text copyright © 1988, 1996 by Jane Goodall. Published by Pocket Books, a division of Simon & Schuster Inc.

Staff Credits

Diane Alimena, Michele Angelucci, Scott Andrews, Jennifer Angel, Carolyn Belanger, Barbara A. Bertell, Suzanne Biron, Peggy Bliss, Stephanie Bradley, James Brady, Anne M. Bray, Sarah M. Carroll, Kerry Cashman, Jonathan Cheney, Joshua D. Clapper, Lisa J. Clark, Bob Craton, Patricia Cully, Patricia M. Dambry, Kathy Dempsey, Leanne Esterly, Emily Ellen, Thomas Ferreira, Jonathan Fisher, Patricia Fromkin, Paul Gagnon, Kathy Gavilanes, Joel Gendler, Holly Gordon, Robert Graham, Ellen Granter, Diane Grossman, Barbara Hollingdale, Linda Johnson, Anne Jones, John Judge, Kevin Keane, Kelly Kelliher, Toby Klang, Sue Langan, Russ Lappa, Carolyn Lock, Rebecca Loveys, Constance J. McCarty, Carolyn B. McGuire, Ranida Touranont McKneally, Anne McLaughlin, Eve Melnechuk, Natania Mlawer, Janet Morris, Karyl Murray, Francine Neumann, Baljit Nijjar, Marie Opera, Jill Ort, Kim Ortell, Joan Paley, Dorothy Preston, Maureen Raymond, Laura Ross, Rashid Ross, Siri Schwartzman, Melissa Shustyk, Laurel Smith, Emily Soltanoff, Jennifer A. Teece, Elizabeth Torjussen, Amanda M. Watters, Merce Wilczek, Amy Winchester, Char Lyn Yeakley. **Additional Credits** Allen Gold, Andrea Golden, Etta Jacobs, Meg Montgomery, Kim Schmidt, Adam Teller, Joan Tobin.

Illustration

Kerry Cashman: 10–11t, 18, 20, 55, 66, 67, 81, 84, 90, 91, 94, 108–109; **John Ceballos:** 91–93; **John Edwards:** 68, 69, 70–71; **Gary Glover:** 58–59, 98, 99, 100–101, 102–103, 104–105; **Barbara Hollingdale:** 13; **Richard McMahon:** 46–47, 54, 112–113, 120; **Kim and James Neale:** 61, 63, 64; **XNR Productions:** 11b. **All charts and graphs by Matt Mayerchak.**

Photography

Photo Research Paula Wehde
Cover image top, Rosenfeld Images Ltd./Science Photo Library; **bottom,** Gary S. and Vivian Chapman/Getty Images.

Page vi, SPL/Photo Researchers, Inc.; **vii,** Richard Haynes; **viii,** Richard Haynes; **x–1,** Alan S. Weiner; **1 both,** Johnson Research and Development Co.; **2t,** Lonnie G. Johnson; **2b,** Robin Samper; **3l,** Johnson Research and Development Co.; **3m,** Lonnie G. Johnson; **3r,** Lonnie G. Johnson.

Chapter 1

Pages 4–5, Barrett and MacKay; **5 inset,** Richard Haynes; **7t,** Michael Nichols/National Geographic Society; **7b,** Manoh Shah/Getty Images, Inc.; **8,** K. & K. Ammann/Bruce Coleman, Inc.; **9,** Wild Chimpanzees.org; **10t,** Wild Chimpanzees.org; **10b,** Dorling Kindersley Media Library; **11l,** Irven De Vore/Anthrophoto File; **11r,** Adrian Warren/Lastrefuge.co.uk; **12,** Mark Richards/PhotoEdit; **13t,** Richard Haynes; **13b,** M.T. Frazier/Photo Researchers, Inc.; **14,** Richard Haynes; **15,** Richard Haynes; **16–17,** Richard Haynes; **18,** Richard Haynes; **19,** Richard Haynes; **20 all,** Richard Haynes; **22,** Shirley Church/Photo Researchers, Inc.; **23 both,** Richard Haynes; **24t,** David Young-Wolff/PhotoEdit; **25b,** Bob Daemmrich; **26,** Dana White/PhotoEdit; **27,** Superstock, Inc.; **28–29,** Panoramic Images; **29t inset,** Linda Burton/Robertstock; **29b inset,** Superstock/PictureQuest; **30,** Photri, Inc.; **31t,** Wolfgang Kaehler/Corbis; **31b,** SPL/Photo Researchers, Inc.; **32,** SPL/Photo Researchers, Inc.; **33 all,** NASA; **34tl,** ARS; **34tr,** USDA; **34bl,** ARS; **34br,** ARS; **35,** Russ Lappa; **36t,** PictureQuest; **36bl,** Bill Cornett; **36br,** Corbis; **37,** Bob Daemmrich; **38t,** Manoh Shah/Getty Images, Inc.; **38b,** Richard Haynes; **40,** Renee Stockdale/Animals Animals.

Chapter 2

Pages 42–43, Flip Nicklin/Minden Pictures; **43 inset,** Richard Haynes; **44b,** David Young-Wolf/PhotoEdit; **44t,** Richard Haynes; **45,** Richard Haynes; **46l,** Bettmann/Corbis; **46m,** Dorling Kindersley; **46r,** The Art Archive/The Picture Desk, Inc.; **47l,** Bridgeman Art Library; **47m,** Science & Society Picture Library; **47r,** Bureau of International Weights & Measures; **48,** Richard Haynes; **49,** Richard Haynes; **50 both,** Richard Haynes; **51,** Richard Haynes; **52 both,** Richard Haynes; **53 both,** Richard Haynes; **54,** Richard Haynes; **56,** Richard Haynes; **57,** Richard Haynes; **60,** Richard Haynes; **60–61b,** Kevin Fleming/Corbis; **62 all,** Richard Haynes; **66,** Seapics; **69,** Richard Haynes; **72l,** Richard Haynes; **72r,** Getty Images, Inc.; **73l,** Stephen Oliver/Dorling Kindersley; **73r,** Stephen Oliver/Dorling Kindersley; **74l,** Mark C. Burnett/Photo Researchers, Inc.; **74r,** Dr. K.S. Kim/Peter Arnold, Inc.; **75,** Index Stock Imagery, Inc.; **75l,** Royalty-Free/Corbis; **75r,** Dorling Kindersley; **76,** Richard Haynes; **77b,** David Young-Wolf/PhotoEdit; **77t,** Index Stock Imagery, Inc.; **78,** Richard Haynes; **79,** Richard Haynes; **80bl,** Getty Images, Inc.; **80bm,** Royalty-Free/Corbis; **80br,** Richard Haynes; **80ml,** Getty Images, Inc.; **80mr,** Getty Images, Inc.; **80t,** Getty Images, Inc.; **84,** Index Stock Imagery, Inc.

Chapter 3

Pages 86–87, Hank Morgan/Photo Researchers, Inc; **87 inset,** Richard Haynes; **88b,** Corbis; **88tl,** Getty Images, Inc.; **88tm,** Casio, Inc.; **88tml,** Corbis; **88tmr,** Corbis; **88tr,** Dorling Kindersley; **89l,** Advertising Archive/The Picture Desk, Inc.; **89m,** Advertising Archive; **89r,** The Granger Collection; **90l,** Masterfile; **90r,** Richard Haynes; **91m,** Phototake; **91r,** Photo Researchers; **94l,** David Young-Wolf/PhotoEdit; **94r,** Richard Haynes; **96 both,** Richard Haynes; **97 both,** Richard Haynes; **99,** Dorling Kindersley; **100,** Dorling Kindersley; **101,** Dorling Kindersley; **102,** Kevin Candland courtesy of IDEO; **102,** Dorling Kindersley; **103,** Dorling Kindersley; **104,** Fisher/Thatcher/Getty Images, Inc.; **106,** Richard Haynes; **107,** Richard Haynes; **108l inset,** Bridgeman Art Library; **108r inset,** Hulton Archive/Getty Images Inc.; **108–109b,** Richard Haynes; **109 inset,** PictureQuest; **110l,** Richard Haynes; **110r,** Superstock; **112l,** The Art Archive; **112m,** Getty Images, Inc.; **112r,** BATA Shoe Museum; **113l,** Corbis; **113ml,** Index Stock Imagery, Inc.; **113r,** SPL/Photo Researchers; **115,** Corbis; **116,** Richard Haynes; **118l,** Richard Haynes; **118,** Dorling Kindersley.

Page 122b, Library of Congress; **122m,** U.S. Dept. of the Interior National Park Service, Edison National Historic Site; **122t,** Dave King/Dorling Kindersley; **123,** U.S. Dept. of the Interior, National Park Service, Edison National Historic Site; **124–125,** AP/Wide World Photos; **125b,** Bettman/Corbis; **125tr,** Smithsonian Institution, EMP-LAR-BB1, Courtesy of the General Electric Lighting Co.; **126b,** Brooks/Brown/Photo Researchers, Inc.; **126m,** U.S. Dept. of the Interior, National Park Service, Edison National Historic Site; **126t,** Everett Collection; **127b,** Tom McCarthy/PhotoEdit; **127t,** U.S. Geological Survey/Science Photo Library/Photo Researchers, Inc.; **128,** Tony Freeman/PhotoEdit; **129t,** Russ Lappa; **129m,** Richard Haynes; **129b,** Russ Lappa; **130,** Richard Haynes; **132,** Richard Haynes; **134,** Morton Beebe/Corbis; **135,** Catherine Karnow/Corbis; **137t,** Dorling Kindersley Media Library; **137b,** Richard Haynes; **153,** Richard Haynes; **154b,** K. & K. Ammann/Bruce Coleman, Inc.; **154t,** Mark C. Burnett/Photo Researchers, Inc.; **156,** Superstock; **157,** SPL/Photo Researchers, Inc.